PURE MATHEMATICS

8. VECTORS IN TWO AND THREE DIMENSIONS

ANTHONY NICOLAIDES

B.Sc. (Eng.), C. Eng. M.I.E.E.
SENIOR LECTURER

P.A.S.S. PUBLICATIONS

PRIVATE ACADEMIC & SCIENTIFIC STUDIES LTD

First Published in Great Britain 1994 by

Private Academic & Scientific Studies Limited

ISBN 1 872684 03 3

Printed and bound in Great Britain
by Hartnolls Ltd, Bodmin, Cornwall

Titles by the same author in the GCE A series.

1. Algebra.
2. Trigonometry.
3. Complex Numbers.
4. Differential Calculus and Applications.
5. Cartesian and Polar Curve Sketching.
6. Coordinate Geometry in two Dimensions.
7. Integral Calculus and Applications.
8. Vectors in two and three dimensions.
9. Determinants, Matrices and Applications.
10. Combinations. Permutations Probabilities.

<u>THE COMPLETE WORKS PURE MATHEMATICS GCE A</u>

PREFACE

This book, which is part of the GCE A level series in Pure Mathematics covers the specialised topic of The Vectors in Two and Three dimensions.

The GCE A level series in Pure Mathematics is comprised of ten books, covering the syllabuses of most examining boards. The books are designed to assist the student wishing to master the subject of Pure Mathematics. The series is easy to follow with minimum help. It can be easily adopted by a student who wishes to study it in the comforts of his home at his pace without having to attend classes formally; it is ideal for the working person who wishes to enhance his knowledge and qualification. The Vectors in Two and Three dimensions books, like all the books in the series, is divided into two parts. In Part I, the theory is comprehensively dealt with, together with many worked examples and exercises. A step by step approach is adopted in all the worked examples. Part II of the book, a special and unique feature acts as a problem solver for all the exercises set at the end of each chapter in Part I.

I am grateful to Mr. Myat Thaw Kaung, an excellent ex-student of mine, who typeset the manuscript superbly with great care on a desktop publishing system.

I am also grateful to Mr. Alex Yau for checking thoroughly this book.

The GCE A is equivalent to the new NVQ level III.

Thanks are due to the following examining bodies who have kindly allowed me to use questions from their past examination papers.

The Associated Examining Board. AEB

The University of London School Examinations. UL

The University of London School Examinations Board and The Associated Examining Board accept no responsibility whatsoever for the accuracy of working in the answers given.

A. Nicolaides

8. VECTORS IN TWO AND THREE DIMENSIONS

1. INTRODUCTION TO VECTORS

1.1 SCALARS

A scalar is a physical quantity that has only magnitude. The following are some examples of scalars. Length, area, volume, work done, electrical resistance, power, energy, mass, density, temperature, and potential. All the above physical quantities have a magnitude, the length is 15 cm, the electrical resistance is 5 Ω, the mass is 1.5 kg, the temperature is 23° C and so on.

1.2 VECTORS

A vector is a physical quantity that has magnitude and direction.
The following are some examples of vectors. Displacement, velocity, force, magnetic field strength, current and acceleration.
Simon Stevin of Bruges, a Mathematician and Engineer, in about 1586, was the first to show that a force can be represented by a line, that is, a vector can by represented by a line, and the addition of forces can be implemented using triangle of forces.

1.3 EQUAL VECTORS

$\overrightarrow{AB}$ and $\overrightarrow{CD}$ are two vectors parallel and equal.

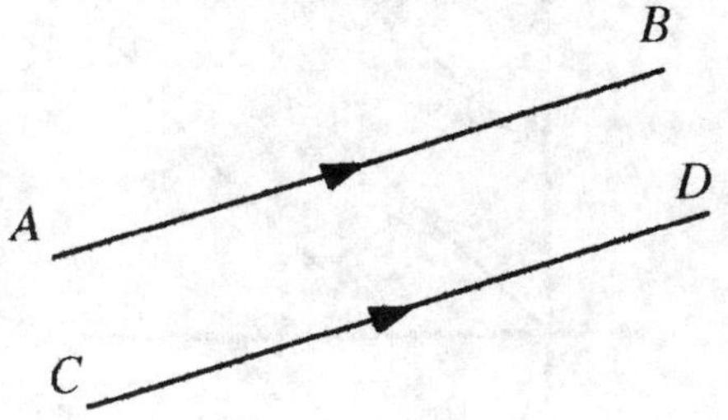

Fig. 8-I/1 Two equal vectors

Two vectors are equal if the following three properties are satisfied.

(1) The vectors are parallel.

(2) The vectors have the same direction and the same sense.

(3) The magnitude of vector, $\overrightarrow{AB}$, denoted by two vertical lines, $\left|\overrightarrow{AB}\right|$, is equal to the magnitude of vector $\overrightarrow{CD}$, $\left|\overrightarrow{CD}\right|$, that is,

$$\left|\overrightarrow{AB}\right| = \left|\overrightarrow{CD}\right|.$$

Note that there is a difference between the two words <u>direction</u> and <u>sense</u>.

The direction of the vector is from A to B and it is represented by $\overrightarrow{AB}$, or from B to A and is represented by $\overrightarrow{BA}$.
The sense of a vector could be clockwise or anticlockwise.

Consider three equal coplanar vectors $\overrightarrow{AB}$, $\overrightarrow{OP}$, and $\overrightarrow{CD}$. Since the three vectors are equal, we can represent them by the same algebraic symbol, **F**

$$\overrightarrow{AB} = \overrightarrow{CD} = \overrightarrow{OP} = \mathbf{F}.$$

1.4 THE MAGNITUDE OF THE VECTORS ARE

$$\left|\overrightarrow{AB}\right| = \left|\overrightarrow{CD}\right| = \left|\overrightarrow{OP}\right| = \left|\mathbf{F}\right| .$$

The vertical lines denote the modulus or the magnitude of the vector and this is always considered to be positive.

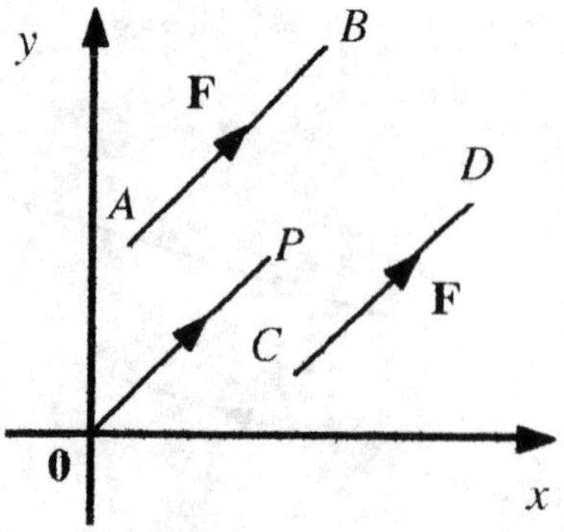

Fig. 8-I/2 Geometrical and algebraic representation of vectors

The word vector was first introduced by W. R. Hamilton, in 1844 in Dublin.

1.5 TRIANGLE OF FORCES

Consider two forces to be applied at a point O at the directions and magnitudes shown in Fig. 8-I/3. It is required to find the total or <u>resultant force</u> applied at the point O.

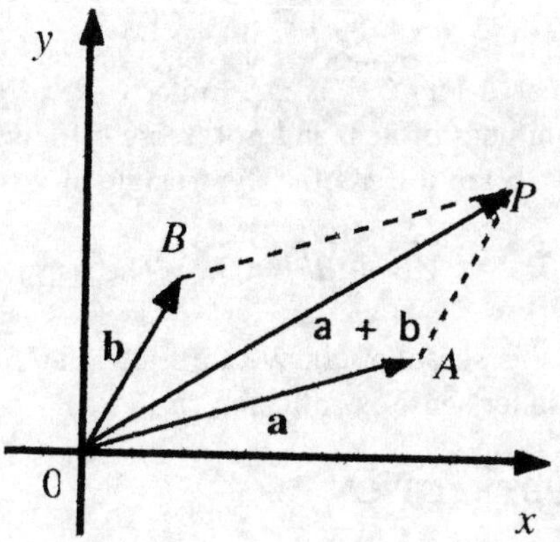

Fig. 8-I/3 Algebra addition of two vectors

Draw from B a line parallel and equal to $\overrightarrow{OA}$, $\overrightarrow{BP}$ and draw from A a line parallel and equal to $\overrightarrow{OB}$, $\overrightarrow{AP}$. The diagonal of the parallelogram $\overrightarrow{OP}$, is the resultant force $\mathbf{a} + \mathbf{b}$. But $\overrightarrow{AP} = \overrightarrow{OB} = \mathbf{b}$ and $\overrightarrow{OA} = \overrightarrow{BP} = \mathbf{a}$, therefore $\overrightarrow{OA} + \overrightarrow{AP} = \overrightarrow{OP}$ from the triangle of forces OAP. If $\overrightarrow{OP} = \mathbf{a}$, $\overrightarrow{OB} = \mathbf{b}$ and $\overrightarrow{OP} = \mathbf{c}$ then

$$\boxed{\mathbf{a} + \mathbf{b} = \mathbf{c}}$$

But also from the triangle of forces OBP, we have

$$\boxed{\mathbf{b} + \mathbf{a} = \mathbf{c}}$$

therefore, $\mathbf{a} + \mathbf{b} = \mathbf{b} + \mathbf{a}$ and the algebra addition is commutative.

1.6 FREE VECTORS

A free vector has no specified point of application. Fig. 8-I/3, shows two free vectors, $\overrightarrow{BP}$ and $\overrightarrow{AP}$.

1.7 POSITION VECTORS

A position vector has a specified point of application, the origin O. Fig. 8-I/3 shows two position vectors, $\overrightarrow{OA}$ and $\overrightarrow{OB}$.

The origin of the vector, $\overrightarrow{OA}$, is O; similarly the origin of the vector, $\overrightarrow{OB}$, is O. The magnitudes of **a**, **b** and **a** + **b** are different and also the directions of **a**, **b** and **a** + **b** are different. The triangle of vectors OAP and OBP,

$\overrightarrow{OA} + \overrightarrow{AP} = \overrightarrow{OP}$, $\overrightarrow{OB} + \overrightarrow{BP} = \overrightarrow{OP}$. The <u>sense</u> of the vectors $\overrightarrow{OA}$, $\overrightarrow{AP}$ is different from the sense of the vectors $\overrightarrow{OB}$ and $\overrightarrow{BP}$, the former sense is clockwise, the latter sense is anticlockwise.

1.8 ALGEBRA SUBTRACTION

If $\overrightarrow{OA}$ = **a** in the direction shown in Fig. 8-I/4 then $\overrightarrow{OA'}$ = − **a** is equal and opposite, $\overrightarrow{OA'}$ is a <u>negative vector</u>, $\overrightarrow{OA}$ and $\overrightarrow{OA'}$ have the same magnitudes and their directions are the same but of <u>opposite sense</u>.

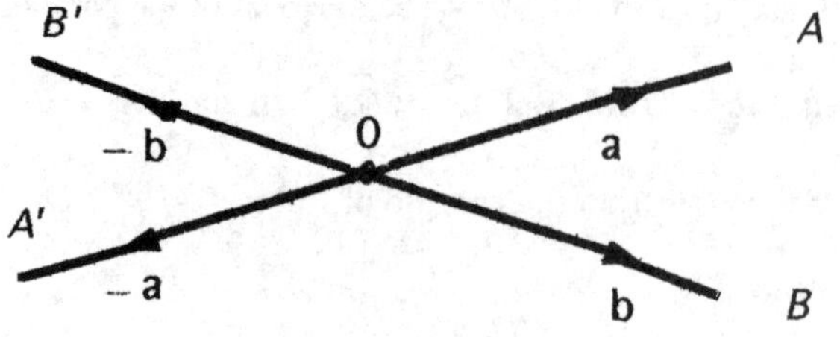

Fig. 8-I/4 Negative vectors

If $\overrightarrow{OA}$ = **a** in the direction shown in Fig. 8-I/4 then $\overrightarrow{OA'}$ = − **a** is equal and opposite to $\overrightarrow{OA}$, this defines a negative vector (− **a**). Similarly for − **b**.

Completing the parallelogram $OBRA'$ as shown in Fig. 8-I/5 then

$\overrightarrow{OR}$ = **b** − **a**

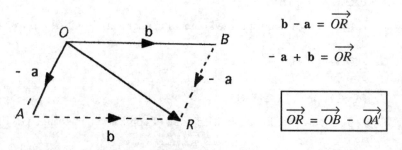

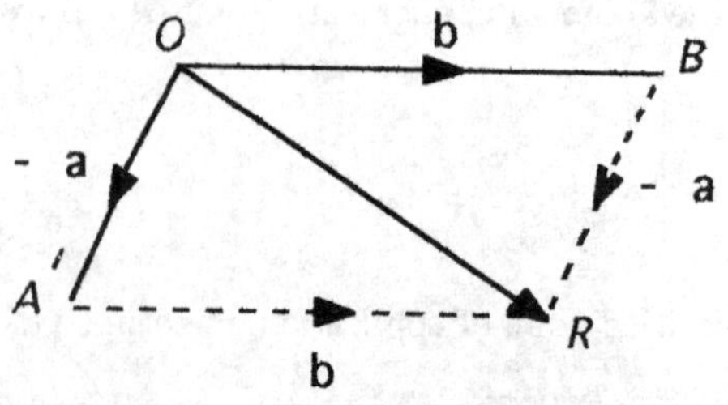

b − **a** = $\overrightarrow{OR}$

− **a** + **b** = $\overrightarrow{OR}$

$$\boxed{\overrightarrow{OR} = \overrightarrow{OB} - \overrightarrow{OA'}}$$

Fig. 8-I/5 Vector subtraction

1.9 THE PARALLELOGRAM OF VECTORS

The sum or resultant of two forces is found by using the parallelogram of forces.

1.10 THE POLYGON OF VECTORS

If we have more than two vectors, the polygon of vectors can be used to obtain the sum or resultant of vectors.

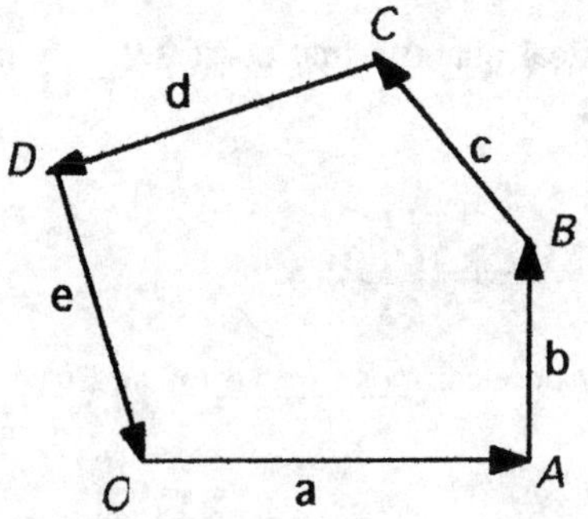

Fig. 8-I/6 The Polygon of vectors

$$\overrightarrow{OA} + \overrightarrow{AB} + \overrightarrow{BC} + \overrightarrow{CD} + \overrightarrow{DO} = 0$$

$$\mathbf{a} + \mathbf{b} + \mathbf{c} + \mathbf{d} + \mathbf{e} = 0.$$

1.11 SCALAR MULTIPLE OR SUBMULTIPLE OF A VECTOR

If there are n equal vectors then $\mathbf{a} + \mathbf{a} + \ldots + \mathbf{a} = n\mathbf{a}$ where n is a scalar integer.

Examples

$$\mathbf{a} + \mathbf{a} + 2\mathbf{a} = 4\mathbf{a}$$

$$\mathbf{a} + \frac{1}{2}\mathbf{a} + \frac{3}{4}\mathbf{a} = \frac{4}{4}\mathbf{a} + \frac{2}{4}\mathbf{a} + \frac{3}{4}\mathbf{a} = \frac{9}{4}\mathbf{a}.$$

WORKED EXAMPLE 1

Distinguish clearly between a vector and a scalar physical quantities and state a few examples of each.

SOLUTION 1

A vector is a physical quantity that possesses magnitude and direction such as displacement, velocity, acceleration, force, momentum, electric current, magnetic force, electric force.

A scalar is a physical quantity that possesses only magnitude such as mass, speed, temperature.

WORKED EXAMPLE 2

Distinguish clearly between position vector and free vector.

SOLUTION 2

Position vector is a vector referred to a fixed point usually the origin of the axes. A position vector shows the displacement of one point relative to a fixed point O.

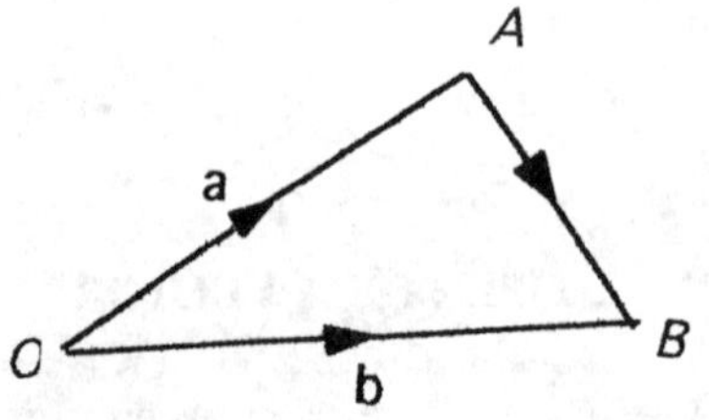

$\overrightarrow{OA} = \mathbf{a} =$ position vector

$\overrightarrow{OB} = \mathbf{b} =$ position vector

$\overrightarrow{AB} = \mathbf{b} - \mathbf{a} =$ free vector

$=$ the displacement of point B relative to the point A, where A is not a fixed point.

Fig. 8-I/7 Position vector

The line of action of $\overrightarrow{AB}$ is different from $\overrightarrow{OA}$ and $\overrightarrow{OB}$ which both are referred to the fixed point O, the origin.

WORKED EXAMPLE 3

Two forces of 50 N and 100 N are applied at a point at the directions of 30° and 75° from the horizontal.

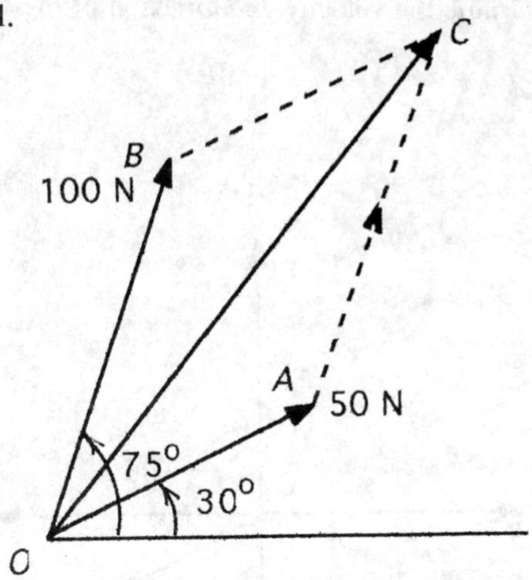

Fig. 8-I/8 Resultant of forces

Determine the resultant force and its direction from the horizontal.

SOLUTION 3

This example can be solved graphically. Draw the line *OA* with a protractor at 30° to the horizontal, scale off along *OA* 5 cm, 1 cm = 10 N, from *A* draw the line *AC*, 75° to the horizontal, and scale off along *AC*, 10 cm, to represent 100 N, join *O* to *C*, $\overrightarrow{OC}$ is the resultant, measure its length and the angle that makes with the horizontal. If a protractor and ruler are not available use calculations.

$\angle OAC = 135°$ and employing the cosine rule

$OC^2 = 50^2 + 100^2 - 2 \times 50 \times 100 \times 0.7071$

$OC^2 = 2500 + 10000 + 7071$

$OC = 139.9 \approx 140$ N the resultant force

$$\frac{AC}{\sin \angle COA} = \frac{140}{\sin 135°} \Rightarrow \frac{100}{\sin \angle COA} = \frac{140}{0.7071}$$

$$\sin \angle COA = \frac{70.71}{140} = 0.505 \Rightarrow \angle COA = 30.33°$$

therefore the direction of the resultant from the horizontal is 30° + 30.33° = 60.3°. Another idea of vectors consider the example.

WORKED EXAMPLE 4

A yacht is sailing at 10 km/h in a SE direction and a tide of 5 km/h is running towards the N, determine the velocity and direction of the yacht.

SOLUTION 4

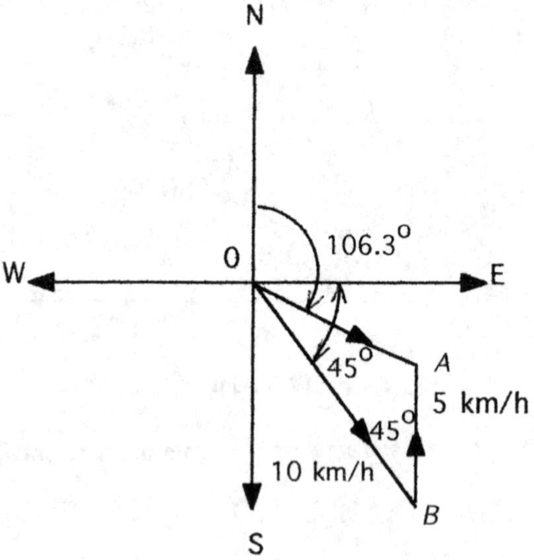

Fig. 8-I/9 The velocity of the yacht

The bearings of the yacht sailing at 10 km/h and the tide of 5 km/h towards N are shown. $\left|\overrightarrow{OA}\right|$ is required and its direction.

$OA^2 = 5^2 + 10^2 - 2 \times 5 \times 10 \cos 45° = 25 + 100 - 100 \times 0.707$

$\overrightarrow{OA}^2 = 125 - 70.7 = 54.3 \Rightarrow \left|\overrightarrow{OA}\right| = 7.47$ km/h.

Using the sine rule

$$\frac{5}{\sin \angle AOB} = \frac{7.37}{\sin 45°}$$

$$\sin \angle AOB = \frac{5 \times \sin 45°}{7.37} = 0.4796472$$

$\angle AOB = 28.66°$.

The bearing of the yacht is $135° - 28.7° = 106.3°$.

WORKED EXAMPLE 5

A particle is moving around a circular orbit. Determine the magnitude and direction of the acceleration using vectors.

SOLUTION 5

Consider a particle moving with constant speed v in a circle of radius r.

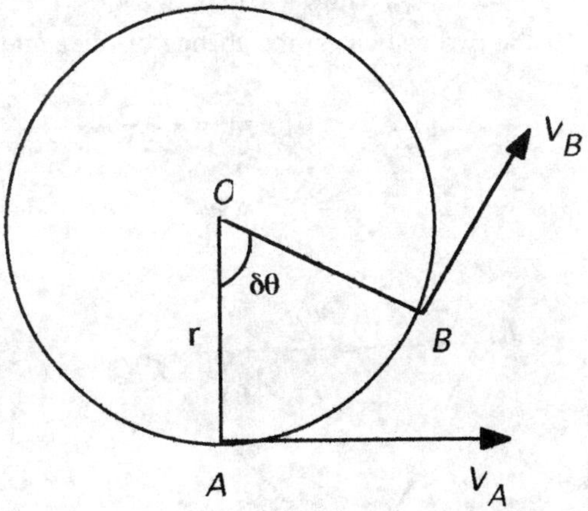

Fig. 8-I/10

A particle travels from A to B in a short interval of time δt, subtending an angle $\delta\theta$ as shown in Fig. 8-I/10

$$\text{speed} = \frac{\text{distance}}{\text{time}}$$

$$v = \frac{\text{arc } AB}{\delta t}$$

$$v = \frac{r\delta\theta}{\delta t}.$$

Let v_A and v_B be the velocities at A an B respectively, these are tangential at A and B.

a = acceleration = change of velocity = $v_B - v_A = v_B + (-v_A)$.

Drawing a vector PQ in the same direction as v_B and equal to v_B, QR in the opposite direction to v_A in the same direction as v_A and equal to v_A.

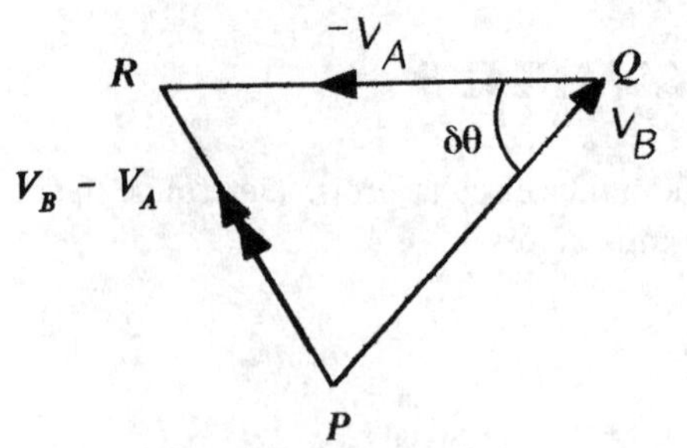

Fig. 8-I/11

PR is the resultant of the two velocities, the change of the angle between v_B and v_A is $\delta\theta$.

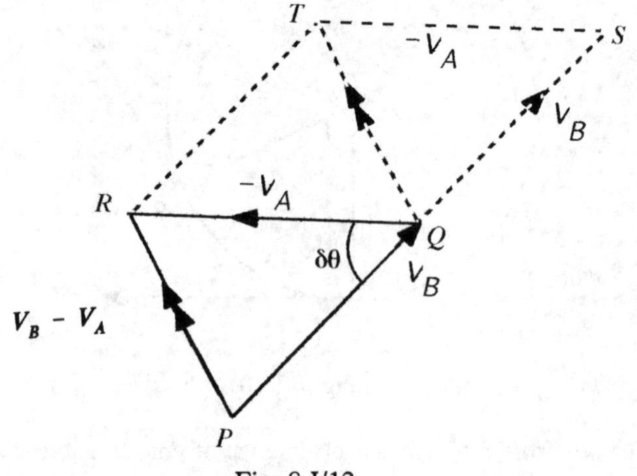

Fig. 8-I/12

Draw the parallelogram $QSTR$, PQ is the magnitude of v_B, RQ is the magnitude of $-v_A$, the resultant PR shows the magnitude and direction of acceleration, the change of velocity. $PR = v\delta\theta = v\,v\dfrac{\delta t}{r}$

$$a = \frac{\text{change in velocity}}{\text{time interval}} = \frac{PR}{\delta t} = \frac{v^2}{r}$$

$$\boxed{a = \frac{v^2}{r}}$$

since $v = r\omega$, $\boxed{a = \omega^2 r}$

The direction of $\overrightarrow{PR}$ is towards the centre O of the circle and the acceleration is called <u>centripetal acceleration</u>. Therefore the magnitude of the acceleration is $\dfrac{v^2}{r}$ or $\omega^2 r$ and it is directed towards the centre. Therefore velocities and accelerations are vector quantities.

EXERCISES 1

1. Distinguish clearly between scalars and vectors.

2. State clearly the three properties that are satisfied for two equal vectors. Distinguish between direction and sense.

3. The vector algebra addition is commutative. Explain and illustrate this statement.

4. Distinguish between a Free Vector and a Position Vector. Illustrate by means of a diagram.

5. Distinguish between positive and negative vectors.

6. Determine the resultant of two vectors using the parallelogram of vectors. Two forces of 100 N and 250 N are applied at a point, O, at the directions of 45° and 60° from the horizontal. Determine the resultant force and its direction from the horizontal. Use sine and cosine rules.

7. The bearing of yacht sailing 25 km/h is 045° and a tide of 5 km/h is running towards the E, determine the velocity and bearing of the yacht.

8. P divides AB in the ratio 2 : 3. Determine the position vector of the point P.

2. VECTORS IN TWO AND THREE DIMENSIONS

2.1 ORTHOGONAL VECTORS

Let **i**, **j**, and **k** be the unit vectors along the x-axis, y-axis and z-axis respectively

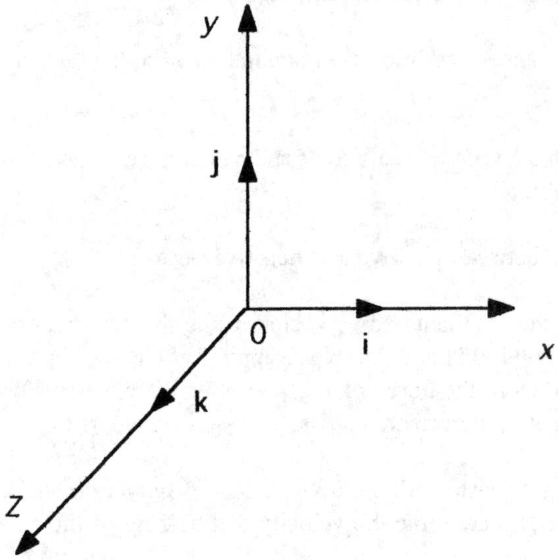

Fig. 8-I/13 The orthogonal unit vectors **i**, **j**, **k**.

x, y and z are three mutually perpendicular axes as shown in Fig. 8-I/13. Consider first for simplicity two dimensions.

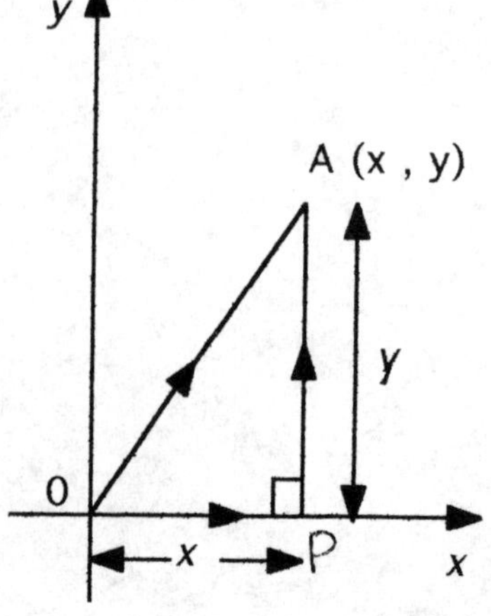

Fig. 8-I/14 The unit vectors **i**, **j**

Consider the position vector $\overrightarrow{OA} = x\mathbf{i} + y\mathbf{j}$ of the point A with coordinates, (x, y) and letting **i** and **j** be the unit vectors along the x-axis and y-axis

respectively then $\overrightarrow{OA} = x\mathbf{i} + y\mathbf{j}$, **i** and **j** denote the directions, therefore, we have x units along the x-axis, and y units along the y-axis.

In column matrix form $\overrightarrow{OA} = \begin{pmatrix} x \\ y \end{pmatrix} = x\mathbf{i} + y\mathbf{j}$.

The components of $\overrightarrow{OA}$ are $x\mathbf{i}$ and $y\mathbf{j}$, $\overrightarrow{OP} + \overrightarrow{PA} = \overrightarrow{OA}$

$$\overrightarrow{OA} = x\mathbf{i} + y\mathbf{j}.$$

2.2 MODULUS OR MAGNITUDE IN TWO DIMENSIONS

$$\left|\overrightarrow{OA}\right| = \sqrt{x^2 + y^2}$$

Extending the idea in three dimensions $\overrightarrow{OA} = x\mathbf{i} + y\mathbf{j} + z\mathbf{k}$

$$= \begin{pmatrix} x \\ y \\ z \end{pmatrix}.$$

Modulus or magnitude in three dimension

$$\left|\overrightarrow{OA}\right| = \sqrt{x^2 + y^2 + z^2}$$

The unit vector.

A unit vector in a given direction is a vector with unit magnitude in that direction. Let **a** be a vector, its magnitude is denoted as $|\mathbf{a}|$ and its unit vector in the direction of **a** is denoted as $\hat{\mathbf{a}}$ and defined

$$\hat{\mathbf{a}} = \frac{\mathbf{a}}{|\mathbf{a}|}$$

WORKED EXAMPLE 6

The following vectors are given:

(i) $\mathbf{a} = 3\mathbf{i} + 5\mathbf{j} - \mathbf{k}$

(ii) $\mathbf{b} = -\mathbf{i} - 2\mathbf{j} + 3\mathbf{k}$

(iii) $\mathbf{c} = 2\mathbf{i} + 3\mathbf{j} - 4\mathbf{k}$
(iv) $\mathbf{d} = -\mathbf{i} - \mathbf{j} - \mathbf{k}$
(v) $\mathbf{e} = \mathbf{i} + \mathbf{j} + \mathbf{k}$.

Determine the magnitudes of the vectors and hence find the corresponding unit vectors.

SOLUTION 6

(i) $\mathbf{a} = 3\mathbf{i} + 5\mathbf{j} - \mathbf{k}$

$|\mathbf{a}|$ = the magnitude or modulus of the vector **a**

$$|\mathbf{a}| = \sqrt{(3)^2 + (5)^2 + (-1)^2} = \sqrt{9 + 25 + 1} = \sqrt{35}$$

$\hat{\mathbf{a}}$ = the unit vector in the direction of the vector **a**.

$$\hat{\mathbf{a}} = \frac{\mathbf{a}}{|\mathbf{a}|} = \frac{1}{\sqrt{35}}(3i + 5j - k)$$

(ii) $\mathbf{b} = -\mathbf{i} - 2\mathbf{j} + 3\mathbf{k}$

$$|\mathbf{b}| = \sqrt{(-1)^2 + (-2)^2 + 3^2} = \sqrt{14}$$

$$\hat{\mathbf{b}} = \frac{\mathbf{b}}{|\mathbf{b}|} = \frac{1}{\sqrt{14}}(-\mathbf{i} - 2\mathbf{j} + 3\mathbf{k})$$ = the unit vector in the direction of the vector **b**.

(iii) $\mathbf{c} = 2\mathbf{i} + 3\mathbf{j} - 4\mathbf{k}$

$$|\mathbf{c}| = \sqrt{2^2 + 3^2 + (-4)^2} = \sqrt{29}$$

$$\hat{\mathbf{c}} = \frac{\mathbf{c}}{|\mathbf{c}|} = \frac{1}{\sqrt{29}}(2\mathbf{i} + 3\mathbf{j} - 4\mathbf{k})$$ = the unit vector in the direction of the vector **c**.

(iv) $\mathbf{d} = -\mathbf{i} - \mathbf{j} - \mathbf{k}$

$$|\mathbf{d}| = \sqrt{(-1)^2 + (-1)^2 + (-1)^2} = \sqrt{3}$$

$$\hat{\mathbf{d}} = \frac{\mathbf{d}}{|\mathbf{d}|} = -\frac{1}{\sqrt{3}}(\mathbf{i} + \mathbf{j} + \mathbf{k})$$ = the unit vector in the direction of the vector **d**.

(v) $\mathbf{e} = \mathbf{i} + \mathbf{j} + \mathbf{k}$

$$|\mathbf{e}| = \sqrt{1^2 + 1^2 + 1^2} = \sqrt{3}$$

$$\hat{\mathbf{e}} = \frac{1}{\sqrt{3}}(\mathbf{i} + \mathbf{j} + \mathbf{k}) = \text{the unit vector in the direction of the vector } \mathbf{e}.$$

2.3 THE COMPONENTS OF A VECTOR IN TWO AND THREE DIMENSIONS

A vector $\overrightarrow{OA}$ can be expressed in two or three dimensions.

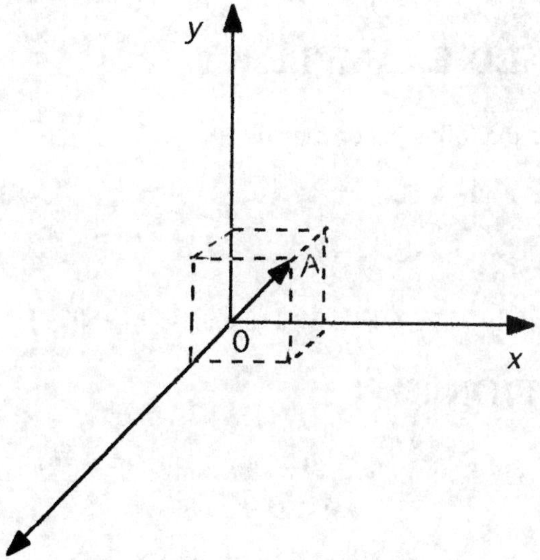

Fig. 8-I/15 The three components of $\overrightarrow{OA}$

If $\overrightarrow{OA}$ is the position vector of the point A with coordinates (x, y, z) and if **i**, **j** and **k** are the unit vectors along the axes ox, oy, and oz respectively the

$\overrightarrow{OA} = x\mathbf{i} + y\mathbf{j} + z\mathbf{k}$ and therefore $x\mathbf{i}$, $y\mathbf{j}$ and $z\mathbf{k}$ are the components of the

vector $\overrightarrow{OA}$ in the axes ox, oy and oz respectively.

$$\overrightarrow{OA} = x\mathbf{i} + y\mathbf{j} + z\mathbf{k}$$

$$= \begin{pmatrix} x \\ y \\ z \end{pmatrix}$$

$\begin{pmatrix} x \\ y \\ z \end{pmatrix}$ is the corresponding column matrix.

WORKED EXAMPLE 7

Find the addition of the vectors $\mathbf{a} = 2\mathbf{i} + 3\mathbf{j} + 5\mathbf{k}$

$\mathbf{b} = \mathbf{i} + 2\mathbf{j} + 3\mathbf{k}.$

SOLUTION 7

$$\mathbf{a} + \mathbf{b} = (2\mathbf{i} + 3\mathbf{j} + 5\mathbf{k}) + (\mathbf{i} + 2\mathbf{j} + 3\mathbf{k}) = 3\mathbf{i} + 5\mathbf{j} + 8\mathbf{k}$$

$$\mathbf{a} + \mathbf{b} = \begin{pmatrix} 2 \\ 3 \\ 5 \end{pmatrix} + \begin{pmatrix} 1 \\ 2 \\ 3 \end{pmatrix} = \begin{pmatrix} 2+1 \\ 3+2 \\ 5+3 \end{pmatrix} = \begin{pmatrix} 3 \\ 5 \\ 8 \end{pmatrix}.$$

WORKED EXAMPLE 8

Determine the following operations

(i) $\mathbf{a} + 2\mathbf{b} + 3\mathbf{c}$

(ii) $3\mathbf{a} - \mathbf{b} + \mathbf{c}$

(iii) $-\mathbf{a} + 4\mathbf{b} - 2\mathbf{c}.$

If $\mathbf{a} = \mathbf{i} + 2\mathbf{j} - 3\mathbf{k}$, $\mathbf{b} = -3\mathbf{j} + 5\mathbf{k}$ and $\mathbf{c} = -4\mathbf{i} - \mathbf{j} + 2\mathbf{k}$.

SOLUTION 8

(i) $\mathbf{a} + 2\mathbf{b} + 3\mathbf{c} = (\mathbf{i} + 2\mathbf{j} - 3\mathbf{k}) + 2(-3\mathbf{j} + 5\mathbf{k}) + 3(-4\mathbf{i} - \mathbf{j} + 2\mathbf{k})$
$= -11\mathbf{i} - 7\mathbf{j} + 13\mathbf{k}$

(ii) $3\mathbf{a} - \mathbf{b} + \mathbf{c} = 3(\mathbf{i} + 2\mathbf{j} - 3\mathbf{k}) - (-3\mathbf{j} + 5\mathbf{k}) + (-4\mathbf{i} - \mathbf{j} + 2\mathbf{k})$
$= -\mathbf{i} + 8\mathbf{j} - 12\mathbf{k}$

(iii) $-\mathbf{a} + 4\mathbf{b} - 2\mathbf{c} = -(\mathbf{i} + 2\mathbf{j} - 3\mathbf{k}) + 4(-3\mathbf{j} + 5\mathbf{k}) - 2(-4\mathbf{i} - \mathbf{j} + 2\mathbf{k})$
$= 7\mathbf{i} - 12\mathbf{j} + 19\mathbf{k}.$

WORKED EXAMPLE 9

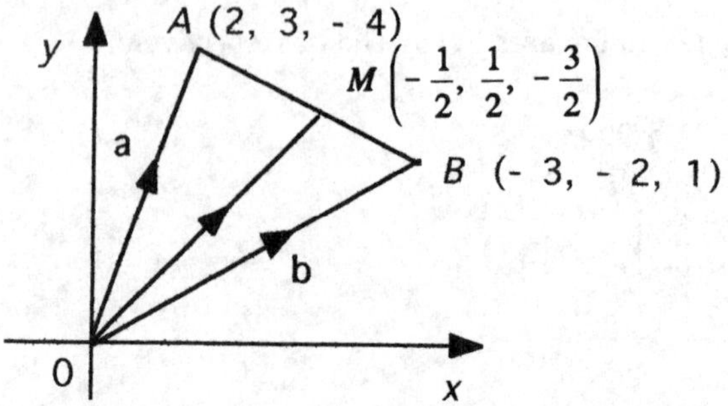

Fig. 8-I/16 Position vector of the mid-point

The position vectors of A and B are $\mathbf{a} = 2\mathbf{i} + 3\mathbf{j} - 4\mathbf{k}$ and $\mathbf{b} = -3\mathbf{i} - 2\mathbf{j} + \mathbf{k}$,

find the position vector of the mid-point of AB. Determine the magnitude of $\overrightarrow{AB}$

SOLUTION 9

The coordinates of A and B are $(2, 3, -4)$ and $(-3, -2, 1)$ respectively, the

mid-point of AB is $M\left(\frac{2-3}{2}, \frac{3-2}{2}, \frac{-4+1}{2}\right) \equiv M\left(-\frac{1}{2}, \frac{1}{2}, -\frac{3}{2}\right)$

hence the position vector of the mid-point is $OM = -\frac{1}{2}\mathbf{i} + \frac{1}{2}\mathbf{j} - \frac{3}{2}\mathbf{k}$.

$$\overrightarrow{AB} = \mathbf{b} - \mathbf{a} = -3\mathbf{i} - 2\mathbf{j} + \mathbf{k} - 2\mathbf{i} - 3\mathbf{j} + 4\mathbf{k} = -5\mathbf{i} - 5\mathbf{j} + 5\mathbf{k}$$

$$\left|\overrightarrow{AB}\right| = \sqrt{(-5)^2 + (-5)^2 + 5^2} = \sqrt{75} = 5\sqrt{3}.$$

WORKED EXAMPLE 10

The position vectors are given by the following coordinates (i) $A\ (1, 2, 3)$ (ii) $B\ (-1, 2, -3)$ (iii) $C\ (0, 3, 5)$ (iv) $D\ (-4, 2, 1)$ and (v) $E\ (3, 0, 4)$. Write down the position vectors in the form $a\mathbf{i} + b\mathbf{j} + c\mathbf{k}$.

SOLUTION 10

(i) $\overrightarrow{OA} = \mathbf{i} + 2\mathbf{j} + 3\mathbf{k}$ (ii) $\overrightarrow{OB} = -\mathbf{i} + 2\mathbf{j} - 3\mathbf{k}$ (iii) $\overrightarrow{OC} = 3\mathbf{j} + 5\mathbf{k}$

(iv) $\overrightarrow{OD} = -4\mathbf{i} + 2\mathbf{j} + \mathbf{k}$ (v) $\overrightarrow{OE} = 3\mathbf{i} + 4\mathbf{k}$.

WORKED EXAMPLE 11

Calculate the moduli of the vectors given:

(a) $\mathbf{u} = \mathbf{i} - 2\mathbf{j} + \sqrt{20}\,\mathbf{k}$ (b) $\mathbf{v} = -3\mathbf{i} + 7\mathbf{j} + 4\mathbf{k}$.

SOLUTION 11

(a) $|\mathbf{u}| = \sqrt{1^2 + (-2)^2 + \left(\sqrt{20}\right)^2} = \sqrt{1 + 4 + 20} = 5$

(b) $|\mathbf{v}| = \sqrt{(-3)^2 + 7^2 + 4^2} = \sqrt{9 + 49 + 16} = \sqrt{74} = 8.6.$

WORKED EXAMPLE 12

Show that the points P, Q, R, S with position vectors 2j, - 2i, - 4j and 2i - 2j respectively, are the vertices of a parallelogram.

SOLUTION 12

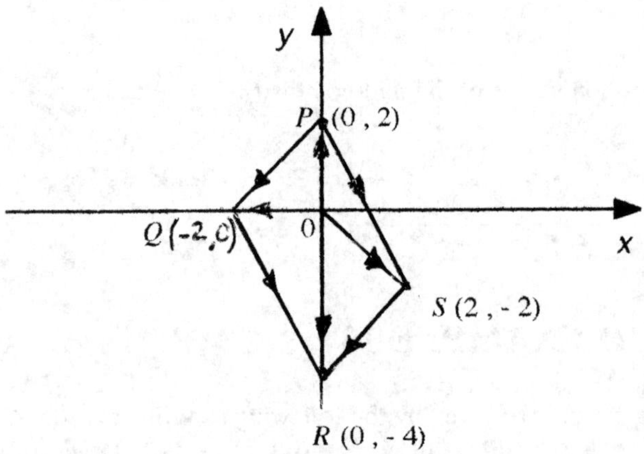

Fig. 8-I/17 Parallelogram

$\overrightarrow{PQ} = \overrightarrow{OQ} - \overrightarrow{OP} = -2j - 2i$, $\quad \overrightarrow{SR} = \overrightarrow{OR} - \overrightarrow{OS} = -4j - 2i + 2j$
$= -2j - 2i$

$\overrightarrow{PQ} = \overrightarrow{SR} = -2j - 2i$

$\overrightarrow{QR} = \overrightarrow{OR} - \overrightarrow{OQ} = -4j + 2i$, $\quad \overrightarrow{PS} = \overrightarrow{OS} - \overrightarrow{OP} = 2i - 2j - 2j = 2i - 4j$

$\overrightarrow{QR} = \overrightarrow{PS} = 2i - 4j$

PQRS is a parallelogram.

2.4 DIRECTION RATIO OF A VECTOR

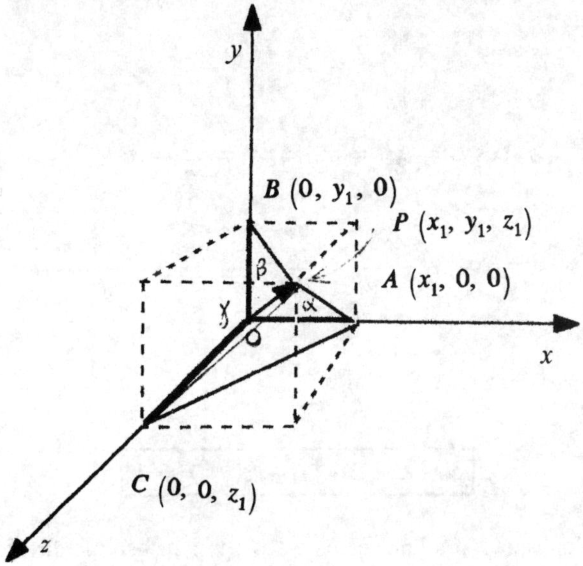

Fig. 8-I/18 Direction Ratios.

Consider a position vector $\overrightarrow{OP} = x_1\mathbf{i} + y_1\mathbf{j} + z_1\mathbf{k}$.

The ratios $x_1 : y_1 : z_1$ are called the direction ratios of the vector $\overrightarrow{OP}$.

2.5 DIRECTION COSINES OF A VECTOR

The position vector $\overrightarrow{OP}$ makes three angles, α, β, γ with x-axis, y-axis and z-axis respectively as shown in the Fig. 8-I/18 above.

Connect P to A, B and C as shown $\angle PAO$, $\angle PBO$, $\angle PCO$ are 90° each as shown in Fig. 8-I/19 below.

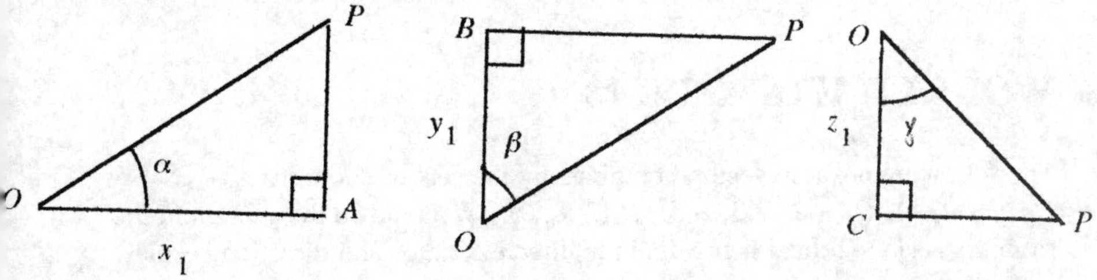

Fig. 8-I/19 Direction cosines

$$\cos\alpha = \frac{x_1}{|\overrightarrow{OP}|} = l, \cos\beta = \frac{y_1}{|\overrightarrow{OP}|} = m, \cos\gamma = \frac{z_1}{|\overrightarrow{OP}|} = n.$$

These cosines are called direction cosines.

Let $|\overrightarrow{OP}| = d$

$$\cos\alpha = \frac{x_1}{d} = l, \cos\beta = \frac{y_1}{d} = m, \cos\gamma = \frac{z_1}{d} = n$$

$$\cos^2\alpha + \cos^2\beta + \cos^2\gamma = \frac{x_1^2}{d^2} + \frac{y_1^2}{d^2} + \frac{z_1^2}{d^2} = \frac{x_1^2 + y_1^2 + z_1^2}{d^2} = \frac{d^2}{d^2} = 1$$

but $|\overrightarrow{OP}| = d = \sqrt{x_1^2 + y_1^2 + z_1^2}$

$$\boxed{\cos^2\alpha + \cos^2\beta + \cos^2\gamma = 1}$$

If the direction ratios of a line vector are $x_1 : y_1 : z_1$ then the direction cosines of this vector are $l : m : n$.

$$\boxed{l^2 + m^2 + n^2 = 1}$$

If $\overrightarrow{OP}$ is a position vector,

$\overrightarrow{OP} = x_1\mathbf{i} + y_1\mathbf{j} + z_1\mathbf{k} = dl\mathbf{i} + dm\mathbf{j} + dn\mathbf{k} = d\,(l\mathbf{i} + m\mathbf{j} + n\mathbf{k})$ since d is a scalar quantity then the vector $l\mathbf{i} + m\mathbf{j} + n\mathbf{k}$ is a unit vector.

$$\mathbf{a} = |\mathbf{a}|\,\hat{\mathbf{a}}$$

$$\hat{\mathbf{a}} = \frac{\mathbf{a}}{|\mathbf{a}|} = \frac{x_1\mathbf{i} + y_1\mathbf{j} + z_1\mathbf{k}}{\sqrt{x_1^2 + y_1^2 + z_1^2}} = \frac{x_1}{d}\mathbf{i} + \frac{y_1}{d}\mathbf{j} + \frac{z_1}{d}\mathbf{k} = l\mathbf{i} + m\mathbf{j} + n\mathbf{k}.$$

WORKED EXAMPLE 13

The following position vectors are given by the sets of coordinates $P\,(-1, 2, 4)$, $Q\,(-2, -3, -5)$, $R\,(7, 8, 9)$. Write down the vectors in the form $x\mathbf{i} + y\mathbf{j} + z\mathbf{k}$ and hence find the direction ratios and direction cosines.

SOLUTION 13

$\overrightarrow{OP} = -\mathbf{i} + 2\mathbf{j} + 4\mathbf{k}$, $\overrightarrow{OQ} = -2\mathbf{i} - 3\mathbf{j} - 5\mathbf{k}$, $\overrightarrow{OR} = 7\mathbf{i} + 8\mathbf{j} + 9\mathbf{k}$ the corresponding direction ratios are $-1 : 2 : 4$, $-2 : -3 : -5$, $7 : 8 : 9$.

The magintudes of the vectors are:

$$\left|\overrightarrow{OP}\right| = \sqrt{(-1)^2 + 2^2 + 4^2} = \sqrt{21}$$

$$\left|\overrightarrow{OQ}\right| = \sqrt{(-2)^2 + (-3)^2 + (-5)^2} = \sqrt{38}$$

$$\left|\overrightarrow{OR}\right| = \sqrt{7^2 + 8^2 + 9^2} = \sqrt{194}$$

the direction cosines are correspondingly

$$\frac{-1}{\sqrt{21}} : \frac{2}{\sqrt{21}} : \frac{4}{\sqrt{21}}, \frac{-2}{\sqrt{38}} : \frac{-3}{\sqrt{38}} : \frac{-5}{\sqrt{38}}, \frac{7}{\sqrt{194}} : \frac{8}{\sqrt{194}} : \frac{9}{\sqrt{194}}.$$

WORKED EXAMPLE 14

Determine the direction cosines of the vector $\overrightarrow{OP} = \mathbf{i} + 2\mathbf{j} + 3\mathbf{k}$ and hence

calculate the angles that $\overrightarrow{OP}$ make with the axes.

SOLUTION 14

$1 : 2 : 3$ are the direction ratios

$$\left|\overrightarrow{OP}\right| = \sqrt{1^2 + 2^2 + 3^2} = \sqrt{14}$$

$\frac{1}{\sqrt{14}} : \frac{2}{\sqrt{14}} : \frac{3}{\sqrt{14}}$ are the direction cosines

$\cos\alpha : \cos\beta : \cos\gamma$

$\cos\alpha = \frac{1}{\sqrt{14}}$, hence $\alpha = 74.5^\circ$

$\cos\beta = \frac{2}{\sqrt{14}}$, hence $\beta = 57.7^\circ$

$\cos\gamma = \frac{3}{\sqrt{14}}$, hence $\gamma = 36.7^\circ$

WORKED EXAMPLE 15

A position vector makes angles of 30° and 60° with the x-axis and z-axis respectively, determine the angle that the vector makes with the y-axis.

SOLUTION 15

$\cos^2 \alpha + \cos^2 \beta + \cos^2 \gamma = 1$

$\cos^2 30^\circ + \cos^2 \beta + \cos^2 60^\circ = 1$

$\cos^2 \beta = 1 - 0.75 - 0.25$

$\cos^2 \beta = 0$

$\boxed{\beta = 90^\circ}$

WORKED EXAMPLE 16

The position vectors $\overrightarrow{OP} = 3\mathbf{i} - 2\mathbf{j} - \mathbf{k}$ and $\overrightarrow{OQ}$ are referred to the origin O.

Determine $\overrightarrow{OQ}$ if the free vector $\overrightarrow{PQ} = -2\mathbf{i} + \mathbf{j} + 4\mathbf{k}$.

Calculate (i) the magnitudes of the vectors $\overrightarrow{OP}$, $\overrightarrow{OQ}$, and $\overrightarrow{PQ}$.

(ii) the units vectors corresponding to $\overrightarrow{OP}$, $\overrightarrow{OQ}$ and $\overrightarrow{PQ}$

(iii) the direction ratios of the vectors $\overrightarrow{OP}$, $\overrightarrow{OQ}$, and $\overrightarrow{PQ}$

(iv) the directions cosines of the vectors and hence the angles with respect to x-axis, y-axis and z-axis.

SOLUTION 16

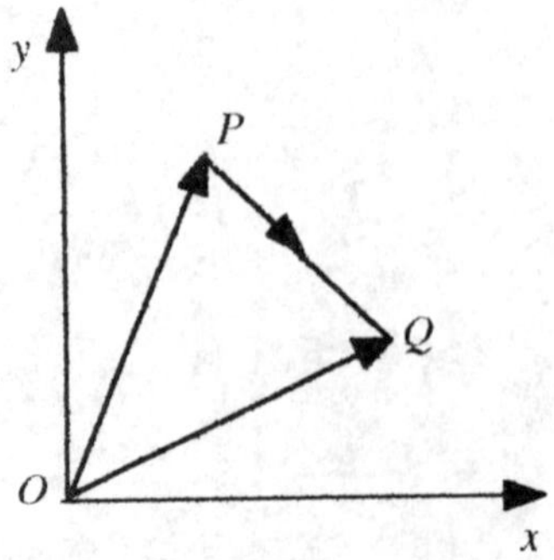

Fig. 8-I/20 Position Vector.

$\overrightarrow{OP} + \overrightarrow{PQ} = \overrightarrow{OQ}$

$3\mathbf{i} - 2\mathbf{j} - \mathbf{k} + (-2\mathbf{i} + \mathbf{j} + 4\mathbf{k}) = \overrightarrow{OQ}$

$\boxed{\overrightarrow{OQ} = \mathbf{i} - \mathbf{j} + 3\mathbf{k}}$

(i) $\left|\overrightarrow{OP}\right| = \sqrt{3^2 + (-2)^2 + (-1)^2} = \sqrt{14}$

$\left|\overrightarrow{OQ}\right| = \sqrt{1^2 + (-1)^2 + 3^2} = \sqrt{11}$

$\left|\overrightarrow{PQ}\right| = \sqrt{(-2)^2 + 1^2 + 4^2} = \sqrt{21}$

(ii) $\overrightarrow{OP} = \left|\overrightarrow{OP}\right| \hat{OP} \qquad \hat{OP} = \dfrac{\overrightarrow{OP}}{|\overrightarrow{OP}|} = \dfrac{3}{\sqrt{14}}\mathbf{i} - \dfrac{2}{\sqrt{14}}\mathbf{j} - \dfrac{1}{\sqrt{14}}\mathbf{k}$

$\overrightarrow{OQ} = \left|\overrightarrow{OQ}\right| \hat{OQ} \qquad \hat{OQ} = \dfrac{\overrightarrow{OQ}}{|\overrightarrow{OQ}|} = \dfrac{1}{\sqrt{11}}\mathbf{i} - \dfrac{1}{\sqrt{11}}\mathbf{j} + \dfrac{3}{\sqrt{11}}\mathbf{k}$

$\overrightarrow{PQ} = \left|\overrightarrow{PQ}\right| \hat{PQ} \qquad \hat{PQ} = \dfrac{\overrightarrow{PQ}}{|\overrightarrow{PQ}|} = -\dfrac{2}{\sqrt{21}}\mathbf{i} + \dfrac{1}{\sqrt{21}}\mathbf{j} + \dfrac{4}{\sqrt{21}}\mathbf{k}$

(iii) $l : m : n$ are the direction ratios.

$3 : -2 : -1$ for $\overrightarrow{OP}$

$1 : -1 : 3$ for $\overrightarrow{OQ}$

$-2 : 1 : 4$ for $\overrightarrow{PQ}$

(iv) $\cos\alpha$, $\cos\beta$ and $\cos\gamma$ are direction cosines

$\dfrac{3}{\sqrt{14}} : -\dfrac{2}{\sqrt{14}} : -\dfrac{1}{\sqrt{14}}$ for $\overrightarrow{OP}$

$\cos\alpha = \dfrac{3}{\sqrt{14}}, \quad \cos\beta = -\dfrac{2}{\sqrt{14}}, \quad \cos\gamma = -\dfrac{1}{\sqrt{14}}$

$\alpha = 36.7^\circ, \beta = 122.3^\circ, \gamma = 105.5^\circ$

$\dfrac{1}{\sqrt{11}} : -\dfrac{1}{\sqrt{11}} : \dfrac{3}{\sqrt{11}}$ for $\overrightarrow{OQ}$

$\cos\alpha = \dfrac{1}{\sqrt{11}}, \quad \cos\beta = -\dfrac{1}{\sqrt{11}}, \quad \cos\gamma = \dfrac{3}{\sqrt{11}}$

$\alpha = 72.5^\circ, \beta = 107.6^\circ, \gamma = 25.2^\circ$

$$-\frac{2}{\sqrt{21}} : \frac{1}{\sqrt{21}} : \frac{4}{\sqrt{21}} \text{ for } \overrightarrow{PQ}$$

$$\cos\alpha = -\frac{2}{\sqrt{21}}, \quad \cos\beta = \frac{1}{\sqrt{21}}, \quad \cos\gamma = \frac{4}{\sqrt{21}}$$

$\alpha = 115.9°$, $\beta = 77.4°$, $\gamma = 29.2°$.

2.6 THE POSITION VECTOR OF THE POINT T DIVIDING PQ IN THE RATION $\lambda : \mu$

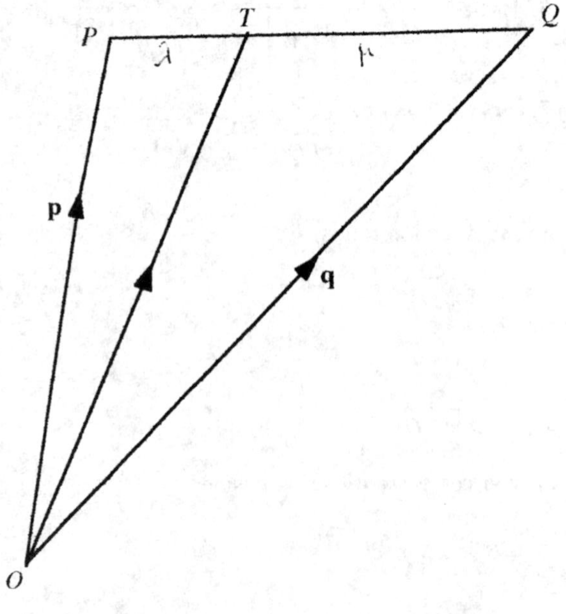

Fig. 8-I/21 Position vector of a point dividing PQ in the ratio $\lambda : \mu$

where **p** and **q** are the position vectors of the points P and Q.

$$\frac{\overrightarrow{PT}}{\overrightarrow{TQ}} = \frac{\lambda}{\mu}$$

$$\frac{\overrightarrow{PT}}{\overrightarrow{TQ}} = \frac{\lambda}{\lambda + \mu}$$

$$\overrightarrow{PT} = \frac{\lambda}{\lambda + \mu}\overrightarrow{PQ}$$

$$\overrightarrow{OT} = \overrightarrow{OP} + \overrightarrow{PT}$$

$$= \mathbf{p} + \frac{\lambda}{\lambda + \mu}(\mathbf{q} - \mathbf{p})$$

$$= \frac{\mathbf{p}(\lambda + \mu) + \lambda(\mathbf{q} - \mathbf{p})}{\lambda + \mu}$$

$$= \frac{\mathbf{p}\lambda + \mathbf{p}\mu + \mathbf{q}\lambda - \mathbf{p}\lambda}{\lambda + \mu}$$

$$\boxed{\overrightarrow{OT} = \frac{\mathbf{p}\mu + \mathbf{q}\lambda}{\lambda + \mu}}$$

2.7 THREE DIMENSION COORDINATE GEOMETRY

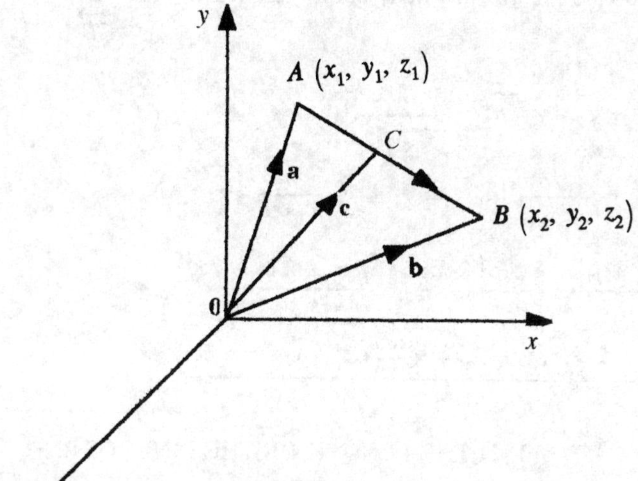

Fig. 8-I/22

$\overrightarrow{OA} = x_1\mathbf{i} + y_1\mathbf{j} + z_1\mathbf{k}$ the position vector of A (x_1, y_1, z_1)

$\overrightarrow{OB} = x_2\mathbf{i} + y_2\mathbf{j} + z_2\mathbf{k}$ the position vector of B (x_2, y_2, z_2)

$\overrightarrow{AB} = \overrightarrow{OB} - \overrightarrow{OA}$ the free vector

$$= (x_2 - x_1)\mathbf{i} + (y_2 - y_1)\mathbf{j} + (z_2 - z_1)\mathbf{k}$$

LENGTH OF $\overrightarrow{AB}$

$$\left|\overrightarrow{AB}\right| = \sqrt{(x_2 - x_1)^2 + (y_2 - y_1)^2 + (z_2 - z_1)^2}$$

DIRECTION RATIOS OF $\overrightarrow{AB}$

$$(x_2 - x_1) : (y_2 - y_1) : (z_2 - z_1)$$

DIRECTION COSINES OF $\overrightarrow{AB}$

$$\frac{x_2 - x_1}{\left|\overrightarrow{AB}\right|} : \frac{y_2 - y_1}{\left|\overrightarrow{AB}\right|} : \frac{z_2 - z_1}{\left|\overrightarrow{AB}\right|}$$

POINT DIVIDING AB in the ratio $\lambda : \mu$

Let C divide the line AB internally in the ratio $\lambda : \mu$, then $\frac{\overrightarrow{AC}}{\overrightarrow{CB}} = \frac{\lambda}{\mu}$

$$\overrightarrow{OC} = \overrightarrow{OA} + \overrightarrow{AC} = \overrightarrow{OA} + \frac{\lambda}{\lambda + \mu}\overrightarrow{AB}$$

$$= \overrightarrow{OA} + \frac{\lambda}{\lambda + \mu}(\mathbf{b} - \mathbf{a}) = \mathbf{a} + \frac{\lambda}{\lambda + \mu}(\mathbf{b} - \mathbf{a})$$

$$= \frac{(\lambda + \mu)\mathbf{a} + \lambda\mathbf{b} - \lambda\mathbf{a}}{\lambda + \mu} = \frac{\mu\mathbf{a} + \lambda\mathbf{b}}{\lambda + \mu}$$

$$= \frac{\mu(x_1\mathbf{i} + y_1\mathbf{j} + z_1\mathbf{k}) + \lambda(x_2\mathbf{i} + y_2\mathbf{j} + z_2\mathbf{k})}{\lambda + \mu}$$

TO FIND THE LENGTH OF THE LINE JOINING $P(x_1, y_1, z_1)$ AND $Q(x_2, y_2, z_2)$

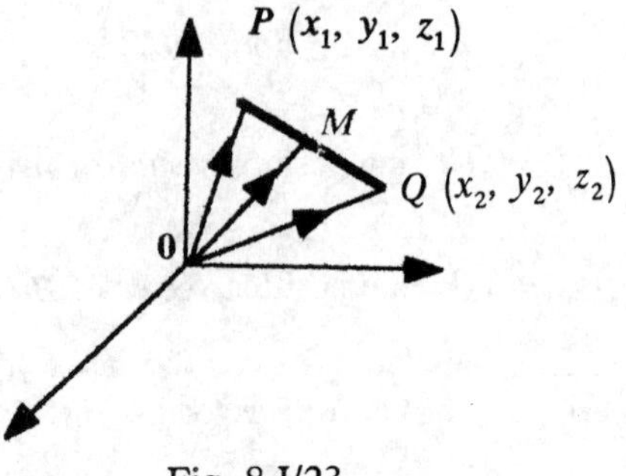

Fig. 8-I/23

The position vectors $\overrightarrow{OP}$ and $\overrightarrow{OQ}$ are $\overrightarrow{OP} = x_1\mathbf{i} + y_1\mathbf{j} + z_1\mathbf{k}$ and

$\overrightarrow{OQ} = x_2\mathbf{i} + y_2\mathbf{j} + z_2\mathbf{k}$.

$$\overrightarrow{PQ} = \overrightarrow{OQ} - \overrightarrow{OP} = (x_2 - x_1)\mathbf{i} + (y_2 - y_1)\mathbf{j} + (z_2 - z_1)\mathbf{k}$$

$$\left|\overrightarrow{PQ}\right| = \sqrt{(x_2 - x_1)^2 + (y_2 - y_1)^2 + (z_2 - z_1)^2}$$

TO FIND THE MIDPOINT OF *PQ*

Let M be the mid-point of PQ, the position vector $\overrightarrow{OM} = \overrightarrow{OP} + \overrightarrow{PM}$

$$= \overrightarrow{OP} + \frac{1}{2}\overrightarrow{PQ}$$

$$= \overrightarrow{OP} + \frac{1}{2}\left(\overrightarrow{OQ} - \overrightarrow{OP}\right)$$

$$= \frac{1}{2}\overrightarrow{OP} + \frac{1}{2}\overrightarrow{OQ}$$

$$\boxed{\overrightarrow{OM} = \frac{1}{2}\left(\overrightarrow{OP} + \overrightarrow{OQ}\right)}$$

$$\overrightarrow{OM} = \frac{1}{2}\left[(x_1 + x_2)\mathbf{i} + (y_1 + y_2)\mathbf{j} + (z_1 + z_2)\mathbf{k}\right]$$

$$M \left(\frac{1}{2}(x_1 + x_2), \frac{1}{2}(y_1 + y_2), \frac{1}{2}(z_1 + z_2)\right)$$

WORKED EXAMPLE 17

A triangle ABC has the following coordinates: A (1, 2, 3), B (− 1, − 2, − 3) and C (3, 4, 6). Write down the position vectors in the form $a\,\mathbf{i} + b\,\mathbf{j} + c\,\mathbf{k}$ and hence

determine the vectors $\overrightarrow{AB}$, $\overrightarrow{BC}$ and $\overrightarrow{AC}$.

Calculate the perimeter and hence the area of the triangle ABC.

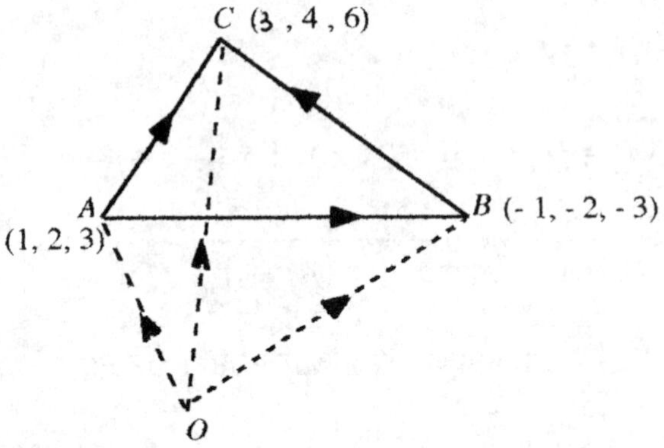

Fig. 8-I/24 The perimeter and area of Δ *ABC*

SOLUTION 17

$$\overrightarrow{AB} = \overrightarrow{OB} - \overrightarrow{OA} = (-\mathbf{i} - 2\mathbf{j} - 3\mathbf{k}) - (\mathbf{i} + 2\mathbf{j} + 3\mathbf{k})$$
$$= -2\mathbf{i} - 4\mathbf{j} - 6\mathbf{k}$$

$$\overrightarrow{BC} = \overrightarrow{OC} - \overrightarrow{OB} = (3\mathbf{i} + 4\mathbf{j} + 6\mathbf{k}) - (-\mathbf{i} - 2\mathbf{j} - 3\mathbf{k})$$
$$= 4\mathbf{i} + 6\mathbf{j} + 9\mathbf{k}$$

$$\overrightarrow{AC} = \overrightarrow{OC} - \overrightarrow{OA} = (3\mathbf{i} + 4\mathbf{j} + 6\mathbf{k}) - (\mathbf{i} + 2\mathbf{j} + 3\mathbf{k})$$
$$= 2\mathbf{i} + 2\mathbf{j} + 3\mathbf{k}$$

$$\overrightarrow{AB} + \overrightarrow{BC} = \overrightarrow{AC}$$

$$\text{L.H.S.} = \overrightarrow{AB} + \overrightarrow{BC} = (-2\mathbf{i} - 4\mathbf{j} - 6\mathbf{k}) + (4\mathbf{i} + 6\mathbf{j} + 9\mathbf{k})$$
$$= 2\mathbf{i} + 2\mathbf{j} + 3\mathbf{k}$$

$$\left|\overrightarrow{AB}\right| = \sqrt{(-2)^2 + (-4)^2 + (-6)^2} = \sqrt{4 + 16 + 36} = \sqrt{56} = 7.48$$

$$\left|\overrightarrow{BC}\right| = \sqrt{4^2 + 6^2 + 9^2} = \sqrt{16 + 36 + 81} = \sqrt{133} = 11.5$$

$$\left|\overrightarrow{AC}\right| = \sqrt{2^2 + 2^2 + 3^2} = \sqrt{17} = 4.12.$$

Each preceding and subsequent calculation is worked out to 3 significant figures.
The perimeter $= 7.48 + 11.5 + 4.12 = 23.1$

s = semi-perimeter

$$= \frac{23.1}{2} = 11.6 \text{ units.}$$

$$\text{Area } \Delta = \sqrt{s(s-a)(s-b)(s-c)}$$

$$= \sqrt{11.6 \times (11.6 - 7.48)(11.6 - 11.5)(11.6 - 4.12)}$$

$$= \sqrt{11.6 \times 4.12 \times 0.1 \times 7.48}$$

$$= 5.98 \text{ square units.}$$

WORKED EXAMPLE 18

The position vectors of the triangle *PQR* are $\overrightarrow{OP} = 2\mathbf{i} + 5\mathbf{j} - 7\mathbf{k}$

$$\overrightarrow{OQ} = -3\mathbf{i} - 2\mathbf{j} + 5\mathbf{k}$$

$$\overrightarrow{OR} = -\mathbf{i} + 3\mathbf{j} - 6\mathbf{k}.$$

Determine the vectors of the sides of the triangle and hence calculate the perimeter and the area of the triangle.

SOLUTION 18

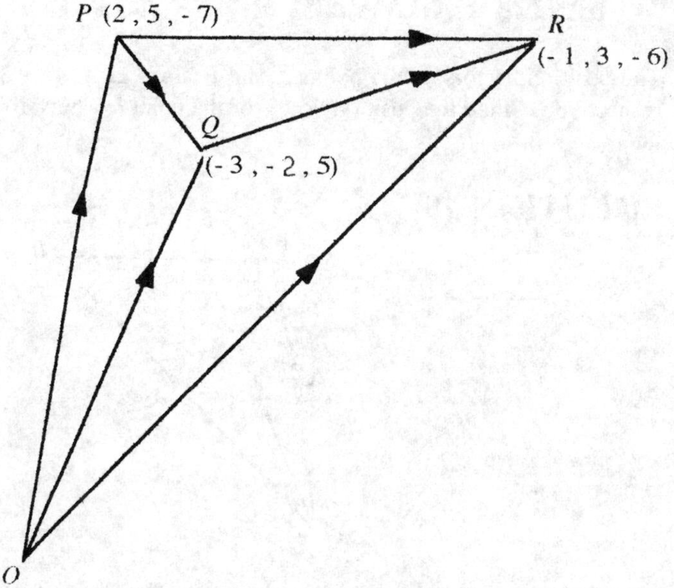

Fig. 8-I/25 Perimeter and area of Δ *PQR*

$$\overrightarrow{PQ} = \overrightarrow{OQ} - \overrightarrow{OP}$$

$$= (-3\mathbf{i} - 2\mathbf{j} + 5\mathbf{k}) - (2\mathbf{i} + 5\mathbf{j} - 7\mathbf{k})$$

$$= -5\mathbf{i} - 7\mathbf{j} + 12\mathbf{k}$$

$\overrightarrow{QR} = \overrightarrow{OR} - \overrightarrow{OQ}$

$= (-\mathbf{i} + 3\mathbf{j} - 6\mathbf{k}) - (-3\mathbf{i} - 2\mathbf{j} + 5\mathbf{k})$

$= 2\mathbf{i} + 5\mathbf{j} - 11\mathbf{k}$

$\overrightarrow{PR} = \overrightarrow{OR} - \overrightarrow{OP} = (-\mathbf{i} + 3\mathbf{j} - 6\mathbf{k}) - (2\mathbf{i} + 5\mathbf{j} - 7\mathbf{k})$
$= -3\mathbf{i} - 2\mathbf{j} + \mathbf{k}$

Each subsequent calculation is worked out to three significant figures.

$$\left|\overrightarrow{PQ}\right| = \sqrt{(-5)^2 + (-7)^2 + (12)^2} = \sqrt{25 + 49 + 144} = \sqrt{218} = 14.8$$

$$\left|\overrightarrow{QR}\right| = \sqrt{2^2 + 5^2 + (-11)^2} = \sqrt{4 + 25 + 121} = \sqrt{150} = 12.3$$

$$\left|\overrightarrow{PR}\right| = \sqrt{(-3)^2 + (-2)^2 + 1^2} = \sqrt{9 + 4 + 1} = \sqrt{14} = 3.74$$

the semi-perimeter $s = \dfrac{14.8 + 12.3 + 3.74}{2} = 15.4$ hence $2s = 30.8$ units.

Area $\Delta = \sqrt{s(s-a)(s-b)(s-c)} = \sqrt{15.4 \times 0.6 \times 3.1 \times 11.66} = 18.3$ square units.

WORKED EXAMPLE 19

The position vectors of the points A and B are $-2\mathbf{i} + 4\mathbf{j} - 3\mathbf{k}$ and $3\mathbf{i} - 5\mathbf{j} + 2\mathbf{k}$ respectively. Find the position vector of the point P which divides AB internally in the ratio 3:2.

SOLUTION 19

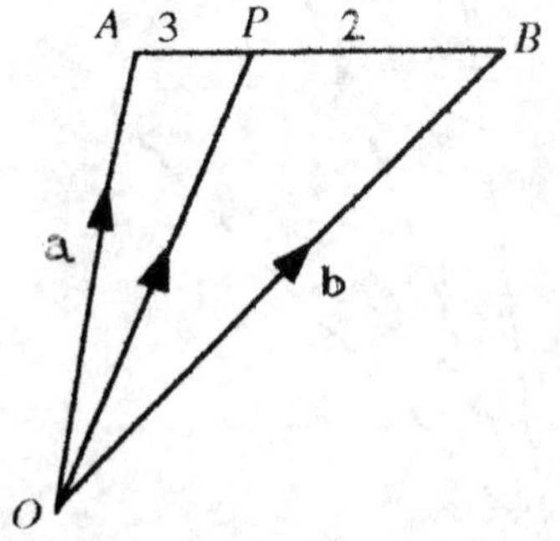

Fig. 8-I/26 Position vector $\overrightarrow{OP}$

$$\overrightarrow{OP} = \frac{\mathbf{a}\mu + \mathbf{b}\lambda}{\lambda + \mu} = \frac{\mathbf{a}2 + \mathbf{b}3}{3 + 2} = \frac{2(-2\mathbf{i} + 4\mathbf{j} - 3\mathbf{k}) + 3(3\mathbf{i} - 5\mathbf{j} + 2\mathbf{k})}{5}$$

$$= \frac{-4\mathbf{i} + 8\mathbf{j} + -6\mathbf{k} + 9\mathbf{i} - 15\mathbf{j} + 6\mathbf{k}}{5} = \frac{5\mathbf{i} - 7\mathbf{j}}{5} = \mathbf{i} - \frac{7}{5}\mathbf{j}.$$

EXERCISES 2

1. The position vectors are given by the following coordinates (i) $A\ (1, 2, 3)$ (ii) $B\ (-1, 2, -3)$ (iii) $C\ (0, 3, 5)$ (iv) $D\ (-4, 2, 1)$ and (v) $E\ (3, 0, 4)$. Write down the vectors in the form $a\mathbf{i} + b\mathbf{j} + c\mathbf{k}$.

2. The position vectors of A, B and C are given $2\mathbf{i} + 3\mathbf{j} - \mathbf{k}$, $-\mathbf{i} + 2\mathbf{j} - 4\mathbf{k}$, $-3\mathbf{i} + \mathbf{j} + \mathbf{k}$ respectively. Write down the coordinates of A, B and C.

3. Calculate the modulus of the vectors given:

   (a) $\mathbf{u} = \mathbf{i} - 2\mathbf{j} + \sqrt{20}\,\mathbf{k}$ (b) $\mathbf{v} = -3\mathbf{i} + 7\mathbf{j} + 4\mathbf{k}$.

4. Determine the magnitude of the lines $\overrightarrow{OP}$, $\overrightarrow{OQ}$, $\overrightarrow{OR}$ where $P\ (3, 4, 5)$, $Q\ (-2, -1, 1)$, $R\ (2, -3, 5)$.

5. If $\mathbf{a} = \begin{pmatrix} 1 \\ 2 \\ 3 \end{pmatrix}$, $\mathbf{b} = \begin{pmatrix} 2 \\ 2 \\ 2 \end{pmatrix}$, $\mathbf{c} = \begin{pmatrix} 3 \\ 0 \\ 5 \end{pmatrix}$,

   find (i) $|\mathbf{a}|$ (ii) $|\mathbf{b} - \mathbf{a}|$ (iii) $\left| 2\mathbf{c} - \frac{1}{2}\mathbf{a} \right|$.

6. The position vectors $\overrightarrow{OP}$, $\overrightarrow{OQ}$, and $\overrightarrow{OR}$ are given by $P\ (-1, -2, -3)$.

   $Q\ (1, 4, 7)$, $R\ (3, -5, 8)$. Determine $\overrightarrow{PQ}$, $\overrightarrow{PR}$ and $\overrightarrow{QR}$ and hence find their moduli.

7. Determine the direction ratios and direction cosines for the following vectors: (i) $\mathbf{u} = \mathbf{i} - 3\mathbf{j} + 5\mathbf{k}$ (ii) $\mathbf{v} = -2\mathbf{i} + 4\mathbf{j} - 6\mathbf{k}$ (iii) $\mathbf{w} = 3\mathbf{i} - 7\mathbf{j} + 11\mathbf{k}$.

8. The direction cosines of a vector are $\frac{5}{7} : \frac{4}{7} : \frac{2\sqrt{2}}{7}$. Calculate the angles that this vector is making with x, y, and z axes respectively. Check that $\cos^2\alpha + \cos^2\beta + \cos^2\gamma = 1$.

9. The angles that a vector make with the x and y axes are 45° and 67.5° respectively. Calculate the angle that it makes with the z-axis.

10. Show that $\cos^2\alpha + \cos^2\beta + \cos^2\gamma = 1$.

11. Show that the position vectors of a point P dividing a line AB in the ratio $\lambda : \mu$ where **a** and **b** are the position vectors of the points P and Q is given by

$$\boxed{\overrightarrow{OP} = \frac{\mathbf{a}\mu + \mathbf{b}\lambda}{\lambda + \mu}}$$

12. The direction cosines of a vector are $\frac{2\sqrt{10}}{9} : \frac{5}{9} : \frac{4}{9}$. Calculate the angles that this vector is making with x, y and z respectively.

13. Deduce that the points with position vectors **a**, **b** and $\mathbf{a}\mu + \mathbf{b}\lambda$ are collinear provided $\lambda + \mu = 1$.

14. Find the direction cosines of the line joining (a, b, c) to (l, m, n).

15. Find the direction cosines of the line joining (1, 2, 3) to (3, − 4, 5).

16. If the direction cosines of a line are in the ratios 3 : 7 : 11 find the actual direction cosines of the line.

17. A line makes angles of 70° and 80° with the positive directions of the x-axis and z-axis respectively. Find the angle it makes with the positive direction of the y-axis.

18. Find the direction cosines of a line that makes equal angles with the three axes.

19. If $\gamma = 2\alpha$ and $\beta = \alpha$. Find the direction cosines.

20. A triangle ABC has the following position vectors: $\overrightarrow{OA} = 2\mathbf{i} - 3\mathbf{j} + \mathbf{k}$

$$\overrightarrow{OB} = \mathbf{i} + 5\mathbf{k}$$

$$\overrightarrow{OC} = -\mathbf{i} + 5\mathbf{j} + 7\mathbf{k}.$$

Determine the free vectors $\overrightarrow{AB}$, $\overrightarrow{BC}$ and $\overrightarrow{AC}$. Calculate the perimeter ABC and hence determine the area of the triangle using Heron's Formula.

3. THE VECTOR EQUATION OF A STRAIGHT LINE

3.1 $\mathbf{r} = \mathbf{a} + \lambda\mathbf{b}$

The vector equation through a fixed point A, of position vector $\mathbf{a} = a_1\mathbf{i} + a_2\mathbf{j} + a_3\mathbf{k}$ and parallel to a vector $\mathbf{b} = b_1\mathbf{i} + b_2\mathbf{j} + b_3\mathbf{k}$.

Let $\overrightarrow{OA}$ be the position vector given as $\mathbf{a} = a_1\mathbf{i} + a_2\mathbf{j} + a_3\mathbf{k}$ and $\mathbf{b} = b_1\mathbf{i} + b_2\mathbf{j} + b_3\mathbf{k}$. It is required to find the vector equation of straight line passing through A and parallel to a vector $\mathbf{b}$.

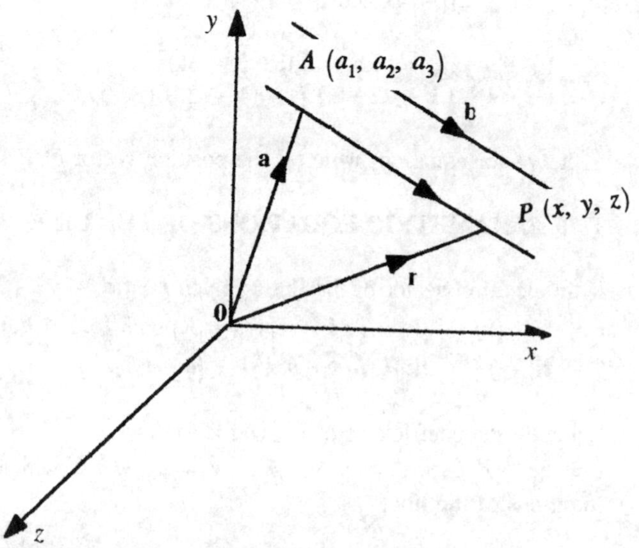

Fig. 8-I/27 Vector equation of a straight line

Let $P\ (x, y\ , z)$ be a point on the straight line whose vector equation is required.

$\overrightarrow{AP} = \lambda\mathbf{b}$ where λ is a scalar parameter. From the triangle OAP we have

$\overrightarrow{OA} + \overrightarrow{AP} = \overrightarrow{OP}$, the clockwise sum of the vectors is equal to the anticlockwise vector.

$\overrightarrow{OA} = \mathbf{a} = a_1\mathbf{i} + a_2\mathbf{j} + a_3\mathbf{k}$ and $\overrightarrow{AP} = \lambda\mathbf{b} = \lambda\left(b_1\mathbf{i} + b_2\mathbf{j} + b_3\mathbf{k}\right)$

$\mathbf{a} + \lambda\mathbf{b} = \mathbf{r}$

$$\boxed{\mathbf{r} = \mathbf{a} + \lambda\mathbf{b}}$$

WORKED EXAMPLE 20

Determine the vector equation of the line which passes through the point $A\ (-3, 2, 4)$ and is parallel to the vector $\mathbf{b} = \mathbf{i} - \mathbf{j} + 3\mathbf{k}$.

SOLUTION 20

Let the vector equation of the line be $\mathbf{r} = \mathbf{a} + \lambda\mathbf{b}$ where
$\mathbf{a} = -3\mathbf{i} + 2\mathbf{j} + 4\mathbf{k}$ and $\mathbf{b} = \mathbf{i} - \mathbf{j} + 3\mathbf{k}$.

$\mathbf{r} = (-3\mathbf{i} + 2\mathbf{j} + 4\,\mathbf{k}) + \lambda\,(\mathbf{i} - \mathbf{j} + 3\mathbf{k})$
$\mathbf{r} = (-3 + \lambda)\,\mathbf{i} + (2 - \lambda)\,\mathbf{j} + (4 + 3\lambda)\,\mathbf{k}$

is the vector equation, which is the position vector of $P\ (x, y, z)$.

3.2 THE PARAMETRIC EQUATIONS OF THE LINE

If the position vector of the line is given $\mathbf{r} = x\mathbf{i} + y\mathbf{j} + z\mathbf{k}$ then
$\mathbf{r} = x\mathbf{i} + y\mathbf{j} + z\mathbf{k} = \left(a_1\mathbf{i} + a_2\mathbf{j} + a_3\mathbf{k}\right) + \lambda\left(b_1\mathbf{i} + b_2\mathbf{j} + b_3\mathbf{k}\right)$
$\quad x\mathbf{i} + y\mathbf{j} + z\mathbf{k} = \left(a_1 + b_1\lambda\right)\mathbf{i} + \left(a_2 + b_2\lambda\right)\mathbf{j} + \left(a_3 + b_3\lambda\right)\mathbf{k}$

Equating the coefficients of **i**, **j** and **k** we have
$x = a_1 + b_1\lambda,\quad y = a_2 + b_2\lambda,\quad z = a_3 + b_3\lambda$ which are the parametric equations of the line.

WORKED EXAMPLE 21

Find the parametric equation of the vector equation of the line

$\mathbf{r} = (-3 + \lambda)\,\mathbf{i} + (2 - \lambda)\,\mathbf{j} + (4 + 3\lambda)\,\mathbf{k}$.

SOLUTION 21

$\mathbf{r} = x\mathbf{i} + y\mathbf{j} + z\mathbf{k} = (-3 + \lambda)\,\mathbf{i} + (2 - \lambda)\,\mathbf{j} + (4 + 3\lambda)\,\mathbf{k}$.

Equating the coefficients of **i**, **j** and **k** we have $x = -3 + \lambda$
$y = 2 - \lambda$
$z = 4 + 3\lambda$

the parametric equations of the line.

3.3 THE CARTESIAN EQUATION OF THE LINE

The parametric equations of the line are $x = a_1 + b_1\lambda$, $y = a_2 + b_2\lambda$, $z = a_3 + b_3\lambda$ and

$$x = a_1 + b_1\lambda \quad \text{or} \quad \frac{x - a_1}{b_1} = \lambda$$

$$y = a_2 + b_2\lambda \quad \text{or} \quad \frac{y - a_2}{b_2} = \lambda$$

$$z = a_3 + b_3\lambda \quad \text{or} \quad \frac{z - a_3}{b_3} = \lambda.$$

The cartesian equations of the line are $\dfrac{x - a_1}{b_1} = \dfrac{y - a_2}{b_2} = \dfrac{z - a_3}{b_3} = \lambda$

$b_1 : b_2 : b_3$ are the direction ratios of the line.

WORKED EXAMPLE 22

Determine the cartesian equations of the line whose parametric equations are $x = -3 + \lambda, y = 2 - \lambda$, and $z = 4 + 3\lambda$ and hence find the direction ratios of the line.

SOLUTION 22

$$x = -3 + \lambda \quad \text{or} \quad \frac{x + 3}{1} = \lambda$$

$$y = 2 - \lambda \quad \text{or} \quad \frac{-2 + y}{-1} = \lambda$$

$$z = 4 + 3\lambda \quad \text{or} \quad \frac{z - 4}{3} = \lambda$$

$$\lambda = \frac{x + 3}{1} = \frac{-2 + y}{-1} = \frac{z - 4}{3}.$$

The direction ratios of the line are $1 : -1 : 3$.

WORKED EXAMPLE 23

A line passes through a fixed point A (4, 5, − 7) and is parallel to a vector $2\mathbf{i} - 3\mathbf{j} + 5\mathbf{k}$. Determine the following:

(i) The vector equation of the line.
(ii) The parametric equations of the line.
(iii) The cartesian equations of the line.

SOLUTION 23

(i) $\mathbf{r} = \mathbf{a} + \lambda\mathbf{b}$ the vector equation of the line,
$\mathbf{r} = (4\mathbf{i} + 5\mathbf{j} - 7\mathbf{k}) + \lambda\,(2\mathbf{i} - 3\mathbf{j} + 5\mathbf{k})$ or
$\mathbf{r} = (4 + 2\lambda)\,\mathbf{i} + (5 - 3\lambda)\mathbf{j} + (-7 + 5\lambda)\,\mathbf{k}.$

(ii) The parametric equations of the line
$\mathbf{r} = x\mathbf{i} + y\mathbf{j} + z\mathbf{k} = (4 + 2\lambda)\,\mathbf{i} + (5 - 3\lambda)\,\mathbf{j} + (-7 + 5\lambda)\,\mathbf{k}$
equating the coefficients of **i**, **j** and **k**

$x = 4 + 2\lambda$ ... (1)
$y = 5 - 3\lambda$ ... (2)
$z = -7 + 5\lambda$ ... (3)
the parametric equations of the line.

(iii) The cartesian equations of the line are found by equating λ in each case of (1), (2) and (3)

$$\lambda = \frac{x - 4}{2} = \frac{y - 5}{-3} = \frac{z + 7}{5}.$$

3.4 A LINE PASSING THROUGH TWO FIXED POINTS

Let the position vectors of the two fixed points be $\overrightarrow{OA} = x_1\mathbf{i} + y_1\mathbf{j} + z_1\mathbf{k} = \mathbf{a}$

and $\overrightarrow{OB} = x_2\mathbf{i} + y_2\mathbf{j} + z_2\mathbf{k} = \mathbf{b}$ respectively.

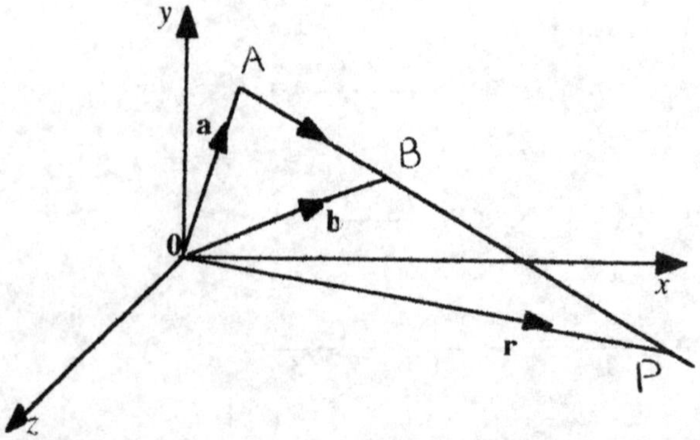

Fig. 8-I/28 Vector equation of a line passing through two fixed points

Let P be a point on AB produced $\overrightarrow{OA} + \overrightarrow{AB} = \overrightarrow{OB}$ from which we have

$$\overrightarrow{AB} = \overrightarrow{OB} - \overrightarrow{OA}$$

$$\overrightarrow{AB} = \mathbf{b} - \mathbf{a}$$

$$\overrightarrow{AP} = t\,\overrightarrow{AB} = t\,(\mathbf{b} - \mathbf{a}).$$

From OAP triangle, we have

$$\mathbf{r} = \overrightarrow{OA} + \overrightarrow{AP} = \mathbf{a} + t\,(\mathbf{b} - \mathbf{a})$$

$$\boxed{\mathbf{r} = \mathbf{a} + t\,(\mathbf{b} - \mathbf{a}).}$$

The vector equation of the line which passes through two fixed points $A\left(x_1, y_1, z_1\right)$ and $B\left(x_2, y_2, z_2\right)$ whose position vectors are **a** and **b** respectively.

This vector equation of the line can be expressed as column matrices

$$\mathbf{r} = x\mathbf{i} + y\mathbf{j} + z\mathbf{k} = \begin{pmatrix} x_1 \\ y_1 \\ z_1 \end{pmatrix} + t \begin{pmatrix} x_2 - x_1 \\ y_2 - y_1 \\ z_2 - z_1 \end{pmatrix}$$

or

$$\begin{aligned} \mathbf{r} &= x\mathbf{i} + y\mathbf{j} + z\mathbf{k} \\ &= \left(x_1\mathbf{i} + y_1\mathbf{j} + z_1\mathbf{k}\right) + t\left[\left(x_2 - x_1\right)\mathbf{i} + \left(y_2 - y_1\right)\mathbf{j} + \left(z_2 - z_1\right)\mathbf{k}\right] \end{aligned}$$

3.5 CONDITION FOR THREE POINTS TO BE COLLINEAR

Let the points A, B and C be collinear as shown in the diagram and let the position vector be **a**, **b** and **c** respectively. The equation of the line BC is given

$\mathbf{r} = \mathbf{b} + \lambda\,(\mathbf{c} - \mathbf{b})$ where **b** is the position vector and $\mathbf{c} - \mathbf{b}$ is the direction vector and λ is a scalar parameter.

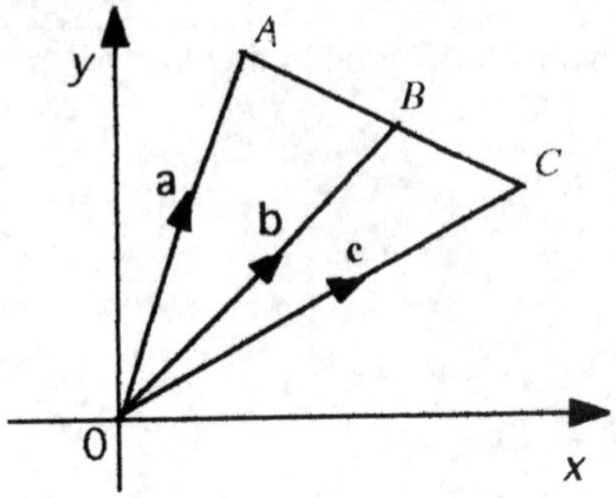

Fig. 8-I/29 Collinear points

The position vector of A must satisfy the equation of BC, substituting $\mathbf{r} = \mathbf{a}$

$$\mathbf{a} = \mathbf{b} + \lambda(\mathbf{c} - \mathbf{b})$$
$$\mathbf{a} + \lambda\mathbf{b} - \mathbf{b} - \lambda\mathbf{c} = 0$$
$$\mathbf{a} + \mathbf{b}(\lambda - 1) - \lambda\mathbf{c} = 0$$

this can be expressed as

$$\mathbf{a} + s\mathbf{b} + t\,\mathbf{c} = 0$$
$$1 + s + t = 0$$

$$s = -t - 1$$
or $$t = -s - 1.$$

WORKED EXAMPLE 24

Prove that the points $A\ (1, -1, 0)$, $B\ (2, 0, 3)$, $C\ (0, -2, -3)$ are collinear.

SOLUTION 24

The position vectors of B and C are $\overrightarrow{OB} = 2\mathbf{i} + 3\mathbf{k}$, $\overrightarrow{OC} = -2\mathbf{j} - 3\mathbf{k}$ and the equation of the line BC is given

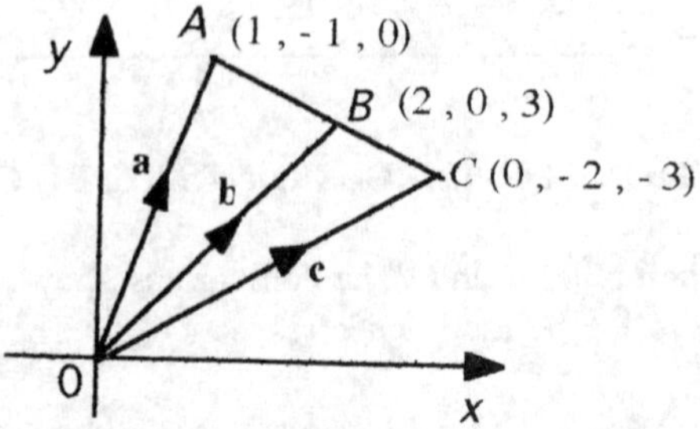

Fig. 8-I/30 Collinear points

$$\mathbf{r} = \mathbf{b} + \lambda (\mathbf{c} - \mathbf{b})$$
$$\mathbf{r} = 2\mathbf{i} + 3\mathbf{k} + \lambda (-2\mathbf{j} - 3\mathbf{k} - 2\mathbf{i} - 3\mathbf{k})$$
$$\mathbf{r} = 2\mathbf{i} + 3\mathbf{k} + \lambda (-2\mathbf{i} - 2\mathbf{j} - 6\mathbf{k})$$

$$\mathbf{r} = (2 - 2\lambda)\,\mathbf{i} - 2\lambda\mathbf{j} + (3 - 6\lambda)\,\mathbf{k}.$$

If A is on the line BC then

$$\mathbf{r} = \mathbf{i} - \mathbf{j}$$
$$\mathbf{i} - \mathbf{j} = (2 - 2\lambda)\,\mathbf{i} - 2\lambda\mathbf{j} + (3 - 6\lambda)\,\mathbf{k}$$
equating the coefficients of **i**, **j** and **k** we have

$$2 - 2\lambda = 1, \quad \lambda = \frac{1}{2}$$

$$-2\lambda = -1, \quad \lambda = \frac{1}{2}$$

$$3 - 6\lambda = 0, \quad \lambda = \frac{1}{2}.$$

WORKED EXAMPLE 25

Three points A, B and C are collinear, the position vectors of A and C are given, $\overrightarrow{OA} = 2\mathbf{i} - 3\mathbf{j} + 4\mathbf{k}$, $\overrightarrow{OC} = -3\mathbf{i} + 2\mathbf{j} + 5\mathbf{k}$, find the position vector of B, for $\lambda = -1$.

SOLUTION 25

The equation of the line on AC is given $\mathbf{r} = \mathbf{a} + \lambda (\mathbf{c} - \mathbf{a})$ since B lies on AC then

$$\begin{aligned} x_1\mathbf{i} + y_1\mathbf{j} + z_1\mathbf{k} &= \mathbf{a} + \lambda (\mathbf{c} - \mathbf{a}) \\ &= (2\mathbf{i} - 3\mathbf{j} + 4\mathbf{k}) + \lambda (-3\mathbf{i} + 2\mathbf{j} + 5\mathbf{k} - 2\mathbf{i} + 3\mathbf{j} - 4\mathbf{k}) \\ &= (2\mathbf{i} - 3\mathbf{j} + 4\mathbf{k}) + \lambda (-5\mathbf{i} + 5\mathbf{j} + \mathbf{k}) \\ &= (2 - 5\lambda)\,\mathbf{i} + (5\lambda - 3)\,\mathbf{j} + (4 + \lambda)\,\mathbf{k} \end{aligned}$$

$$x_1 = 2 - 5\lambda = 2 - 5(-1) = 7$$
$$y_1 = 5\lambda - 3 = 5(-1) - 3 = -8$$
$$z_1 = 4 + \lambda = 4 - 1 = 3$$

therefore the position vector of B is $\boxed{\overrightarrow{OB} = 7\mathbf{i} - 8\mathbf{j} + 3\mathbf{k}.}$

EXERCISES 3

1. Determine the position and direction vectors for the following:

(a) $\dfrac{x+1}{1} = \dfrac{y+2}{2} = \dfrac{z+3}{3} = \lambda$

(b) $\dfrac{x-1}{2} = \dfrac{y-2}{-3} = \dfrac{z-3}{4} = t$

(c) $\dfrac{x}{3} = \dfrac{y+3}{-4} = \dfrac{z-1}{2} = \mu$

(d) $\dfrac{x+a}{p} = \dfrac{y+b}{q} = \dfrac{z+c}{r} = s.$

2. Find the direction ratios and hence the direction cosines of the vectors of question 1.

3. The line $\dfrac{x+1}{1} = \dfrac{y+2}{2} = \dfrac{z+3}{3}$ is parallel to the line

$\dfrac{x+a}{l} = \dfrac{y+b}{m} = \dfrac{z+c}{n}$ which passes through the point $(-3, -4, -5)$.

Deduce the values of a, b, c, l, m, and n.

4. The line $\dfrac{x+a}{-3} = \dfrac{y+b}{-4} = \dfrac{z+c}{-5}$ is parallel to the line

$\dfrac{x-1}{l} = \dfrac{y-2}{m} = \dfrac{z-3}{n}$ and passes through the point $(2, 2, 2)$. Deduce

the value of a, b, c, l, m, and n.

5. Determine the unit vectors in the direction of the lines of question 1.

6. Find the vector equation of the line which passes through the point $A\ (-1, 2, 5)$ and is parallel to the direction vector $2\mathbf{i} - 3\mathbf{j} + 7\mathbf{k}$.

7. Find the vector equation of the line which passes through the point $\mathbf{a} = \mathbf{i} - \mathbf{j} + 3\mathbf{k}$ and is parallel to the direction vector $\mathbf{b} = 2\mathbf{i} + 3\mathbf{j} - 5\mathbf{k}$.

8. Find the vector equation of the line which passes through a point with position vector $\mathbf{a} = a_1\mathbf{i} + a_2\mathbf{j} + a_3\mathbf{k}$ and is parallel to the direction vector $\mathbf{b} = b_1\mathbf{i} + b_2\mathbf{j} + b_3\mathbf{k}$.

9. Find the vector equation of the line which passes through the points $A\ (1, -2, 3)$ and $B\ (-2, 4, 7)$.

10. Find the vector equation of the line which passes through two points with position vectors **w** and **u**.

11. Find the vector equation of the line which passes through two points with position vector $\mathbf{a} = 2\mathbf{i} + 2\mathbf{j} + 2\mathbf{k}$, and $\mathbf{b} = 3\mathbf{i} + 3\mathbf{j} + 3\mathbf{k}$.

12. Explain the difference of the vector equations of a line

$$\mathbf{r} = \mathbf{a} + \lambda\mathbf{b}$$
$$\mathbf{r} = \mathbf{a} + \lambda\,(\mathbf{b} - \mathbf{a}).$$

13. Write the following vector equations

$$\mathbf{r}_1 = (\mathbf{i} - 3\mathbf{j} + 2\mathbf{k}) + \lambda\,(-2\mathbf{i} + 3\mathbf{j} - 4\mathbf{k})$$
$$\mathbf{r}_2 = (2\mathbf{i} + \mathbf{j} - \mathbf{k}) + \mu\,(\mathbf{i} + 7\mathbf{j} - \mathbf{k})$$
$$\mathbf{r}_3 = (\mathbf{i} + \mathbf{j} + \mathbf{k}) + \nu\,(2\mathbf{i} + 2\mathbf{j} - 3\mathbf{k})$$

in column vector forms.

14. The vector equations of three lines are given

(a) $\mathbf{r}_1 = (3\mathbf{j} - 5\mathbf{k}) + t\,(2\mathbf{i} - 3\mathbf{j} + 7\mathbf{k})$

(b) $\mathbf{r}_2 = (\mathbf{i} - \mathbf{j} + 7\mathbf{k}) + \mu\,(\mathbf{i} + 3\mathbf{j} + 4\mathbf{k})$

(c) $\mathbf{r}_3 = (-2\mathbf{i} + \mathbf{j} - 4\mathbf{k}) + \lambda\,(-3\mathbf{i} + 5\mathbf{j} + \mathbf{k})$.

Find three points, A, B and C on each line for three values of the parameters (a) $t = 1, 2, -3$ (b) $\mu = 0, -2, 1$ (c) $\lambda = -2, -1, 4$.

15. Show that the point with position vector $\mathbf{i} + 5\mathbf{j} + 13\mathbf{k}$ lies on the line l with vector equation

$$\mathbf{r} = 5\mathbf{i} - \mathbf{j} + 7\mathbf{k} + \lambda\,(-2\mathbf{i} + 3\mathbf{j} + 3\mathbf{k}).$$

16. Show that the point with position vector $3\mathbf{i} - 2\mathbf{j} + 4\mathbf{k}$ lies on the line l with vector equation

$$\mathbf{r} = (5\mathbf{j} + 7\mathbf{k}) + \mu\,(3\mathbf{i} - 7\mathbf{j} - 3\mathbf{k}).$$

17. A line passes through the point $(-2, 4, -5)$ and is parallel to the direction vector $3\mathbf{i} + 5\mathbf{j} + \mathbf{k}$. Three points on the line are $A\ (-2, 4, -5)$, $B\ (-5, -1, -6)$, $C\ (4, 14, -3)$. Find the values of the parameters for these points.

4. PAIRS OF LINES

The vector equations of a pair of lines are given as $\mathbf{r}_1 = \mathbf{a}_1 + \lambda \mathbf{b}_1$ and $\mathbf{r}_2 = \mathbf{a}_2 + \mu \mathbf{b}_2$ where $\mathbf{a}_1 = x_1 \mathbf{i} + y_1 \mathbf{j} + z_1 \mathbf{k}$, $\mathbf{a}_2 = x_2 \mathbf{i} + y_2 \mathbf{j} + z_2 \mathbf{k}$ are fixed points and the lines are parallel to $\mathbf{b}_1 = x_1' \mathbf{i} + y_1' \mathbf{j} + z_1' \mathbf{k}$ and $\mathbf{b}_2 = x_2' \mathbf{i} + y_2' \mathbf{j} + z_2' \mathbf{k}$ respectively.

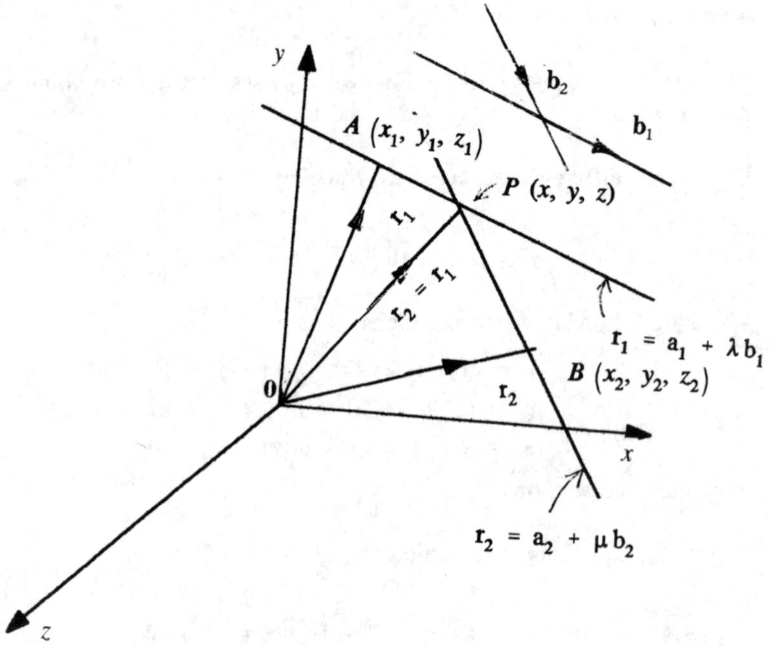

Fig. 8-I/31 Pairs of lines

The line $l_1 : \mathbf{r}_1 = \mathbf{a}_1 + \lambda \mathbf{b}_1$, passes through the fixed point A and it is parallel to the vector $\mathbf{b}_1$.
The line $l_2 : \mathbf{r}_2 = \mathbf{a}_2 + \mu \mathbf{b}_2$, passes through the fixed point B and it is parallel to the vector $\mathbf{b}_2$.

The direction vectors $\mathbf{b}_1$ and $\mathbf{b}_2$ may be parallel, intersect or neither (skew vectors). The most important case to consider in details is the intersection of the line l_1, and l_2 or the intersection of the direction $\mathbf{b}_1$ and $\mathbf{b}_2$.

4.1 THE INTERSECTION OF A PAIR OF LINES l_1 AND l_2

Fig. 8-I/31 shows the case of the two lines l_1 and l_2 that intersect at a point P with coordinates (x, y, z), the vector equations are equal at this point

$\mathbf{r}_1 = \mathbf{r}_2 \qquad \mathbf{a}_1 + \lambda \mathbf{b}_1 = \mathbf{a}_2 + \mu \mathbf{b}_2$
where λ and μ are such parameters that satisfy this equality.

4.2 PARALLEL LINES

The direction vectors b_1 and b_2 are parallel.

4.3 SKEW LINES

The direction vectros b_1 and b_2 are neither parallel nor intersect.

WORKED EXAMPLE 26

The following pairs of lines are given

(i) $l_1 : r_1 = (3\mathbf{i} + \mathbf{j} - 4\mathbf{k}) + \lambda (2\mathbf{i} - 3\mathbf{j} + \mathbf{k})$
$l_2 : r_2 = (-2\mathbf{i} + 4\mathbf{j} + \mathbf{k}) + \mu (-\mathbf{i} + 4\mathbf{j} - 7\mathbf{k})$

(ii) $l_1 : r_1 = (-2\mathbf{i} - 2\mathbf{j} - 4\mathbf{k}) + \lambda (-\mathbf{i} + 2\mathbf{j} + 3\mathbf{k})$
$l_2 : r_2 = (\mathbf{i} + \mathbf{j} + \mathbf{k}) + \mu (\mathbf{i} - 7\mathbf{j} + 2\mathbf{k})$

(iii) $l_1 : r_1 = (8\mathbf{i} - 8\mathbf{j} + 18\mathbf{k}) + \lambda (2\mathbf{i} + 2\mathbf{j} + 6\mathbf{k})$
$l_2 : r_2 = (2\mathbf{i} + 2\mathbf{j} + 2\mathbf{k}) + \mu (2\mathbf{i} - 14\mathbf{j} + 4\mathbf{k})$

(iv) $l_1 : r_1 = (\mathbf{i} + \mathbf{j} + \mathbf{k}) + \lambda (3\mathbf{i} + 4\mathbf{j} + 5\mathbf{k})$
$l_2 : r_2 = (4\mathbf{i} - 4\mathbf{j} + 9\mathbf{k}) + \mu (6\mathbf{i} + 8\mathbf{j} + 10\mathbf{k})$

(v) $l_1 : r_1 = (2\mathbf{i} + 2\mathbf{j} + 2\mathbf{k}) + \lambda (-\mathbf{i} + 7\mathbf{j} + 9\mathbf{k})$
$l_2 : r_2 = (8\mathbf{i} - 8\mathbf{j} + 9\mathbf{k}) + \mu (4\mathbf{i} - 2\mathbf{j} + 2\mathbf{k})$.

Determine whether the pair of lines above are parallel, intersect or are skew. Find the position vector of the point of intersection.

SOLUTION 26

Examine the direction ratios of the direction vectors.

(i) The direction ratios of l_1 are $2 : -3 : 1$
l_2 are $-1 : 4 : -7$

and since these direction ratios are not equal the lines are not parallel. If the lines intersect, then have a common point. Equating the coefficients of **i**, **j** and **k** we have

$$3 + 2\lambda = -2 - \mu \quad \text{or} \quad 2\lambda = -5 - \mu \quad \ldots (1)$$
$$1 - 3\lambda = 4 + 4\mu \quad \text{or} \quad 3\lambda = -3 - 4\mu \quad \ldots (2)$$
$$-4 + \lambda = 1 - 7\mu \quad \text{or} \quad \lambda = 5 - 7\mu \quad \ldots (3)$$

Solving equations (1) and (3) in order to find the values of λ and μ
$2(5 - 7\mu) = -5 - \mu$ or $10 - 14\mu = -5 - \mu$ or $13\mu = 15$,
$\mu = 15/13$ and substituting in (3) $\lambda = 5 - 105/13 = -40/13$. If the lines intersect then equation (2) is true for these values, but equation (2) is not verified and the lines are skew.

(ii) The direction ratios of l_1 and l_2 are $-1 : 2 : 3$ and $1 : -7 : 2$, the lines are not parallel.

Equating the coefficients of **i**, **j** and **k** we have

$$-2 - \lambda = 1 + \mu \text{ or } \lambda = -3 - \mu \quad \ldots (1)$$
$$-2 + 2\lambda = 1 - 7\mu \text{ or } 2\lambda = 3 - 7\mu \quad \ldots (2)$$
$$-4 + 3\lambda = 1 + 2\mu \text{ or } 3\lambda = 5 + 2\mu \quad \ldots (3)$$

Solving equations (1) and (2)

$$2\lambda = -6 - 2\mu \quad \ldots. (1) \times 2$$
$$2\lambda = 3 - 7\mu \quad \ldots (2)$$
$$-6 - 2\mu = 3 - 7\mu \text{ or } 5\mu = 9 \text{ or } \mu = \frac{9}{5}, \lambda = -3 - \frac{9}{5} = -\frac{24}{5}.$$

Substituting these values $\lambda = -\frac{24}{5}$ and $\mu = \frac{9}{5}$ in equation (3),

we find that $3\left(-\frac{24}{5}\right) \neq 5 + 2\left(\frac{9}{5}\right)$.

The lines are again skew.

(iii) The direction ratios are $2 : 2 : 6$ and $2 : -14 : 4$ or $1 : 1 : 3$ and $1 : -7 : 2$ which are not equal therefore the lines are not parallel.

Equating the coefficient of **i**, **j** and **k** for the two lines we have

$$8 + 2\lambda = 2 + 2\mu \text{ or } 2\lambda = -6 + 2\mu \text{ or } \lambda = -3 + \mu \quad \ldots (1)$$
$$-8 + 2\lambda = 2 - 14\mu \text{ or } 2\lambda = 10 - 14\mu \text{ or } \lambda = 5 - 7\mu \quad \ldots (2)$$
$$18 + 6\lambda = 2 + 4\mu \text{ or } 6\lambda = -16 + 4\mu \text{ or } 3\lambda = -8 + 2\mu \quad \ldots (3)$$

Solving (1) and (2)

$$-3 + \mu = 5 - 7\mu \text{ or } 8\mu = 8 \text{ or } \boxed{\mu = 1}$$

$$\lambda = -3 + 1 = -2 \text{ or } \boxed{\lambda = -2}$$

Substituting these values in (3) $-6 = -8 + 2 = -6$, verifies these equations and the values of $\mu = 1$ and $\lambda = -2$ make the two vector equations equal $\mathbf{r}_1 = \mathbf{r}_2$, the lines therefore intersect.

$$l_1 : \mathbf{r}_1 = (8\mathbf{i} - 8\mathbf{j} + 18\mathbf{k}) - 2(2\mathbf{i} + 2\mathbf{j} + 6\mathbf{k})$$
$$= 4\mathbf{i} - 12\mathbf{j} + 6\mathbf{k}$$

$l_2 : \mathbf{r}_2 = (2\mathbf{i} + 2\mathbf{j} + 2\mathbf{k}) + 2\mathbf{i} - 14\mathbf{j} + 4\mathbf{k}$
$= 4\mathbf{i} - 12\mathbf{j} + 6\mathbf{k}$

$\mathbf{r}_1 = \mathbf{r}_2$ and the position vector of $\overrightarrow{OP} = 4\mathbf{i} - 12\mathbf{j} + 6\mathbf{k}$.

(iv) The direction ratios are for l_1 : $3 : 4 : 5$
for l_2 : $6 : 8 : 10$
or $3 : 4 : 5$, the direction ratios are equal and the lines are parallel.

(v) The direction ratios are for l_1 : $-1 : 7 : 9$
for l_2 : $4 : -2 : +2$.

$2 - \lambda = 8 + 4\mu$ ... (1) $\quad 2 + 7\lambda = -8 - 2\mu$ ... (2)
$2 + 9\lambda = 9 + 2\mu$ ... (3).

Solving (1) and (2) we have $\lambda = -6 - 4\mu$ from (1), $7\lambda = -10 - 2\mu$, from (2), $7(-6 - 4\mu) = -10 - 2\mu$, $-42 - 28\mu = -10 - 2\mu$,

$26\mu = -32$, $\mu = -\dfrac{16}{13}$ and $\lambda = -6 + \dfrac{64}{13} = -\dfrac{14}{13}$. Substituting

these values in (3) $2 - \dfrac{126}{13} \neq 9 - \dfrac{32}{13}$ or $-\dfrac{100}{13} \neq \dfrac{85}{13}$. These

lines are neither parallel nor do they intersect. They are skew lines. Observe that the dot product of the direction vectors is zero.
$(-\mathbf{i} + 7\mathbf{j} + 9\mathbf{k}) \cdot (4\mathbf{i} - 2\mathbf{j} + 2\mathbf{k}) = -4 - 14 + 18 = 0$ see next page. The skew lines are perpandicular.

4.4 ANGLE BETWEEN A PAIR OF LINE

Consider the general vector equation $\mathbf{r} = \mathbf{a} + s\mathbf{b}$
where $\mathbf{r} = x\,\mathbf{i} + y\,\mathbf{j} + z\,\mathbf{k}$

$\mathbf{a} = a_1\mathbf{i} + a_2\mathbf{j} + a_3\mathbf{k}$ the position vector

$\mathbf{b} = b_1\mathbf{i} + b_2\mathbf{j} + b_3\mathbf{k}$ the direction vector

and s is the parameter.

Therefore the vector equations of any two lines are:

$$l_1 : \mathbf{r} = (a_1\mathbf{i} + a_2\mathbf{j} + a_3\mathbf{k}) + \lambda\,(b_1\mathbf{i} + b_2\mathbf{j} + b_3\mathbf{k})$$

$$l_2 : \mathbf{r} = (a_1'\mathbf{i} + a_2'\mathbf{j} + a_3'\mathbf{k}) + \mu\,(b_1'\mathbf{i} + b_2'\mathbf{j} + b_3'\mathbf{k}).$$

The angle between a pair of lines depends only on their directions and <u>not</u> on their positions.

The direction vectors are

$$\mathbf{v}_1 = b_1\mathbf{i} + b_2\mathbf{j} + b_3\mathbf{k}$$

$$\mathbf{v}_2 = b_1'\mathbf{i} + b_2'\mathbf{j} + b_3'\mathbf{k}.$$

The direction ratios are $b_1 : b_2 : b_3$ for $\mathbf{v}_1$ and $b_1' : b_2' : b_3'$ for $\mathbf{v}_2$.

The direction cosines are $\frac{b_1}{|\mathbf{v}_1|}, \frac{b_2}{|\mathbf{v}_1|}, \frac{b_3}{|\mathbf{v}_1|}$ for $\mathbf{v}_1$ and $\frac{b_1'}{|\mathbf{v}_2|}, \frac{b_2'}{|\mathbf{v}_2|}, \frac{b_3'}{|\mathbf{v}_2|}$.

DOT OR SCALAR PRODUCT

$$\begin{aligned}\mathbf{v}_1 . \mathbf{v}_2 &= (b_1\mathbf{i} + b_2\mathbf{j} + b_3\mathbf{k}).(b_1'\mathbf{i} + b_2'\mathbf{j} + b_3'\mathbf{k}) \\ &= b_1 b_1' + b_2 b_2' + b_3 b_3' \text{ where}\end{aligned}$$

$\boxed{\mathbf{v}_1 . \mathbf{v}_2 = |\mathbf{v}_1|\,|\mathbf{v}_2| \cos\theta}$ and $\mathbf{i} . \mathbf{j} = \mathbf{i} . \mathbf{k} = \mathbf{j} . \mathbf{k} = 0$, $\mathbf{i}.\mathbf{i} = \mathbf{j}.\mathbf{j} = \mathbf{k}.\mathbf{k} = 1$

since $\cos 0 = 1$ and $\cos 90° = 0$

$$b_1 b_1' + b_2 b_2' + b_3 b_3' = \sqrt{b_1^2 + b_2^2 + b_3^2}\sqrt{b_1'^2 + b_2'^2 + b_3'^2} \cos\theta$$

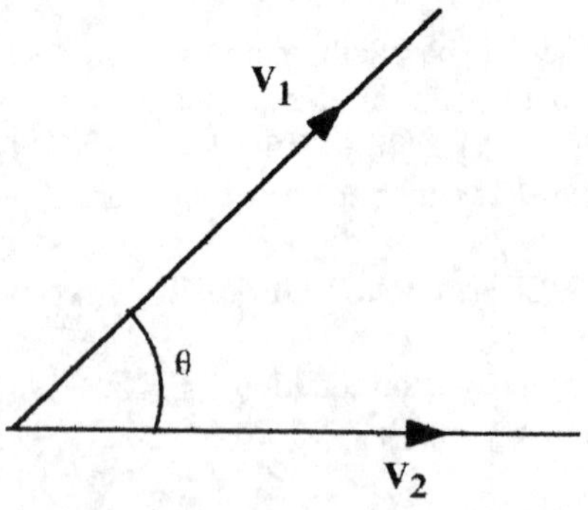

Fig. 8-I/32 Scalar product

WORKED EXAMPLE 27

Find the acute angles between l_1 and l_2, giving your answer correct to the nearest 0.1 of a degree.

(i) $l_1 : \mathbf{r} = \mathbf{i} + \mathbf{j} + \mathbf{k} + \lambda(-2\mathbf{i} + \mathbf{j} + 5\mathbf{k})$

$l_2 : \mathbf{r} = 2\mathbf{i} + 3\mathbf{j} + 4\mathbf{k} + \mu(\mathbf{i} + 2\mathbf{j} - 7\mathbf{k})$

(ii) $l_1 : \mathbf{r} = 2\mathbf{i} + 3\mathbf{j} + 5\mathbf{k} + s(\mathbf{i} + \mathbf{j} + 2\mathbf{k})$

$l_2 : \mathbf{r} = 4\mathbf{j} + 6\mathbf{k} + t(-\mathbf{i} + 2\mathbf{j} + 3\mathbf{k})$

(iii) $l_1 : \mathbf{r} = -3\mathbf{i} + 2\mathbf{j} - \mathbf{k} + \lambda(\mathbf{i} + \mathbf{j} + \mathbf{k})$

$l_2 : \mathbf{r} = 2\mathbf{i} + 3\mathbf{j} - 4\mathbf{k} + \mu(2\mathbf{i} - 3\mathbf{j} + \mathbf{k})$.

SOLUTION 27

(i) $\mathbf{v}_1 = -2\mathbf{i} + \mathbf{j} + 5\mathbf{k}$

$\mathbf{v}_2 = \mathbf{i} + 2\mathbf{j} - 7\mathbf{k}$

$$\mathbf{v}_1 \cdot \mathbf{v}_2 = (-2\mathbf{i} + \mathbf{j} + 5\mathbf{k}) \cdot (\mathbf{i} + 2\mathbf{j} - 7\mathbf{k})$$

$$= \sqrt{(-2)^2 + (1)^2 + (5)^2}\ \sqrt{1^2 + 2^2 + (-7)^2}\ \cos\theta$$

$$-2 + 2 - 35 = \sqrt{30}\ \sqrt{54}\ \cos\theta$$

$$\cos\theta = -0.869581991 \Rightarrow \theta = 150.4^\circ$$

$\theta = 29.6^\circ$ the acute angle to the nearest 0.1 of a degree

(ii) $\mathbf{v}_1 = (\mathbf{i} + \mathbf{j} + 2\mathbf{k})$

$\mathbf{v}_2 = (-\mathbf{i} + 2\mathbf{j} + 3\mathbf{k})$

$$\mathbf{v}_1 \cdot \mathbf{v}_2 = (\mathbf{i} + \mathbf{j} + 2\mathbf{k}) \cdot (-\mathbf{i} + 2\mathbf{j} + 3\mathbf{k})$$

$$= \sqrt{1^2 + 1^2 + 2^2}\ \sqrt{1^2 + 2^2 + 3^2}\ \cos\theta$$

$$-1 + 2 + 6 = \sqrt{6}\ \sqrt{14}\ \cos\theta$$

$$\cos\theta = \frac{7}{\sqrt{6}\ \sqrt{14}}$$

$$\theta = 40.2^\circ$$

(iii) $\mathbf{v}_1 = \mathbf{i} + \mathbf{j} + \mathbf{k}$

$\mathbf{v}_2 = 2\mathbf{i} - 3\mathbf{j} + \mathbf{k}$

$$\mathbf{v}_1 \cdot \mathbf{v}_2 = (\mathbf{i} + \mathbf{j} + \mathbf{k}) \cdot (2\mathbf{i} - 3\mathbf{j} + \mathbf{k})$$

$$= \sqrt{1^2 + 1^2 + 1^2}\ \sqrt{2^2 + 3^2 + 1^2}\ \cos\theta$$

$$2 - 3 + 1 = \sqrt{3}\ \sqrt{14}\ \cos\theta$$

$$\cos\theta = \frac{0}{\sqrt{3}\ \sqrt{14}}$$

$$\theta = 90^\circ$$

EXERCISES 4

1. The line l_1 is parallel to the vector $2\mathbf{i} + 3\mathbf{j} - \mathbf{k}$ and passes through the point A with position vector $-\mathbf{i} + 3\mathbf{j} + 5\mathbf{k}$ relative to the origin O.

   Write down the vector equation for l_1. The line l_2 is parallel to the vector $-\mathbf{i} + 2\mathbf{j} + 5\mathbf{k}$ and passes through the point B with position vector $2\mathbf{i} + 3\mathbf{j} + 4\mathbf{k}$ relative to the origin O.

   Write down the vector equation for l_2. Determine whether the two lines l_1 and l_2 intersect or not.

2. $\mathbf{a} = 2\mathbf{i} + 3\mathbf{j} + 4\mathbf{k}$
   $\mathbf{b} = \mathbf{i} - 2\mathbf{j} + 3\mathbf{k}$
   $\mathbf{c} = 3\mathbf{i} + \mathbf{j} - 2\mathbf{k}$.

   Find $\mathbf{b} + \mathbf{c}$ then find $\mathbf{a}.\mathbf{b}$, $\mathbf{a}.\mathbf{c}$ and $\mathbf{a}.(\mathbf{b} + \mathbf{c})$. State your conclusions.

3. A triangle ABC with coordinates $A\ (1, 2, 3)$, $B\ (3, 4, 6)$, $C\ (-1, -2, -3)$

   find the vectors of $\overrightarrow{AB}$, $\overrightarrow{BC}$ and $\overrightarrow{AC}$. Hence calculate the area of the

   triangle using $\Delta = \sqrt{s(s-a)(s-b)(s-c)}$.

4. A vector makes angles of 30°, 60° with respect to x-axis and y-axis. Determine the angle that the vector makes with the z-axis. (You may use $\cos^2\alpha + \cos^2\beta + \cos^2\gamma = 1$).

5. The vectors $\mathbf{a}$ and $\mathbf{b}$ are given by

   $$\mathbf{a} = t\,\mathbf{i} + \mathbf{j} + 3\mathbf{k}$$
   $$\mathbf{b} = -2\mathbf{i} + \lambda\mathbf{j} + 3\mathbf{k}.$$

   (a) Find a relation between the scalars t and λ if the vectors $\mathbf{a}$ and $\mathbf{b}$ are perpendicular.

   (b) Find the values of the scalars t and λ if $\mathbf{a}$ is parallel to $\mathbf{b}$.

6. The vectors $\mathbf{a}$ and $\mathbf{b}$ are given by

   $$\mathbf{a} = 7\mathbf{i} + 2\lambda\mathbf{j} - 9\mathbf{k}$$
   $$\mathbf{b} = 7\mathbf{i} + 4\mathbf{j} + \mu\mathbf{k}.$$

   (a) If $\mathbf{a}$ and $\mathbf{b}$ are perpendicular determine a relation between the scalars λ and μ.
   (b) If $\lambda = -1$ and $\mu = 2$, find the acute angle between the vectors $\mathbf{a}$ and $\mathbf{b}$.
   (c) What are the values of λ and μ if the vectors $\mathbf{a}$ and $\mathbf{b}$ are to be parallel.

7. With respect to an origin O, the position vectors of the points A, B and C are given as follows:

$$\mathbf{a} = \overrightarrow{OA} = 2\mathbf{i} + 5\mathbf{j} - 7\mathbf{k}$$

$$\mathbf{b} = \overrightarrow{OB} = -3\mathbf{i} - 2\mathbf{j} + 4\mathbf{k}$$

$$\mathbf{c} = \overrightarrow{OC} = \mathbf{i} + 6\mathbf{j} + 11\mathbf{k}.$$

(a) Find the vectors $\overrightarrow{AB}$, $\overrightarrow{AC}$, $\overrightarrow{BC}$.

(b) Determine the acute angle $\angle ABC$.

(i) using the cosine rule

(ii) using the scalar product.

8. With respect to an origin O, the position vectors of the points P, Q and R are given as follows:

$$\mathbf{p} = \overrightarrow{OP} = \mathbf{i} + \mathbf{j} + \mathbf{k}$$

$$\mathbf{q} = \overrightarrow{OQ} = 2\mathbf{i} + 3\mathbf{j} + 4\mathbf{k}$$

$$\mathbf{r} = \overrightarrow{OR} = -5\mathbf{i} + 4\mathbf{j} - 3\mathbf{k}.$$

(a) Find the vectors $\overrightarrow{PQ}$ and $\overrightarrow{PR}$.

(b) Calculate the acute angle $\angle RPQ$

(i) using the cosine rule

(ii) using the scalar product.

9. (a) The position vectors $\overrightarrow{OP}$, $\overrightarrow{OQ}$ and $\overrightarrow{OR}$ are given by $P\,(-3, 0, 4)$, $Q\,(1, 3, 0)$, $R\,(-3, 0, 0)$. Determine $\overrightarrow{PQ}$, $\overrightarrow{PR}$ and $\overrightarrow{QR}$ and hence find their moduli.

(b) Determine the magnitudes of the following vectors and the corresponding unit vectors.

(i) $\mathbf{a} = 3\mathbf{i} - 4\mathbf{j} + 5\mathbf{k}$

(ii) $\mathbf{b} = -3\mathbf{i} + 5\mathbf{k}$

(iii) $\mathbf{r} = \mathbf{i} + \mathbf{j} + \mathbf{k}$

(iv) $\mathbf{r} = a\,\mathbf{i} + b\,\mathbf{j} + c\,\mathbf{k}$

(v) $\mathbf{p} = x\,\mathbf{i} + y\,\mathbf{j} + z\,\mathbf{k}$.

10. Calculate the acute angle between the vector **u** and **v** when:

(a) $\mathbf{u} = 2\mathbf{i} - 3\mathbf{j} + 4\mathbf{k}$
$\mathbf{v} = -\mathbf{i} + \mathbf{j} - \mathbf{k}$

(b) $\mathbf{u} = (1, 2, 3)$ and $\mathbf{v} = (-1, -2, -3)$.

11. The position vectors are given by the following sets of coordinates:

(i) $A\ (0, 3)$ (ii) $B\ (-1, 2, 3)$ (iii) $C\ (-1, -4, -9)$

(iv) $D\ (0, 0, 4)$, (v) $E\ (-4, 0, 5)$.

Write down the position vectors in the form $a\mathbf{i} + b\mathbf{j} + c\mathbf{k}$.

12. The position vectors of A, B and C are given $-7\mathbf{i} + 7\mathbf{k}$, $2\mathbf{j} - 3\mathbf{k}$, $-\mathbf{k}$ respectively. Write down the set of coordinates of A, B and C.

13. Find the moduli of the following vectors:

(i) $\mathbf{u} = 2\mathbf{i} - 2\mathbf{j} + \mathbf{k}$ (ii) $\mathbf{v} = 5\mathbf{i} + 5\mathbf{j} - 6\mathbf{k}$ (iii) $\mathbf{w} = -\mathbf{i} - \mathbf{j} + 2\mathbf{k}$.

14. Determine the magnitude of the lines $\overrightarrow{OP}$, $\overrightarrow{OQ}$, $\overrightarrow{OR}$ where $P\ (-1, 4, -5)$, $Q\ (1, 2, 5)$, $R\ (-2, -4, -6)$.

15. If $\mathbf{a} = \begin{pmatrix} 4 \\ -5 \\ 6 \end{pmatrix}$, $\mathbf{b} = \begin{pmatrix} 2 \\ -3 \\ 5 \end{pmatrix}$, and $\mathbf{c} = \begin{pmatrix} 1 \\ 3 \\ 0 \end{pmatrix}$.

Find (i) $|\mathbf{a}|$ (ii) $|\mathbf{a} - \mathbf{c}|$ (iii) $|\mathbf{b} + \mathbf{a} + \mathbf{c}|$.

16. The following vectors are given by (i) $\mathbf{u} = 3\mathbf{i} - \mathbf{j} - 5\mathbf{k}$
$\mathbf{v} = -2\mathbf{i} + 5\mathbf{j} + 4\mathbf{k}$

(ii) $\mathbf{a} = 3\mathbf{j} + \mathbf{k}$
$\mathbf{b} = \mathbf{i} - \mathbf{k}$

(iii) $\mathbf{w} = \mathbf{i} - \mathbf{j} - 7\mathbf{k}$
$\mathbf{z} = -2\mathbf{i} + 2\mathbf{j} + \mathbf{k}$.

Determine the scalar products and hence find the acute angles between the pair of vectors.

17. The magnitudes of two vectors are 1 and 2 and their acute angle is 30°, find their scalar product.

18. Determine the following scalar products:

(i) $\mathbf{i} \cdot \mathbf{j} \cdot \mathbf{k}$ (ii) $\mathbf{i} \cdot \mathbf{i} = \mathbf{j} \cdot \mathbf{j} = \mathbf{k} \cdot \mathbf{k}$

(iii) $\mathbf{i} \cdot \mathbf{i} \cdot \mathbf{i}$ (iv) $\mathbf{i} \cdot \mathbf{j} = \mathbf{j} \cdot \mathbf{k} = \mathbf{k} \cdot \mathbf{i}$.

19. Determine **a** . **b** if

(a) $\mathbf{a} = 2\mathbf{i} - 3\mathbf{j} - 5\mathbf{k}$, $\mathbf{b} = \mathbf{i} + 2\mathbf{j} + \mathbf{k}$

(b) $\mathbf{a} = -\mathbf{j} - \mathbf{k}$, $\mathbf{b} = \mathbf{i} + \mathbf{j} + \mathbf{k}$

(c) $\mathbf{a} = (3, 4, 5)$, $\mathbf{b} = (-1, -1, -1)$

(d) $\mathbf{a} = (2, 2, 2)$, $\mathbf{b} = (2, 2, 2)$.

20. Given that $\mathbf{u} = 3t\,\mathbf{i} + 2t^2\mathbf{j} + \mathbf{k}$ and $\mathbf{v} = (1 - t)\mathbf{i} + 3\mathbf{j} - \mathbf{k}$ where t is a scalar variable, determine

(a) the values of t for which **u** and **v** are perpendicular,
(b) the angle between the vector **u** and **v** when $t = -2$.

21. Given that $\mathbf{a} = 2t^2\mathbf{i} + (1 - 2t)\mathbf{j} + t\mathbf{k}$

$$\mathbf{b} = 2t\mathbf{i} - 2t\mathbf{j} - 4t^2\mathbf{k}$$

where t is a scalar variable, determine the value of t for which the vectors are at right angles.

22. The vectors **p** and **q** are given as $3\mathbf{i} - 5\mathbf{j} + \mathbf{k}$ and $-2\mathbf{i} - \mathbf{j} + 2\mathbf{k}$ determine the scalar product **p** . **q** and hence find the acute angle between the vectors.

23. The position vectors of the points A and B are given

$$\mathbf{a} = \mathbf{i} + 3\mathbf{j} + \mathbf{k}$$
$$\mathbf{b} = 2\mathbf{i} - 2\mathbf{j} - 3\mathbf{k}$$

determine the scalar product **a** . **b** and hence find the tangent of the acute angle between the vectors.

24. The following position vectors of the points A, B, C, D and E are given:

$$\mathbf{a} = 3\mathbf{j} - 5\mathbf{k}$$
$$\mathbf{b} = \mathbf{i} + 2\mathbf{j} - 3\mathbf{k}$$
$$\mathbf{c} = -2\mathbf{i} - \mathbf{j} + \mathbf{k}$$
$$\mathbf{d} = 3\mathbf{i} + 2\mathbf{j} + \mathbf{k}$$
$$\mathbf{e} = 3\mathbf{i} + 4\mathbf{j} + 5\mathbf{k}.$$

Determine:

(a) (i) $2\mathbf{a} - 3\mathbf{e}$ (ii) $\mathbf{b} + 3\mathbf{d} + \mathbf{e}$ (iii) $2\mathbf{b} - 4\mathbf{d} + 2\mathbf{e}$.

(b) (i) $|\mathbf{b} \cdot \mathbf{e}|$ (ii) $|\mathbf{a} - \mathbf{e}|$ (iii) $|\mathbf{d} - \mathbf{a}|$

(iv) $|\mathbf{d} \cdot \mathbf{e}|$ (v) $|(\mathbf{a} \cdot \mathbf{b}) \cdot \mathbf{c}|$

(c) the direction cosines of each vector.

(d) the angle (i) between **a** and **e**
(ii) between 2**a** and **d**
(iii) between **c** and 2**e**.

25. The vector equations of the three lines are given below:

$$l_1 : \mathbf{r} = 2\mathbf{i} + 3\mathbf{j} + 4\mathbf{k} + \lambda\,(2\mathbf{i} - 3\mathbf{j} + 5\mathbf{k})$$
$$l_2 : \mathbf{r} = 2\mathbf{i} - 5\mathbf{j} + \mathbf{k} + \mu\,(4\mathbf{i} - 6\mathbf{j} + 10\mathbf{k})$$
$$l_3 : \mathbf{r} = -\mathbf{i} + \mathbf{j} + 3\mathbf{k} + \nu\,(\mathbf{i} - \mathbf{j} + 2\mathbf{k}).$$

Find which pair of lines (i) are parallel to each other (ii) are skew (iii) intersect with each other.

26. Find the perpendicular distance from the point $A\,(2, -3, 4)$ to the line with vector equation $\mathbf{r} = -\mathbf{i} + 2\mathbf{j} + 4\mathbf{k} + \lambda\,(2\mathbf{i} - 3\mathbf{j} + 5\mathbf{k})$.

27. Find the perpendicular distance from the point $A\,(1, 2, 3)$ to the line with vector equation $\mathbf{r} = \mathbf{i} + 3\mathbf{j} + 5\mathbf{k} + \mu\,(4\mathbf{i} + 3\mathbf{j} + 2\mathbf{k})$.

28. A line passes through the point (x_1, y_1, z_1) and is parallel to the direction vector $a\mathbf{i} + b\mathbf{j} + c\mathbf{k}$. Write down the vector equation of the line in parametric form and hence find the cartesian form of the line.

29. Prove that a line that passes through a point $A\,(x_1, y_1, z_1)$ and is parallel to the vector $\mathbf{b} = a\mathbf{i} + b\mathbf{j} + c\mathbf{k}$ is given by the vector equation

$$\mathbf{r} = \mathbf{a} + \lambda\mathbf{b}$$

where λ is a parameter.

30. A line passes through two points $A\,(x_1, y_1, z_1)$ and $B\,(x_2, y_2, z_2)$ show that the vector equation of the line is given

$$\mathbf{r} = (x_1\mathbf{i} + y_1\mathbf{j} + z_1\mathbf{k}) + \lambda\left[(x_2 - x_1)\mathbf{i} + (y_2 - y_1)\mathbf{j} + (z_2 - z_1)\mathbf{k}\right].$$

31. Write down the vector equations of the lines corresponding to the following cartesian equations:

(i) $\dfrac{x+1}{1} = \dfrac{y-2}{2} = \dfrac{z+3}{3}$

(ii) $\dfrac{x-3}{-3} = \dfrac{y+1}{5} = \dfrac{z-5}{7}$

(iii) $\dfrac{x-2}{-1} = \dfrac{y-1}{-2} = \dfrac{z-4}{-3}$

(iv) $\dfrac{x-1}{0} = \dfrac{y-2}{0} = \dfrac{z}{2}$.

32. The vector equations of two lines l_1, l_2 are given:

$$l_1 : \mathbf{r} = (2\mathbf{i} - 3\mathbf{j} + 4\mathbf{k}) + \lambda(-\mathbf{i} - 3\mathbf{j} + 2\mathbf{k})$$

$$l_2 : \mathbf{r} = (3\mathbf{i} + 2\mathbf{k}) + \mu(\mathbf{i} - 2\mathbf{j} - 3\mathbf{k}).$$

Show that the lines intersect and find the position vector of the point of intersection.

33. The cartesian equations of two lines are given $y = m_1 x + c_1$, $y = m_2 x + c_2$ find the vector equations of the lines and hence show that the acute angle of the intersection of the lines is given $\tan^{-1} \dfrac{m_1 - m_2}{1 + m_1 m_2}$.

34. Determine by means of vectors the perpendicular distance from a point $A\ (x_1, y_1)$ to the line $ax + by + c = 0$.

35. Find the distance between the pair of parallel lines

$$\mathbf{r} = (\mathbf{i} + \mathbf{j} + \mathbf{k}) + \lambda(-2\mathbf{i} - 3\mathbf{j} - 4\mathbf{k}) : l_1$$

$$\mathbf{r} = (2\mathbf{i} - 3\mathbf{j} - \mathbf{k}) + \mu(-2\mathbf{i} - 3\mathbf{j} - 4\mathbf{k}) : l_2$$

36. Find the distance between the pair of parallel lines

$$\frac{x-1}{2} = \frac{y+2}{3} = \frac{z-3}{1} \qquad \frac{x+3}{2} = \frac{y-3}{3} = \frac{z+1}{1}.$$

5. COORDINATE GEOMETRY IN 3 DIMENSIONS

THE EQUATION OF A PLANE

A plane may be located if we know a fixed point on the plane and the plane is known to be perpendicular to a given direction.
Let $A\ (-2,\ 3,\ 5)$ be a fixed point on the plane which is perpendicular to the line with direction ratios $3 : 4 : 7$.

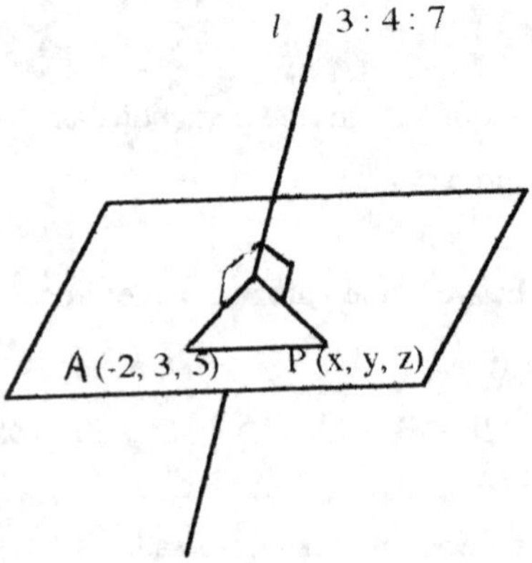

Fig. 8-I/33 The equation of a plane.

Since the line l is perpendicular to the plane then it is perpendicular to any line in the plane.
Let $P\ (x, y, z)$ be a general point on the plane, then AP is perpendicular to the line l.
The direction ratios of AP are $(x + 2) : (y - 3) : (z - 5)$ and since the line is perpendicular to AP

$$3\ (x + 2) + 4\ (y - 3) + 7\ (z - 5) = 0$$
$$3x + 6 + 4y - 12 + 7z - 35 = 0$$

$$\boxed{3x + 4y + 7z = 41}$$

therefore $P\ (x, y, z)$ is a point on the plane $3x + 4y + 7z = 41$

In general, $\boxed{ax + by + cz = d}$ represents the cartesian equation of a plane, where $a : b : c$ are the direction ratios of a normal to the plane.
If a plane is normal to a line with direction ratios $a : b : c$ and contains the point (x_1, y_1, z_1) then the equation of the plane is written directly as

$ax + by + cz = ax_1 + by_1 + cz_1$.

WORKED EXAMPLE 28

Find the equation of the plane for the point A $(0, -3, -7)$ on the plane which is perpendicular to the line with direction ratios $1 : 2 : 3$.

SOLUTION 28

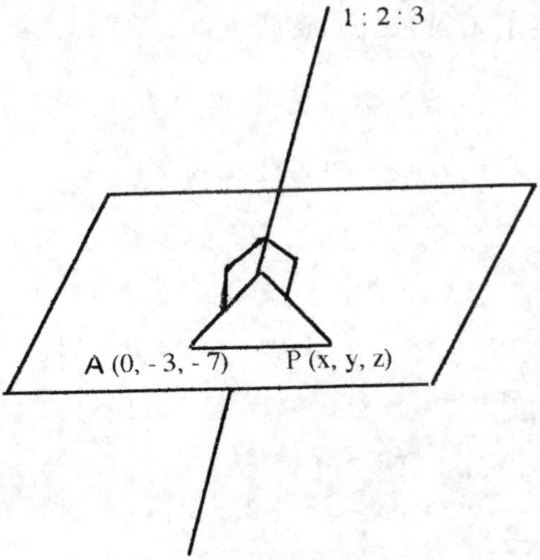

Fig. 8-I/34 Equation of the plane

The direction ratios of AP are $x : (y + 3) : (z + 7)$ and since the line is perpendicular to AP

$$1\,(x) + 2\,(y + 3) + 3\,(z + 7) = 0$$
$$x + 2y + 6 + 3z + 21 = 0$$

therefore this is $\boxed{x + 2y + 3z = -27}$

the equation of the plane and P $(x, y\ z)$ is a point on it.

WORKED EXAMPLE 29

Find the equation of the plane which contains three points with coordinates A $(1, 2, 3)$, B $(-2, 3, -1)$, C $(-1, 4, 2)$.

SOLUTION 29

The equation of the plane is $ax + by + cz = d$, where $a : b : c$ are the direction ratios of the line which is perpendicular to the plane.

Since A (1, 2, 3) lies on the plane then this will satisfy the equation.

$$a + 2b + 3c = d \quad \dots (1)$$

Since B (− 2, 3, − 1) lies also on the plane then this will also satisfy the equation

$$-2a + 3b - c = d \quad \dots (2)$$

and finally C (− 1, 4, 2) lies on the plane then

$$-a + 4b + 2c = d \quad \dots (3)$$

Solving equations (1), (2) and (3) in terms of d

$$a + 2b + 3c = d \quad \dots (1)$$

$$-2a + 3b - c = d \quad \dots (2)$$

$$-a + 4b + 2c = d \quad \dots (3)$$

adding (1) and (3)

$$6b + 5c = 2d \quad \dots (4)$$

(1) × 2 $\quad 2a + 4b + 6c = 2d$

(2) $\quad -2a + 3b - c = d$

$$7b + 5c = 3d \quad \dots (5)$$

(5) − (4) $\boxed{b = d}$

Substituting this value in (4), $6d + 5c = d$

$$5c = -5d$$

$$\boxed{c = -d}$$

From (1) $\quad a + 2b + 3c = d$

$$a + 2d - 3d = d$$

$$a = d + 3d - 2d = 2d$$

$$\boxed{a = 2d}$$

$a = 2d$, $b = d$, $c = -d$.

The plane through A, B, and C is given by

$$2\,dx + 1\,dy - 1\,dz = d$$

$$\boxed{2x + y - z = 1}$$

If a plane contains the origin, then $O\ (0, 0, 0)$ satisfies the equation $ax + by + cz = d$ where $d = 0$.

Any plane through the origin has an equation

$$\boxed{ax + by + cz = 0}$$

WORKED EXAMPLE 30

Find the equation of the plane which contains the two lines

$$l_1 : \frac{x + 2}{4} = \frac{y + 6}{3} = \frac{z - 2}{2}$$

$$l_2 : \frac{x - 3}{1} = \frac{y + 1}{2} = \frac{z - 7}{3}.$$

SOLUTION 30

The lines must be parallel or intersecting.

Let $l_1 : \dfrac{x + 2}{4} = \dfrac{y + 6}{3} = \dfrac{z - 2}{2} = t$ ... (1)

and $l_2 : \dfrac{x - 3}{1} = \dfrac{y + 1}{2} = \dfrac{z - 7}{3} = s$ ... (2)

where t and s are scalar parameters.

From (1) $3(x + 2) = 4(y + 6)$

$3x - 4y = 24 - 6$

$\boxed{3x - 4y = 18}$ ... (3)

From (2) $2(x - 3) = y + 1$

$2x - y = 6 + 1$

$\boxed{2x - y = 7}$ ... (4)

Solve (3) and (4)

$$\begin{aligned} 3x - 4y &= 18 \quad &\dots (3) \\ -8x + 4y &= -28 \quad &\dots (4) \times (-4) \end{aligned}$$

$$-5x = -10$$

$$\boxed{x = 2} \text{ and } \boxed{y = -3}$$

From (1) and (2)

$2(y + 6) = 3(z - 2)$ $\qquad$ $3(y + 1) = 2(z - 7)$

$2y - 3z = -12 - 6$ $\qquad$ $3y - 2z = -3 - 14$

$\boxed{2y - 3z = -18}$ ... (5) $\quad$ $\boxed{3y - 2z = -17}$ ... (6)

(5) × 3 $\qquad$ $6y - 9z = -54$ ... (7)

(6) × (− 2) $\qquad$ $-6y + 4z = 34$ ... (8)

adding (7) and (8) $\qquad$ $-5z = -20$, $\boxed{z = 4}$ $\boxed{y = -3}$

Equation (1) and (2) are consistent

$\boxed{x = 2}$ $\quad$ $\boxed{y = -3}$ and $\boxed{z = 4}$

therefore the lines intersect at P (2, − 3, 4)

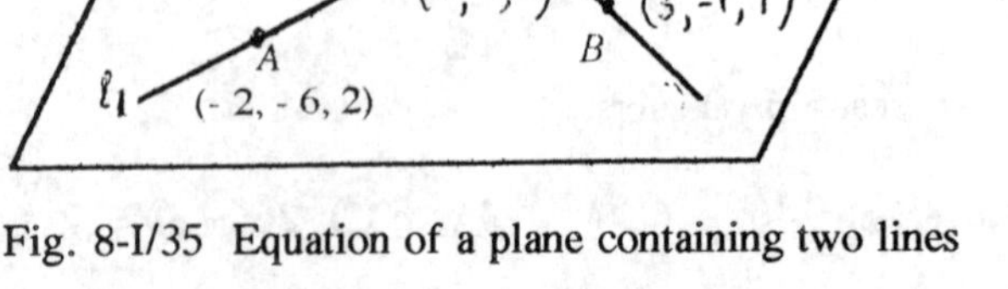

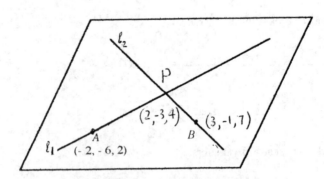

Fig. 8-I/35 Equation of a plane containing two lines

$$l_1 : \frac{x + 2}{4} = \frac{y + 6}{3} = \frac{z - 2}{2} = t = 1$$

$$l_2 : \frac{x - 3}{1} = \frac{y + 1}{2} = \frac{z - 7}{3} = s = -1$$

when $t = 0, x = -2, y = -6, z = 2$; $A(-2, -6, 2)$
when $s = 0, x = 3, y = -1, z = 7$; $B(3, -1, 7)$.

For each value of t corresponds to one and only one point on l_1. For each value of s corresponds to one and only one point on l_2. Find the plane containing the points $A(-2, -6, 2)$, $B(3, -1, 7)$, $C(2, -3, 4)$.

Since these points lie on the plane, then will satisfy the equation of the plane

$$ax + by + cz = d$$
$$-2a - 6b + 2c = d \quad \dots (1)$$
$$3a - b + 7c = d \quad \dots (2)$$
$$2a - 3b + 4c = d \quad \dots (3)$$

Adding (1) and (3)

$$\boxed{-9b + 6c = 2d} \quad \dots (4)$$

adding (1) $\times$ 3 and (2) $\times$ 2

$$-6a - 18b + 6c = 3d$$
$$6a - 2b + 14c = 2d$$

$$-20b + 20c = 5d$$

or $\boxed{-4b + 4c = d} \quad \dots (5)$

(4) $\times$ 2 $\quad -18b + 12c = 4d$
(5) $\times -3$ $\quad +12b - 12c = -3d$

$$-6b = d$$

$$\boxed{b = -\frac{d}{6}} \quad \dots (6)$$

$$4c = d + 4b = d - \frac{4d}{6} = \frac{2d}{6} = \frac{d}{3}$$

$$\boxed{c = \frac{d}{12}} \quad \dots (7)$$

From (1) $\quad -2a - 6\left(-\frac{d}{6}\right) + 2\left(\frac{d}{12}\right) = d$

$$-2a = d - d - \frac{1}{6}d$$

$$\boxed{a = \frac{1}{12}d} \quad \dots (8)$$

Substituting (6), (7) and (8) in plane equation

$$\frac{1}{12}dx - \frac{1}{6}dy + \frac{1}{12}dx = d$$

therefore the equation of the plane is

$$\boxed{x - 2y + z = 12}$$

This example can be solved alternatively. Let l_3 be a line perpendicular to both lines l_1 and l_2, with direction ratio $a : b : c$.

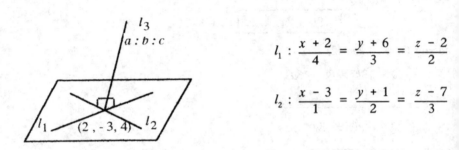

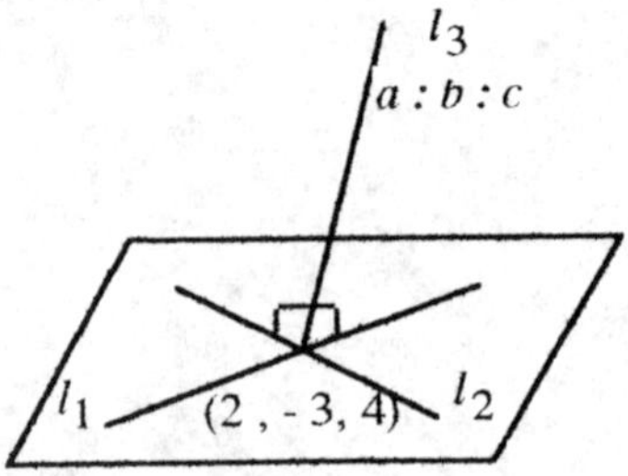

$$l_1 : \frac{x+2}{4} = \frac{y+6}{3} = \frac{z-2}{2}$$

$$l_2 : \frac{x-3}{1} = \frac{y+1}{2} = \frac{z-7}{3}$$

Fig. 8-I/36 Equation of a plane containing two lines.

Since l_3 is perpendicular to l_1 then

$$4a + 3b + 2c = 0 \quad \ldots (1)$$

Since l_3 is perpendicular to l_2 then

$$a + 2b + 3c = 0 \quad \ldots (2)$$

Solving (1) and (2) simultaneously

(1) $\qquad 4a + 3b + 2c = 0$

(2) $\times\ -4 \qquad -4a - 8b - 12c = 0$

$$-5b - 10c = 0$$

$$\frac{b}{c} = -\frac{2}{1}$$

From (2) $\qquad a - 4c + 3c = 0, \ a = c$

$$\frac{a}{c} = \frac{1}{1}$$

$$\frac{a/c}{b/c} = \frac{1}{-2} = -\frac{1}{2}$$

$$\frac{a}{b} = -\frac{1}{2}$$

$$a : b : c = 1 : -2 : 1.$$

The intersection of l_1 and l_2 is $(2, -3, 4)$

$x - 2y + z = (1)(2) + (-2)(-3) + (1)(4) = 12$

$$\boxed{x - 2y + z = 12}$$

51. THE PERPENDICULAR DISTANCE OF THE POINT $A\ (x_1, y_1, z_1)$ FROM THE PLANE $ax + by + cz = d$ IS

$$\left| \frac{ax_1 + by_1 + cz_1 - d}{\sqrt{a^2 + b^2 + c^2}} \right|.$$

Let the equation of a plane π be $ax + by + cz = d$ and the point $A\ (x_1, y_1, z_1)$.

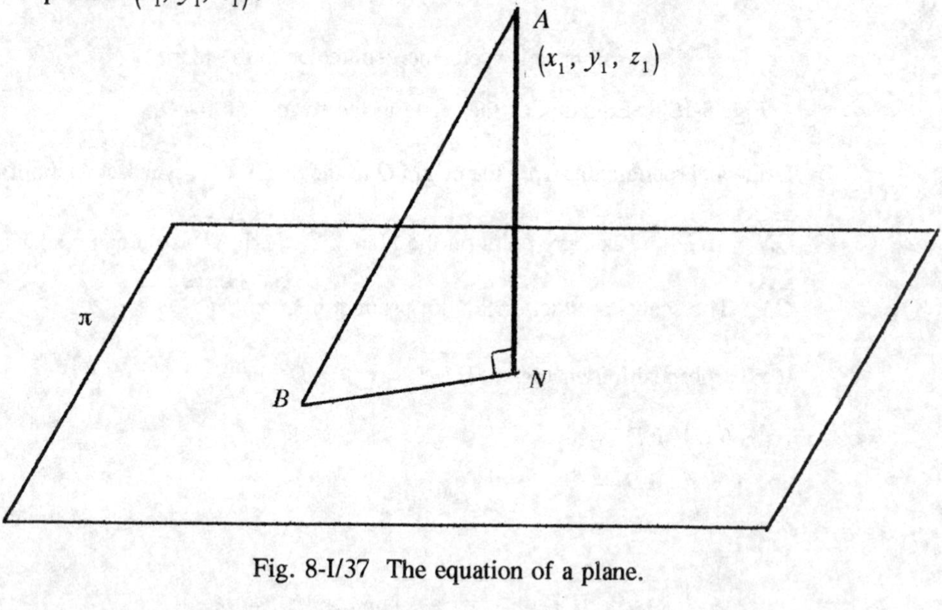

Fig. 8-I/37 The equation of a plane.

AN is drawn perpendicular to the plane π, B is a point on the plane, so that BN is perpendicular to AN.

The direction ratios of AN are $a : b : c$ and the corresponding direction

cosines are $l = \dfrac{a}{\sqrt{a^2 + b^2 + c^2}}$, $m = \dfrac{b}{\sqrt{a^2 + b^2 + c^2}}$,

$n = \dfrac{c}{\sqrt{a^2 + b^2 + c^2}}$.

5.2 EQUATION OF A PLANE

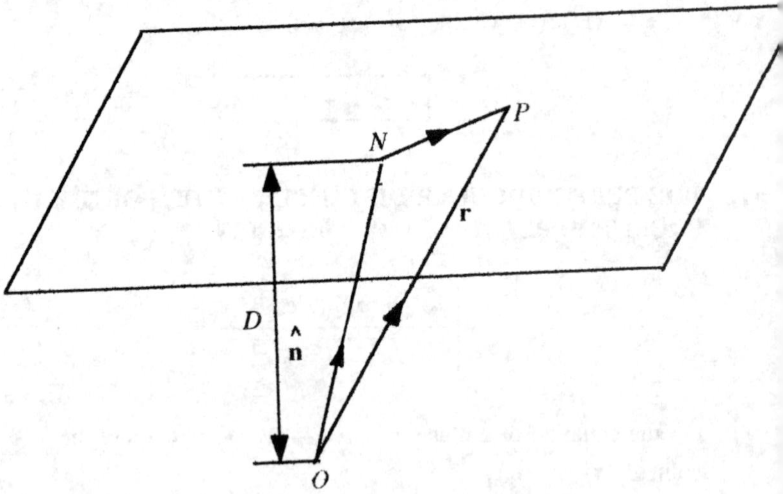

$\hat{\mathbf{n}}$ = unit vector perpendicular to the plane

Fig. 8-I/38 Equation of the plane in the form $\mathbf{r} \cdot \hat{\mathbf{n}} = D$.

Draw a perpendicular from the origin O to the plane, ON, where N is the foot $\overrightarrow{ON} = \hat{\mathbf{n}} D$. Take any point on the plane P, where $\overrightarrow{NP}$ is perpendicular to $\overrightarrow{ON}$. The scalar product or the dot product is given $\overrightarrow{NP} \cdot \overrightarrow{ON} = O$.

If $\mathbf{r}$ is the position vector of P, $\overrightarrow{NP} = \mathbf{r} - \hat{\mathbf{n}} D$

$$(\mathbf{r} - \hat{\mathbf{n}} D) \cdot \hat{\mathbf{n}} D = 0$$

$$\mathbf{r} \cdot \hat{\mathbf{n}} - \hat{\mathbf{n}} \cdot \hat{\mathbf{n}} D = 0$$

but $\quad \hat{\mathbf{n}} \cdot \hat{\mathbf{n}} = 1$

$$\boxed{\mathbf{r} \cdot \hat{\mathbf{n}} = D} \Rightarrow \boxed{\mathbf{r} \cdot \hat{\mathbf{n}} = d} \text{ where } \frac{D}{|\mathbf{n}|} = d$$

the standard form of the vector equation of the plane.

5.3 DISTANCE OF A PLANE FROM THE ORIGIN

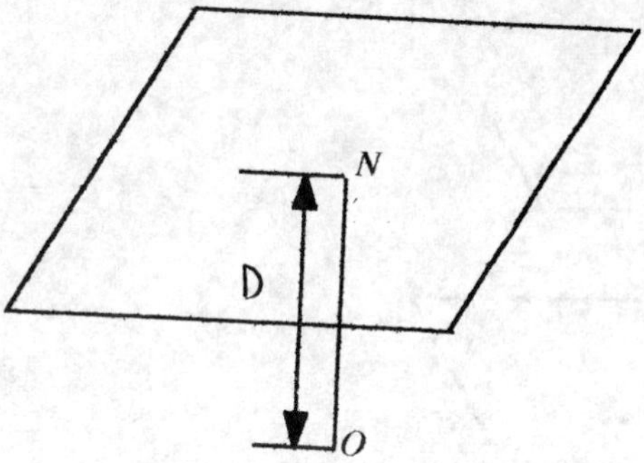

$$ax + by + cz = d$$

Fig. 8-I/40 Distance of a plane from the origin.

ON is perpendicular to the plane Π, the direction cosines $l : m : n$ where

$$l = \frac{a}{\sqrt{a^2 + b^2 + c^2}}, \quad m = \frac{b}{\sqrt{a^2 + b^2 + c^2}} \text{ and } n = \frac{c}{\sqrt{a^2 + b^2 + c^2}}.$$

The coordinates of N are (Dl, Dm, Dn) and since N lies on Π,

$$D = \frac{d}{\sqrt{a^2 + b^2 + c^2}}.$$

Dividing each term, $ax + by + cz = d$, by $\sqrt{a^2 + b^2 + c^2}$, we have

$$\frac{a}{\sqrt{a^2 + b^2 + c^2}}x + \frac{b}{\sqrt{a^2 + b^2 + c^2}}y + \frac{c}{\sqrt{a^2 + b^2 + c^2}}z = D$$

$$lx + my + nz = D$$

5.4 THE DISTANCE BETWEEN TWO PARALLEL PLANES

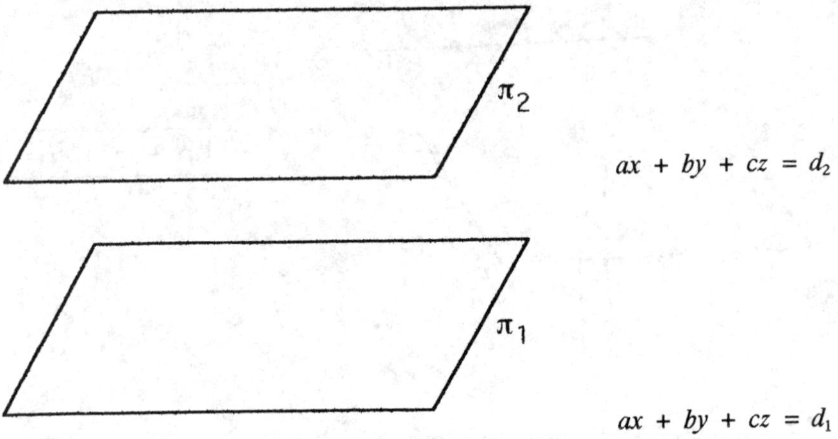

Fig. 8-I/39 Distance between two parallel planes.

The distance from the origin to the plane π_2 is $\dfrac{d_2}{\sqrt{a^2 + b^2 + c^2}}$ and the distance from the origin to the plane π_1 is $\dfrac{d_1}{\sqrt{a^2 + b^2 + c^2}}$. Therefore the distance between the two parallel planes is $\dfrac{d_2 - d_1}{\sqrt{a^2 + b^2 + c^2}}$

WORKED EXAMPLE 31

Find the distance between the two parallel planes given by the cartesian equation $x + 3y - \sqrt{15}\,z = 6$, and $x + 3y - \sqrt{15}\,z = 1$.

SOLUTION 31

$$\frac{d_2 - d_1}{\sqrt{a^2 + b^2 + c^2}} = \frac{6 - 1}{\sqrt{1^2 + 3^2 + 15}} = \frac{5}{5} = 1.$$

5.5 THE PARAMETRIC FORM OF THE VECTOR EQUATION OF A PLANE

Consider three points A, B and C with position vectors **a**, **b** and **c** respectively.

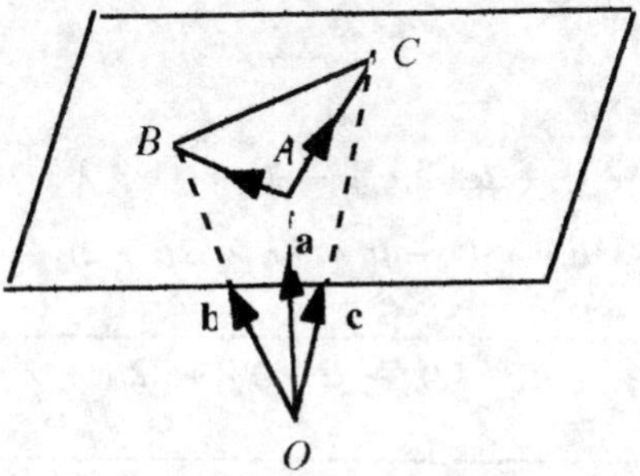

Fig. 8-I/41 Parametric form of a plane.

$\overrightarrow{AB} = \mathbf{b} - \mathbf{a}$, $\overrightarrow{AC} = \mathbf{c} - \mathbf{a}$.

The plane, through the point with position vector **a** and parallel to $\overrightarrow{AB}$ and $\overrightarrow{AC}$, has a vector equation

$$\boxed{\mathbf{r} = \mathbf{a} + s\,\overrightarrow{AB} + t\,\overrightarrow{AC}}$$

where s and t are independent parameters

$$\mathbf{r} = \mathbf{a} + s\,(\mathbf{b} - \mathbf{a}) + t\,(\mathbf{c} - \mathbf{a})$$

$$\mathbf{r} = \mathbf{a}\,(1 - s - t) + s\,\mathbf{b} + t\,\mathbf{c}$$

$$\boxed{\mathbf{r} = \lambda\mathbf{a} + s\,\mathbf{b} + t\,\mathbf{c}} \quad \dots (1)$$

where $\lambda = 1 - s - t$, therefore $\lambda + s + t = 1$.

Equation (1) represents the parametric form of the vector equation of a plane through three points with position vectors **a**, **b**, and **c**.

WORKED EXAMPLE 32

Find the vector equation of the plane containing the points A (2, 1, 0), B (3, − 1, 1), and C (0, − 2, − 1),

(a) in parametric form (b) in cartesian form,
(c) in scalar product form.

SOLUTION 32

(a) The parametric equation of this plane is

$$\mathbf{r} = \lambda(2\mathbf{i} + \mathbf{j}) + \mu(3\mathbf{i} - \mathbf{j} + \mathbf{k}) + \nu(-2\mathbf{j} - \mathbf{k})$$

where $\lambda + \mu + \nu = 1$.

$$\nu = 1 - \lambda - \mu$$

$$\mathbf{r} = \lambda(2\mathbf{i} + \mathbf{j}) + \mu(3\mathbf{i} - \mathbf{j} + \mathbf{k}) + (1 - \lambda - \mu)(-2\mathbf{j} - \mathbf{k})$$

$$\mathbf{r} = (2\lambda + 3\mu)\mathbf{i} + (\lambda - \mu + 2\lambda + 2\mu - 2)\mathbf{j} + (\mu - 1 + \lambda + \mu)\mathbf{k}$$

$$\boxed{\mathbf{r} = (2\lambda + 3\mu)\mathbf{i} + (3\lambda + \mu - 2)\mathbf{j} + (2\mu + \lambda - 1)\mathbf{k}}$$

(b) $x = 2\lambda + 3\mu$

$y = 3\lambda + \mu - 2$

$z = 2\mu + \lambda - 1.$

Eliminating λ and μ from these equations

$$x = 2\lambda + 3\mu, \quad -3y = -9\lambda - 3\mu + 6$$

$$\boxed{x - 3y = -7\lambda + 6}$$

$$-2y = -6\lambda - 2\mu + 4, \qquad z = 2\mu + \lambda - 1$$

$$\boxed{-2y + z = -5\lambda + 3}$$

$$x - 3y = -\frac{7(-2y + z - 3)}{-5} + 6$$

$$+5x - 15y = 7(-2y + z - 3) + 30$$

$$5x - 15y + 14y - 7z + 21 - 30 = 0$$

$$\boxed{5x - y - 7z = 9}$$

(c) the cartesian form of the plane. Therefore the scalar form of the equation is

$$\boxed{\mathbf{r} \cdot (5\mathbf{i} - \mathbf{j} - 7\mathbf{k}) = 9}.$$

5.6 PLANE PASSING THROUGH A GIVEN POINT AND PERPENDICULAR TO A GIVEN DIRECTION.

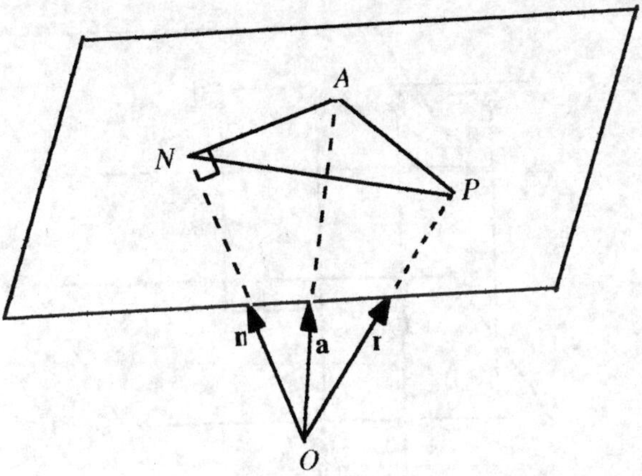

Fig. 8-I/42 Equation of a plane.

Let A be the given point and its position vector is $\overrightarrow{OA} = \mathbf{a}$.

Let the unit vector in the given direction by $\hat{\mathbf{n}}$, $\overrightarrow{ON} = n\hat{\mathbf{n}}$ where n is the

length of ON. As $\overrightarrow{ON}$ is perpendicular to the plane it is perpendicular to $\overrightarrow{AP}$.

$$(\mathbf{r} - \mathbf{a}) \cdot \hat{\mathbf{n}} = 0$$

$$\boxed{\mathbf{r} \cdot \hat{\mathbf{n}} = \mathbf{a} \cdot \hat{\mathbf{n}}}$$

the vector equation of the plane

$$\boxed{\mathbf{r} \cdot \hat{\mathbf{n}} = n}$$

the perpendicular form, where n is positive as the scalar product $\mathbf{a} \cdot \hat{\mathbf{n}}$ is positive and the angle between the vectors is acute.

$ON = n$, the projection of OA.

5.7 PERPENDICULAR DISTANCE OF A POINT FROM A PLANE

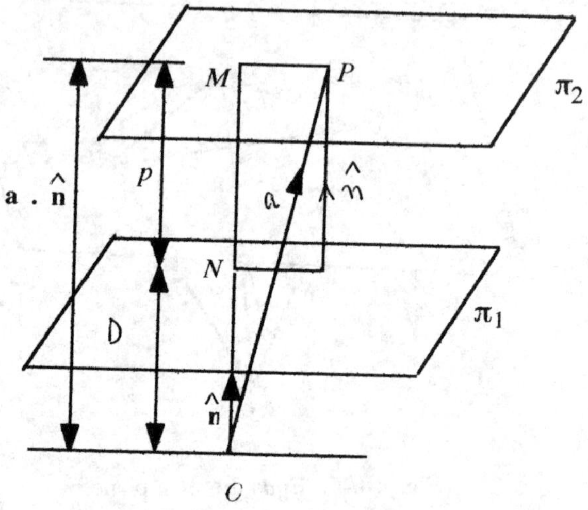

Fig. 8-I/43 Perpendicular distance of a point from a plane

Consider a plane π_1 with equation $\mathbf{r} \cdot \hat{\mathbf{n}} = D$ where D is the distance from the origin to the plane π_1, and let a point P with position vector $(\overrightarrow{OP})$.

The equation of the plane π_2 through P parallel to the plane Π_1 has an equation $\mathbf{r} \cdot \hat{\mathbf{n}} = \mathbf{a} \cdot \hat{\mathbf{n}} = OM$.

MN = distance of P from the plane π

$$p = \mathbf{a} \cdot \hat{\mathbf{n}} - D$$

P and O are on opposite sides of π_1.

WORKED EXAMPLE 33

Find the distance of the point with position vector $\mathbf{i} + \mathbf{j} + \mathbf{k}$ from a plane π with equation $\mathbf{r} \cdot (2\mathbf{i} + 3\mathbf{j} + 4\mathbf{k}) = 5$.

SOLUTION 33

$p = \mathbf{a}.\hat{\mathbf{n}} - D$

$$= (\mathbf{i} + \mathbf{j} + \mathbf{k}).\frac{(2\mathbf{i} + 3\mathbf{j} + 4\mathbf{k})}{\sqrt{2^2 + 3^2 + 4^2}} - \frac{5}{\sqrt{2^2 + 3^2 + 4^2}}$$

$$= (\mathbf{i} + \mathbf{j} + \mathbf{k}).\frac{(2\mathbf{i} + 3\mathbf{j} + 4\mathbf{k})}{\sqrt{29}} - \frac{5}{\sqrt{29}}$$

$$= \frac{1}{\sqrt{29}}(2 + 3 + 4) - \frac{5}{\sqrt{29}} = \frac{4}{\sqrt{29}}$$

therefore the point P and the origin are on opposite sides of the plane.

WORKED EXAMPLE 34

Find the distance of the point (1, 2, 3) from the plane (a) and find the distances of the point (1, 1, 1) from the planes (b) and (c).

(a) $\mathbf{r}.(-\mathbf{i} - \mathbf{j} - \mathbf{k}) = 2$

(b) $\mathbf{r}.(2\mathbf{i} - 3\mathbf{j} + 5\mathbf{k}) = 10$

(c) $\mathbf{r}.(3\mathbf{i} + 4 + 7\mathbf{k}) = 5$.

SOLUTION 34

(a) $p = \mathbf{a}.\hat{\mathbf{n}} - D$

$$= (\mathbf{i} + 2\mathbf{j} + 3\mathbf{k}).\frac{(-\mathbf{i} - \mathbf{j} - \mathbf{k})}{\sqrt{3}} - \frac{2}{\sqrt{3}}$$

$$= -\frac{1}{\sqrt{3}} - \frac{2}{\sqrt{3}} - \frac{3}{\sqrt{3}} - \frac{2}{\sqrt{3}} = -\frac{8}{\sqrt{3}}$$

the negative sign indicates that the point and the origin are on the same side of the plane.

(b) $p = \mathbf{a} . \hat{\mathbf{n}} - D$

$$= (\mathbf{i} + \mathbf{j} + \mathbf{k}) . \frac{(2\mathbf{i} - 3\mathbf{j} + 5\mathbf{k})}{\sqrt{38}} - \frac{10}{\sqrt{38}}$$

$$= \frac{2}{\sqrt{38}} - \frac{3}{\sqrt{38}} + \frac{5}{\sqrt{38}} - \frac{10}{\sqrt{38}} = - \frac{6}{\sqrt{38}}$$

the negative sign indicates that the point and the origin are on the same side of the plane.

(c) $p = \mathbf{a} . \hat{\mathbf{n}} - D$

$$= (\mathbf{i} + \mathbf{j} + \mathbf{k}) . \left(\frac{3\mathbf{i} + 4\mathbf{j} + 7\mathbf{k}}{\sqrt{74}} \right) - \frac{5}{\sqrt{74}}$$

$$= \frac{3}{\sqrt{74}} + \frac{4}{\sqrt{74}} + \frac{7}{\sqrt{74}} - \frac{5}{\sqrt{74}} = \frac{9}{\sqrt{74}}$$

the positive sign indicates that the point and the origin are on opposite sides of the plane.

WORKED EXAMPLE 35

(a) Find the perpendicular distance of the point (1, − 1, − 1) from the plane $\mathbf{r} . (\mathbf{i} + \mathbf{j} + \mathbf{k}) = 1$

(b) Find the perpendicular distance of the point (− 1, 2, − 3) from the plane $\mathbf{r} . (\mathbf{i} + \mathbf{j} - \mathbf{k}) = 2$.

SOLUTION 35

(a) $p = \mathbf{a} . \hat{\mathbf{n}} - D$

$$= (\mathbf{i} - \mathbf{j} - \mathbf{k}) . \frac{(\mathbf{i} + \mathbf{j} + \mathbf{k})}{\sqrt{3}} - \frac{1}{\sqrt{3}}$$

$$= \frac{1}{\sqrt{3}} - \frac{1}{\sqrt{3}} - \frac{1}{\sqrt{3}} - \frac{1}{\sqrt{3}} = - \frac{2}{\sqrt{3}}$$

the point and the origin are on the same side.

(b) $p = \mathbf{a} . \hat{\mathbf{n}} - D$

$$= (-\mathbf{i} + 2\mathbf{j} - 3\mathbf{k}) . \frac{(\mathbf{i} + \mathbf{j} - \mathbf{k})}{\sqrt{3}} - \frac{2}{\sqrt{3}}$$

$$= -\frac{1}{\sqrt{3}} + \frac{2}{\sqrt{3}} + \frac{3}{\sqrt{3}} - \frac{2}{\sqrt{3}} = \frac{2}{\sqrt{3}}$$

the point and the origin are on opposite sides of the plane.

WORKED EXAMPLE 36

Determine whether the points (1, − 2, 1), (− 2, 1, 3) are on the same or opposite sides of the plane $\mathbf{r} . (\mathbf{i} + 2\mathbf{j} - \mathbf{k}) = 1$.

SOLUTION 36

$p = \mathbf{a} . \hat{\mathbf{n}} - D$

$$= (\mathbf{i} - 2\mathbf{j} + \mathbf{k}) . \frac{(\mathbf{i} + 2\mathbf{j} - \mathbf{k})}{\sqrt{6}} - \frac{1}{\sqrt{6}}$$

$$= \frac{1}{\sqrt{6}} - \frac{4}{\sqrt{6}} - \frac{1}{\sqrt{6}} - \frac{1}{\sqrt{6}} = -\frac{5}{\sqrt{6}}$$

$p = \mathbf{a} . \hat{\mathbf{n}} - D$

$$= (-2\mathbf{i} + \mathbf{j} + 3\mathbf{k}) . \frac{(\mathbf{i} + 2\mathbf{j} - \mathbf{k})}{\sqrt{6}} - \frac{1}{\sqrt{6}}$$

$$= -\frac{2}{\sqrt{6}} + \frac{2}{\sqrt{6}} - \frac{3}{\sqrt{6}} - \frac{1}{\sqrt{6}} = -\frac{4}{\sqrt{6}}$$

the points are on the same side of the plane since they are both of the same sign and the points and the origin are on the same side.

5.8 THE ANGLE BETWEEN TWO PLANES

Consider two planes Π_1 and Π_2 whose vector equations are $\mathbf{r} . \hat{\mathbf{n}}_1 = D_1$ and $\mathbf{r} . \hat{\mathbf{n}}_2 = D_2$.

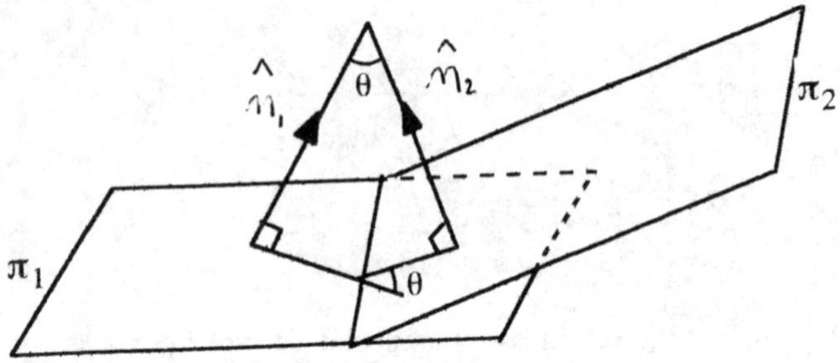

Fig. 8-I/44 Angle between two planes

The angle between the planes Π_1 and Π_2 is equal to the angle between the normals to Π_1 and Π_2, θ

$$\boxed{\cos\theta = \hat{\mathbf{n}}_1 \cdot \hat{\mathbf{n}}_2}$$

WORKED EXAMPLE 37

Find the angle, to the nearest degree, between the planes whose vector equations are $\mathbf{r} \cdot (2\mathbf{i} + 3\mathbf{j} + 4\mathbf{k}) = 5$ and $\mathbf{r} \cdot (+\mathbf{i} + 2\mathbf{j} + 3\mathbf{k}) = 7$.

SOLUTION 37

$$\cos\theta = \frac{(2\mathbf{i} + 3\mathbf{j} + 4\mathbf{k})}{\sqrt{2^2 + 3^2 + 4^2}} \cdot \frac{(+\mathbf{i} + 2\mathbf{j} + 3\mathbf{k})}{\sqrt{1^2 + 2^2 + 3^2}}$$

$$= \frac{+2 + 6 + 12}{\sqrt{29}\sqrt{14}} = \frac{20}{\sqrt{29}\sqrt{14}}$$

$$\theta = 7^{\circ}.$$

WORKED EXAMPLE 38

Determine the condition that two planes (i) are parallel
(ii) are perpendicular.

SOLUTION 38

(i) For the planes to be parallel the angle must be zero, $\cos\theta = \cos 0^\circ = 1$ $= \hat{\mathbf{n}}_1 . \hat{\mathbf{n}}_2$, the unit vectors must be equal $\boxed{\hat{\mathbf{n}}_1 = \hat{\mathbf{n}}_2}$

(ii) For the planes to be perpendicular the angle must be 90°, $\cos 90^\circ = 0$,

therefore, $\boxed{\hat{\mathbf{n}}_1 . \hat{\mathbf{n}}_2 = 0}$.

WORKED EXAMPLE 39

Find the cosine of the acute angle between the two planes whose equations are

(a) $\mathbf{r} . (2\mathbf{i} - 3\mathbf{j} + 7\mathbf{k}) = 1$ and $\mathbf{r} . (\mathbf{i} + \mathbf{j} + 2\mathbf{k}) = 2$

(b) $\mathbf{r} . (\mathbf{i} - 3\mathbf{k}) = 5$ and $\mathbf{r} . (2\mathbf{i} + \mathbf{j} - \mathbf{k}) = 3$.

SOLUTION 39

(a) $\cos\theta = \hat{\mathbf{n}}_1 . \hat{\mathbf{n}}_2$

$$= \frac{(2\mathbf{i} - 3\mathbf{j} + 7\mathbf{k})}{\sqrt{2^2 + 3^2 + 7^2}} . \frac{(\mathbf{i} + \mathbf{j} + 2\mathbf{k})}{\sqrt{1 + 1 + 4}}$$

$$= \frac{2 - 3 + 14}{\sqrt{62}\,\sqrt{6}} = \frac{13}{\sqrt{372}} = 0.674$$

(b) $\cos\theta = \hat{\mathbf{n}}_1 . \hat{\mathbf{n}}_2$

$$= \frac{\mathbf{i} - 3\mathbf{k}}{\sqrt{1 + 3^2}} . \frac{2\mathbf{i} + \mathbf{j} - \mathbf{k}}{\sqrt{2^2 + 1^2 + 1^2}}$$

$$= \frac{2 + 3}{\sqrt{10}\,\sqrt{6}} = \frac{5}{\sqrt{60}} = 0.65$$

5.9 THE ANGLE BETWEEN A LINE AND A PLANE

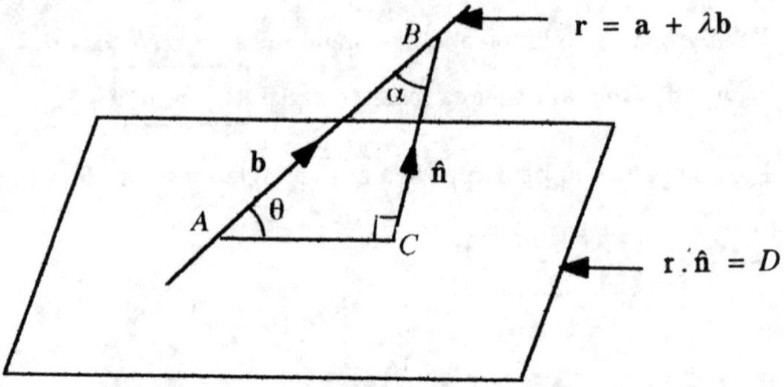

Fig. 8-I/45 The angle between a line and a plane

Consider the vector equation of a line to be $\mathbf{r} = \mathbf{a} + \lambda\mathbf{b}$ and the plane $\mathbf{r} \cdot \hat{\mathbf{n}} = D$.

Let α be the angle between the line and the normal to the plane

$$\cos\alpha = \frac{\mathbf{b} \cdot \hat{\mathbf{n}}}{|\mathbf{b}|}$$

If θ is the angle between the line and the plane, $\theta + \alpha = \frac{\pi}{2}$

$$\cos\alpha = \frac{BC}{AB} = \sin\theta$$

$$\boxed{\sin\theta = \frac{\mathbf{b} \cdot \hat{\mathbf{n}}}{|\mathbf{b}|}}$$

WORKED EXAMPLE 40

Determine the angle between the line with vector equation $\mathbf{r} = (2\mathbf{i} + \mathbf{j} - \mathbf{k}) + \lambda\,(2\mathbf{i} + 3\mathbf{j} + \mathbf{k})$ and the plane $\mathbf{r} \cdot (3\mathbf{i} + 4\mathbf{j} + 5\mathbf{k}) = 7$.

SOLUTION 40

$$\sin\theta = \frac{\mathbf{b} \cdot \hat{\mathbf{n}}}{|\mathbf{b}|}$$

The direction vector $\mathbf{b} = 2\mathbf{i} + 3\mathbf{j} + \mathbf{k}$

$$|\mathbf{b}| = \sqrt{4 + 9 + 1} = \sqrt{14}$$

$$\hat{\mathbf{n}} = \frac{3\mathbf{i} + 4\mathbf{j} + 5\mathbf{k}}{\sqrt{3^2 + 4^2 + 5^2}} = \frac{3}{\sqrt{50}}\mathbf{i} + \frac{4}{\sqrt{50}}\mathbf{j} + \frac{5}{\sqrt{50}}\mathbf{k}$$

$$\sin\theta = \frac{\mathbf{b}\,.\,\hat{\mathbf{n}}}{\sqrt{14}}$$

$$= \frac{(2\mathbf{i} + 3\mathbf{j} + \mathbf{k})\,.\left(\frac{3}{\sqrt{50}}\mathbf{i} + \frac{4}{\sqrt{50}}\mathbf{j} + \frac{5}{\sqrt{50}}\mathbf{k}\right)}{\sqrt{14}}$$

$$= \frac{1}{\sqrt{50}\,\sqrt{14}}(6 + 12 + 5) = \frac{23}{\sqrt{700}} = 0.8693$$

$$\theta = 60.4^\circ.$$

WORKED EXAMPLE 41

Find the sine of the angle between the line and plane whose equations are

(a) $\mathbf{r} = (\mathbf{i} + 2\mathbf{j} - 5\mathbf{k}) + \lambda\,(2\mathbf{i} - 3\mathbf{j} + 4\mathbf{k})$, $\quad \mathbf{r}\,.\,(2\mathbf{i} - 3\mathbf{j} + 5\mathbf{k}) = 1$

(b) $\mathbf{r} = (-\,2\mathbf{i} + 3\mathbf{j} + 7\mathbf{k}) + \lambda\,(+\,4\mathbf{i} + \mathbf{j} + \mathbf{k})$, $\mathbf{r}\,.\,(3\mathbf{i} + \mathbf{j} + \mathbf{k}) = 5.$

SOLUTION 41

(a) $\sin\theta = \dfrac{\mathbf{b}\,.\,\hat{\mathbf{n}}}{|\mathbf{b}|}$ $\qquad \mathbf{b} = 2\mathbf{i} - 3\mathbf{j} + 4\mathbf{k}$

$$|\mathbf{b}| = \sqrt{2^2 + 3^2 + 4^2} = \sqrt{29}$$

$$\hat{\mathbf{n}} = \frac{2\mathbf{i} - 3\mathbf{j} + 5\mathbf{k}}{\sqrt{2^2 + 3^2 + 5^2}} = \frac{1}{\sqrt{38}}(2\mathbf{i} - 3\mathbf{j} + 5\mathbf{k})$$

$$\sin\theta = \frac{(2\mathbf{i} - 3\mathbf{j} + 4\mathbf{k})\,.\,(2\mathbf{i} - 3\mathbf{j} + 5\mathbf{k})}{\sqrt{29}\,\sqrt{38}} = \frac{4 + 9 + 20}{\sqrt{29}\,\sqrt{38}}$$

$$\sin\theta = 0.994.$$

(b) $\sin\theta = \dfrac{\mathbf{b}\,.\,\hat{\mathbf{n}}}{|\mathbf{b}|} = \dfrac{(+\,4\mathbf{i} + \mathbf{j} + \mathbf{k})}{\sqrt{18}}\,.\,\dfrac{(3\mathbf{i} + \mathbf{j} + \mathbf{k})}{\sqrt{11}}$

$$= \frac{12 + 1 + 1}{\sqrt{198}} = \frac{14}{\sqrt{198}} = 0.995.$$

5.10 THE INTERSECTION OF TWO PLANES IS A LINE

Let two planes π_1 and π_2 with equations $\mathbf{r} \cdot \hat{\mathbf{n}}_1 = D_1$ and $\mathbf{r} \cdot \hat{\mathbf{n}}_2 = D_2$ respectively, intersect in a line.

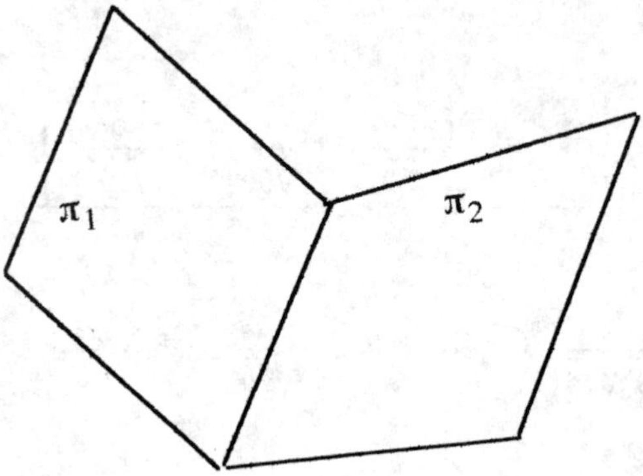

Fig. 8-I/46 The intersection of two planes.

The equation of the plane passing through the intersection has an equation

$$\mathbf{r} \cdot \left(\hat{\mathbf{n}}_1 - k\,\hat{\mathbf{n}}_2\right) = D_1 - kD_2.$$

WORKED EXAMPLE 42

Find the equation of the line of intersection of the two planes with equations

$\pi_1 : \mathbf{r} \cdot (2\mathbf{i} - \mathbf{j} + 2\mathbf{k}) = 3$

$\pi_2 : \mathbf{r} \cdot (-3\mathbf{i} + 2\mathbf{j} - \mathbf{k}) = 5.$

SOLUTION 42

Let $\mathbf{r} = x\,\mathbf{i} + y\,\mathbf{j} + z\,\mathbf{k}$, $(x\,\mathbf{i} + y\,\mathbf{j} + z\,\mathbf{k}) \cdot (2\mathbf{i} - \mathbf{j} + 2\mathbf{k}) = 3$

$$\boxed{2x - y + 2z = 3} \quad \ldots (1)$$

$$(x\,\mathbf{i} + y\,\mathbf{j} + z\,\mathbf{k}) \cdot (-3\mathbf{i} + 2\mathbf{j} - \mathbf{k}) = 5$$

$$\boxed{-3x + 2y - z = 5} \quad \ldots (2)$$

Eliminating y from (1) and (2)

$$\begin{array}{rl} 4x - 2y + 4z &= 6 \\ -\ 3x + 2y - z &= 5 \\ \hline x + 3z &= 11 \\ x &= 11 - 3z. \end{array}$$

Eliminating z from (1) and (2)

$$\begin{array}{rl} 2x - y + 2z &= 3 \\ -\ 6x + 4y - 2z &= 10 \\ \hline -\ 4x + 3y &= 13 \\ x &= \frac{3}{4}y - \frac{13}{4} \end{array}$$

$$x = 11 - 3z = \frac{3}{4}y - \frac{13}{4} = \lambda$$

$$x = \lambda, \quad \frac{11 - \lambda}{3} = z, \quad y = \frac{4}{3}\lambda + \frac{13}{3}.$$

Any point on the line of the intersection is $\left(\lambda, \frac{4}{3}\lambda + \frac{13}{3}, \frac{11 - \lambda}{3}\right)$

or $\left(3\mu, 4\mu + \frac{13}{3}, \frac{11}{3} - \mu\right)$ where $\lambda = 3\mu$.

The position vector therefore, of any point on the line is given

$$\boxed{\mathbf{r} = \frac{13}{3}\mathbf{j} + \frac{11}{3}\mathbf{k} + \mu(3\mathbf{i} + 4\mathbf{j} - 1\mathbf{k})}$$

5.11 THE PARAMETRIC FORM FOR THE VECTOR EQUATION OF A PLANE

The plane, through the point with position vector **a** and parallel to **b** and **c**, has equation

$$\boxed{\mathbf{r} = \mathbf{a} + s\,\mathbf{b} + t\,\mathbf{c}}$$

where s and t are independent parameters.

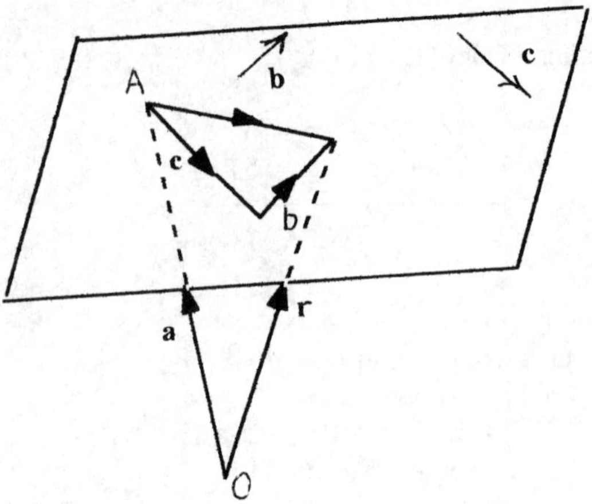

Fig. 8-I/47 The parametric form for the vector equation of a plan.

Fig. 8-I/47 shows a plane through the point A with position vector **a** and parallel to the direction vectors **b** and **c** as shown.

WORKED EXAMPLE 43

Two planes with parametric equations

$\Pi_1 : \mathbf{r} = (2\mathbf{i} - 3\mathbf{j} + \mathbf{k}) + s\,(-\mathbf{i} + 2\mathbf{j} + 3\mathbf{k}) + t\,(3\mathbf{i} + \mathbf{j} + 4\mathbf{k})$

$\Pi_2 : \mathbf{r} = (-\mathbf{i} + 2\mathbf{j} - 4\mathbf{k}) + \lambda\,(\mathbf{i} + \mathbf{j} + \mathbf{k}) + \mu\,(-3\mathbf{i} + 3\mathbf{j} + 2\mathbf{k})$

intersect find the vector equation of the line of intersection.

SOLUTION 43

$$\mathbf{r} = (2\mathbf{i} - 3\mathbf{j} + \mathbf{k}) + s\,(-\mathbf{i} + 2\mathbf{j} + 3\mathbf{k}) + t\,(3\mathbf{i} + \mathbf{j} + 4\mathbf{k}) \quad \ldots (a)$$

$$\boxed{\mathbf{r} = (2 - s + 3t)\,\mathbf{i} + (-3 + 2s + t)\,\mathbf{j} + (1 + 3s + 4t)\,\mathbf{k}} \quad \ldots (1)$$

$$\mathbf{r} = (-\mathbf{i} + 2\mathbf{j} - 4\mathbf{k}) + \lambda\,(\mathbf{i} + \mathbf{j} + \mathbf{k}) + \mu\,(-3\mathbf{i} + 3\mathbf{j} + 2\mathbf{k}) \quad \ldots (b)$$

$$\boxed{\mathbf{r} = (-1 + \lambda - 3\mu)\,\mathbf{i} + (2 + \lambda + 3\mu)\,\mathbf{j} + (-4 + \lambda + 2\mu)\,\mathbf{k}} \quad \ldots (2)$$

These planes meet when

$$2 - s + 3t = -1 + \lambda - 3\mu \quad \ldots (3)$$
$$-3 + 2s + t = 2 + \lambda + 3\mu \quad \ldots (4)$$
$$1 + 3s + 4t = -4 + \lambda + 2\mu \quad \ldots (5)$$

Eliminating the two parameters s and t.

Eliminate firstly s

$$\begin{array}{lrcll} (3)\times 2 & 4 - 2s + 6t &=& -2 + 2\lambda - 6\mu & \text{adding} \\ (4) & -3 + 2s + t &=& 2 + \lambda + 3\mu & \\ \hline & 1 + 7t &=& 3\lambda - 3\mu & \dots (6) \end{array}$$

$$\begin{array}{lrcll} (3)\times 3 & 6 - 3s + 9t &=& -3 + 3\lambda - 9\mu & \text{adding} \\ (5) & 1 + 3s + 4t &=& -4 + \lambda + 2\mu & \\ \hline & 7 + 13t &=& -7 + 4\lambda - 7\mu & \dots (7) \end{array}$$

Eliminate secondly t

$$\begin{array}{lrcll} (6)\times 13 & 13 + 91t &=& 39\lambda - 39\mu & \text{adding} \\ (7)\times(-7) & -49 - 91t &=& 49 - 28\lambda + 49\mu & \\ \hline & -36 &=& 49 + 11\lambda + 10\mu & \end{array}$$

$$11\lambda + 10\mu = -85 \qquad \lambda = -\frac{10}{11}\mu - \frac{85}{11}$$

substituting in (b)

$$\mathbf{r} = (-\mathbf{i} + 2\mathbf{j} - 4\mathbf{k}) + \left(-\frac{10}{11}\mu - \frac{85}{11}\right)(\mathbf{i} + \mathbf{j} + \mathbf{k}) + \mu(-3\mathbf{i} + 3\mathbf{j} + 2\mathbf{k})$$

$$\mathbf{r} = (-\mathbf{i} + 2\mathbf{j} - 4\mathbf{k}) - \frac{10}{11}\mu(\mathbf{i} + \mathbf{j} + \mathbf{k}) - \frac{85}{11}(\mathbf{i} + \mathbf{j} + \mathbf{k}) + \mu(-3\mathbf{i} + 3\mathbf{j} + 2\mathbf{k})$$

$$\boxed{\mathbf{r} = \left(-\frac{96}{11}\mathbf{i} - \frac{63}{11}\mathbf{j} - \frac{129}{11}\mathbf{k}\right) + \mu\left(-\frac{43}{11}\mathbf{i} + \frac{23}{11}\mathbf{j} + \frac{12}{11}\mathbf{k}\right)}$$

the vector equation of the line of intersection of the planes.

EXERCISES 5

1. Determine the equation of the plane when $A\ (-1, -2, -3)$ is a point on the plane which is perpendicular to the line with direction ratios $2 : 3 : 4$.

2. Determine the equation of the plane when $A\ (2\ , -3, 4)$ is a point on the plane which is perpendicular to the line with direction ratios $l : m : n$.

3. Find the equation of the plane which contains three fixed points: $A\ (-3, 4, 7)$, $B\ (0, -2, 5)$ and $C\ (2, 0, -3)$.

4. Find the equation of the plane which contains three fixed points: $A\ (0, 0, 0)$, $B\ (1, -2, -3)$, $C\ (-2, 1, 2)$.

5. Find the equations of the planes passing through the fixed points and whose normals have the given direction ratios

   (i) $A\ (0, 0, 1)$, $1 : -2 : 3$
   (ii) $B\ (1, 0, 0)$, $4 : -5 : 6$
   (iii) $C\ (1, 3, 0)$, $-1 : 2 : 4$.

6. Find the equations of the planes passing through the set of points.

   (i) $A\ (1, 1, 0)$, $B\ (2, -2, 3)$, $C\ (0, 0, 2)$
   (ii) $P\ (0, 1, 0)$, $Q\ (-1, 3, -4)$, $R\ (1, 0, 2)$
   (iii) $D\ (-1, -2, -3)$, $E\ (0, 3, 0)$, $F\ (1, 2, 4)$.

7. Find the point of intersection of the line
   $l : \mathbf{r} = (2\mathbf{i} - 3\mathbf{j} + \mathbf{k}) + \lambda\,(-3\mathbf{i} + \mathbf{j} - 3\mathbf{k})$ and the plane
   $\pi : \mathbf{r} \,.\, (\mathbf{i} + \mathbf{j} + \mathbf{k}) = 3$.

8. Find the point of intersection of the line
   $l : \mathbf{r} = (-\mathbf{i} + 4\mathbf{j} - 5\mathbf{k}) + t\,(2\mathbf{i} - \mathbf{j} - \mathbf{k})$ and the plane
   $\pi : \mathbf{r} \,.\, (2\mathbf{i} - 2\mathbf{j} + 4\mathbf{k}) = 5$.

9. Find the point of intersection of the line
   $l : \mathbf{r} = (\mathbf{i} + \mathbf{j} + \mathbf{k}) + \mu\,(2\mathbf{i} - 3\mathbf{j} + 4\mathbf{k}) = 1$ and the plane
   $\pi : \mathbf{r} \,.\, (2\mathbf{i} + 5\mathbf{j} - 7\mathbf{k}) = 2$.

10. Find the point of intersection of the line $\dfrac{x + 1}{2} = \dfrac{y - 3}{3} = \dfrac{z + 2}{4} = \lambda$ and the plane $x + y + 2z = 4$.

11. Find the point of intersection of the line $x = y = z = \lambda$ and the plane $\mathbf{r} \,.\, (\mathbf{i} + 2\mathbf{j} + 3\mathbf{k}) = 7$.

12. The vector equations of a line and a plane are given

$l : \mathbf{r} = 2\mathbf{i} - 3\mathbf{j} + \mathbf{k} + \lambda(-2\mathbf{i} + 5\mathbf{j} + \mathbf{k})$

$\pi : \mathbf{r} \,.\, (-2\mathbf{i} - \mathbf{j} + \mathbf{k}) = 2$ respectively.

Show that the line, l and the plane π are parallel.

13. The vector equations of a line and a plane are given

$l : \mathbf{r} = (-\mathbf{i} + 2\mathbf{j} - 5\mathbf{k}) + \mu(\mathbf{i} - 7\mathbf{j} + 4\mathbf{k})$

$\pi : \mathbf{r} \,.\, (3\mathbf{i} + \mathbf{j} + \mathbf{k}) = 5$ respectively.

Show that the line, l and the plane, π are parallel.

14. Show that the line l whose vector equation is $\mathbf{r} = (\mathbf{i} - 3\mathbf{j} + 4\mathbf{k}) + t(-5\mathbf{i} + 7\mathbf{j} - 8\mathbf{k})$ is parallel to the plane π whose vector equation is $\mathbf{r} \,.\, (-2\mathbf{i} + 2\mathbf{j} + 3\mathbf{k}) = 1$ and find the distance between the line l and the plane π.

15. Determine whether the following lines

(i) $\mathbf{r} = \mathbf{i} + \mathbf{j} + \mathbf{k} + \lambda(-3\mathbf{i} + 4\mathbf{j} - 5\mathbf{k})$

(ii) $\mathbf{r} = \mathbf{j} + 2\mathbf{k} + t(2\mathbf{i} - 3\mathbf{j} + \mathbf{k})$

(iii) $\mathbf{r} = 2\mathbf{i} - 3\mathbf{j} - 7\mathbf{k} + \mu(3\mathbf{i} + 5\mathbf{j} + 9\mathbf{k})$.

are parallel to the plane $\mathbf{r} \,.\, (2\mathbf{i} - 3\mathbf{j} + \mathbf{k}) = d$ and find the acute angle between the line and the plane.

16. Find the vector equations of the following planes in the form $\mathbf{r} \,.\, \mathbf{n} = d$:

(i) $\mathbf{r} = \mathbf{i} + \mathbf{j} + \mathbf{k} + \lambda(2\mathbf{i} - \mathbf{j} + 3\mathbf{k}) + s(-2\mathbf{i} + 3\mathbf{j} - 7\mathbf{k})$

(ii) $\mathbf{r} = 2\mathbf{j} - 3\mathbf{k} + \mu(-3\mathbf{i} + 4\mathbf{j} - \mathbf{k}) + v(2\mathbf{i} + 5\mathbf{j} - 5\mathbf{k})$

(iii) $\mathbf{r} = (1 - t - s)\,\mathbf{a} + t\,\mathbf{b} + s\,\mathbf{c}$

where $\mathbf{a} = 2\mathbf{i} - 3\mathbf{j} - \mathbf{k}$, $\mathbf{b} = -3\mathbf{i} + 4\mathbf{j} + \mathbf{k}$, $\mathbf{c} = 3\mathbf{j} - 5\mathbf{k}$ are position vectors.

17. Find the cartesian equations of the following planes:

(i) $\mathbf{r} \,.\, (2\mathbf{i} + 3\mathbf{j} + 4\mathbf{k}) = 3$

(ii) $\mathbf{r} \,.\, (-3\mathbf{i} + 2\mathbf{j} - \mathbf{k}) = 1$

(iii) $\mathbf{r} \,.\, (\mathbf{i} - 2\mathbf{j} + 3\mathbf{k}) = 0$.

18. Find the vector equation in the form $\mathbf{r} \,.\, \mathbf{n} = d$ of the planes containing the following pairs of lines

(i) $\mathbf{r} = (2\mathbf{i} - 3\mathbf{j} + 5\mathbf{k}) + \lambda(3\mathbf{j} - 4\mathbf{k})$, $\mathbf{r} = (2\mathbf{i} - 3\mathbf{j} + 5\mathbf{k}) + \mu(\mathbf{i} + 3\mathbf{k})$

(ii) $\mathbf{r} = (2\mathbf{i} - 3\mathbf{k}) + \lambda(2\mathbf{i} - 3\mathbf{j})$, $\mathbf{r} = (2\mathbf{i} - 3\mathbf{k}) + \mu(3\mathbf{i} - \mathbf{j} - \mathbf{k})$

(iii) $\mathbf{r} = (2\mathbf{i} + 7\mathbf{k}) + \lambda(\mathbf{i} + \mathbf{j} - \mathbf{k})$, $\mathbf{r} = (2\mathbf{i} + 7\mathbf{k}) + \mu(2\mathbf{i} - 3\mathbf{j} + \mathbf{k})$.

19. Find the vector equation of the plane containing the position vectors of three points **a** = 2**j** − 3**k**, **b** = − 2**i** + 7**j**, **c** = (**i** + **j** + **k**).

20. Find the vector equation of the plane containing the three points $A\ (-1, -2, -3)$, $B\ (3, 4, 5)$, $C\ (-6, -7, 8)$.

21. Determine the distance between the two parallel planes

$\pi_1 : \mathbf{r} \cdot (\mathbf{i} + \mathbf{j} + \mathbf{k}) = 1$

$\pi_2 : \mathbf{r} \cdot (\mathbf{i} + \mathbf{j} + \mathbf{k}) = 2.$

22. Find the perpendicular distance of the point (1, 2, 3) from the following planes:

(i) $\mathbf{r} \cdot (3\mathbf{i} + 4\mathbf{j} + 5\mathbf{k}) = 12$

(ii) $\mathbf{r} \cdot (6\mathbf{i} + 7\mathbf{j} + 8\mathbf{k}) = 5$

(iii) $\mathbf{r} \cdot (\mathbf{i} + \mathbf{j} + \mathbf{k}) = 1.$

23. Two right angled cones have their bases contained in the planes $\mathbf{r} \cdot (\mathbf{i} + 2\mathbf{j} + 3\mathbf{k}) = 4$, $\mathbf{r} \cdot (\mathbf{i} + 2\mathbf{j} + 3\mathbf{k}) = 7$, determine the distance between the circular bases.

24. Show that the point (− 3, 4, − 5) lies in the plane π whose equation is

$$\mathbf{r} \cdot (2\mathbf{i} - 3\mathbf{j} - 12\mathbf{k}) = 42.$$

25. Find the sine of the angle between the line and the plane whose equation are

(i) $\mathbf{r} = 2\mathbf{j} + 3\mathbf{k} + \lambda\,(2\mathbf{i} + \mathbf{j} - 3\mathbf{k})$, $\mathbf{r} \cdot (\mathbf{i} + \mathbf{j} + \mathbf{k}) = 8$

(ii) $\dfrac{x + 1}{3} = \dfrac{y - 1}{4} = \dfrac{z + 2}{5} = \lambda$ and $x + y + z = 3.$

26. A perpendicular line is drawn from the point (1, 1, 1) to the plane $\mathbf{r} \cdot (-3\mathbf{i} + \mathbf{j} - 2\mathbf{k}) = 25$. Find the vector equation of the line and hence find the coordinates of the point of intersection.

27. The position vector of a point A is − 2**i** + 3**j** + 5**k**, a perpendicular line is drawn from A to intersect the plane $3x - 5y - z = 5$ at B, find the coordinates of B and the reflection point C of A.

28. The position vectors of three points A, B and C are given:

$\mathbf{a} = \mathbf{i} - \mathbf{j} - \mathbf{k}, \ \mathbf{b} = 2\mathbf{i} + 5\mathbf{j} + 7\mathbf{k}, \ \mathbf{c} = -\mathbf{i} - 2\mathbf{j} + 3\mathbf{k}.$

Find the vectors $\overrightarrow{AB}$ and $\overrightarrow{AC}$ and hence find the vector equation of the plane ABC, repeat to procedure by finding the vectors $\overrightarrow{BC}$ and $\overrightarrow{BA}$ and hence find the vector equation of the plane ABC, in the form $\mathbf{r} \cdot \mathbf{n} = d$.

29. Show that the angle between a line with vector equation $\mathbf{r} = \mathbf{a} + \lambda\mathbf{b}$ and a plane with vector equation $\mathbf{r} \cdot \hat{\mathbf{n}} = d$ is given by

$$\boxed{\sin \theta = \frac{\mathbf{b} \cdot \hat{\mathbf{n}}}{|\mathbf{b}|}.}$$

30. The position vector of two points A and B are given as $\mathbf{a} = 2\mathbf{i} - 3\mathbf{j} + 4\mathbf{k}$ and $\mathbf{b} = -3\mathbf{i} + 2\mathbf{j} - \mathbf{k}$, find the vector equation of the line AB.

Determine the sine of the acute angle between the line AB and the plane with vector equation $\mathbf{r} \cdot (-4\mathbf{i} + 5\lambda - 7\mathbf{k}) = 27$.

31. The vector equation of a line is given $\mathbf{r} = (2\mathbf{i} - 5\mathbf{j} - 9\mathbf{k}) + \lambda(-7\mathbf{i} + 2\mathbf{j} + 3\mathbf{k})$ and the vector equation of a plane is given $\mathbf{r} \cdot (\mathbf{i} + 2\mathbf{j} + 3\mathbf{k}) = 33$. Find the angle between the line and the plane.

32. A line is parallel to the vector $3\mathbf{i} - 5\mathbf{j} + 7\mathbf{k}$ and passes through the point $(2, 2, 2)$. Find the cosine of the angle of the line and the plane with vector equation $\mathbf{r} \cdot (-\mathbf{j} + 5\mathbf{k}) = 5$.

33. Find the vector equations of the planes in parametric form containing the following pairs of lines:

(a) $\mathbf{r} = 2\mathbf{i} - 3\mathbf{j} + 4\mathbf{k} + \lambda(\mathbf{i} + 5\mathbf{j} - 7\mathbf{k})$,
$\mathbf{r} = \mathbf{i} + \mathbf{j} + 9\mathbf{k} + \mu(-3\mathbf{i} + 4\mathbf{j} + 8\mathbf{k})$

(b) $\mathbf{r} = \mathbf{i} + 5\mathbf{j} + 9\mathbf{k} + \lambda(\mathbf{i} + 3\mathbf{j} - 2\mathbf{k})$,
$\mathbf{r} = 2\mathbf{i} + 5\mathbf{j} - \mathbf{k} + \mu(3\mathbf{j} + 5\mathbf{k})$.

6. VECTOR PRODUCTS

6.1 INTRODUCTION OF VECTOR PRODUCT (OR CROSS PRODUCT)

If **a** and **b** are vectors, the vector product is given by

$\boxed{\mathbf{a} \times \mathbf{b} = (ab \sin\theta)\,\hat{\mathbf{n}}}$ in a direction perpendicular to the plane containing **a** and **b** in the sense of a right handed screw turned from **a** to **b**.

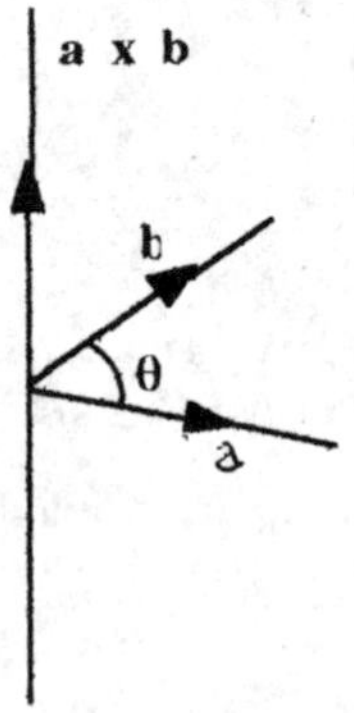

Fig. 8-I/48 Turned from **a** to **b**

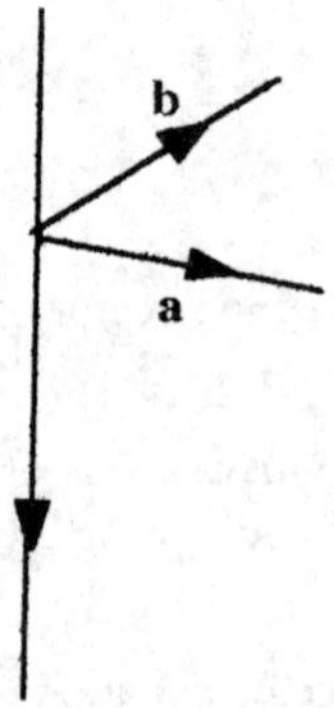

Fig. 8-I/49 Turned from **b** to **a**

The direction of $\mathbf{b} \times \mathbf{a}$ $(ab \sin\theta)$ is the opposite to the direction $\mathbf{a} \times \mathbf{b}$.

$$\boxed{\mathbf{a} \times \mathbf{b} = -\,\mathbf{b} \times \mathbf{a}}\,.$$

The vector product is not commutative.

Let $\mathbf{a} = x_1\mathbf{i} + y_1\mathbf{j} + z_1\mathbf{k}$

$\mathbf{b} = x_2\mathbf{i} + y_2\mathbf{j} + z_2\mathbf{k}$.

To find the vector product

$$\mathbf{a} \times \mathbf{b} = (x_1\mathbf{i} + y_1\mathbf{j} + z_1\mathbf{k}) \times (x_2\mathbf{i} + y_2\mathbf{j} + z_2\mathbf{k}).$$

Consider the following parallel and perpendicular vectors:

$\mathbf{i} \times \mathbf{i} = \mathbf{j} \times \mathbf{j} = \mathbf{k} \times \mathbf{k} = (1)\,(1) \sin 0 = 0$

$$\boxed{\mathbf{i} \times \mathbf{i} = \mathbf{j} \times \mathbf{j} = \mathbf{k} \times \mathbf{k} = 0}$$

therefore the vector product of parallel vectors is zero.

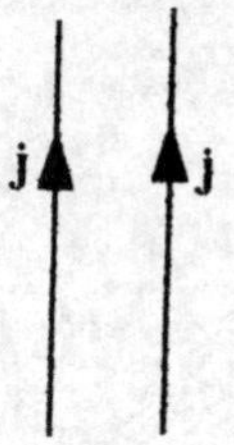

y-direction

Fig. 8-I/50

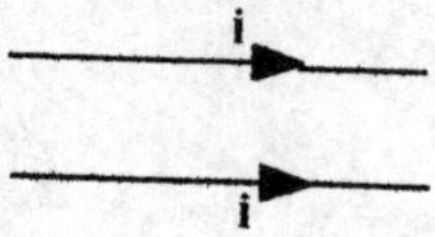

x-direction

Fig. 8-I/51

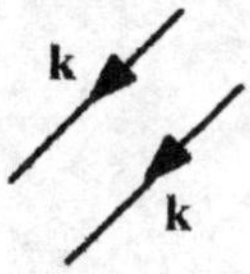

z-direction.

Fig. 8-I/52

Perpendicular vector

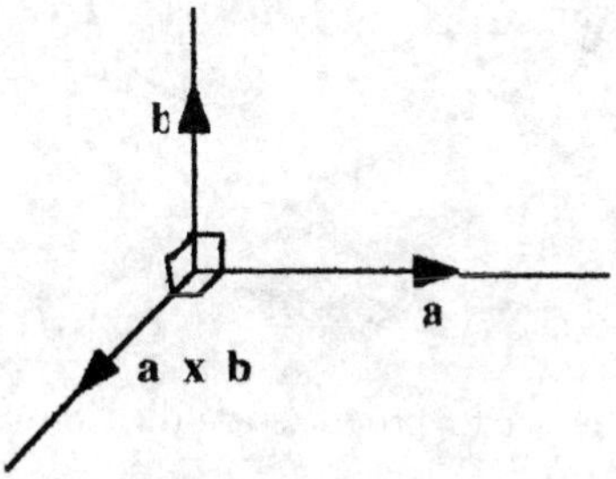

Turned from **a** to **b**

Fig. 8-I/53

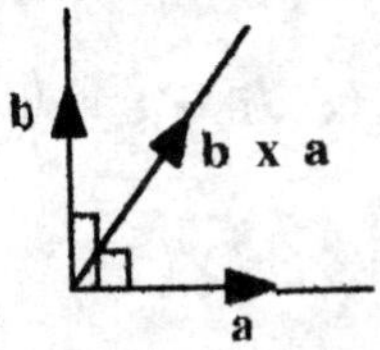

Turned from **b** to **a**

Fig. 8-I/54

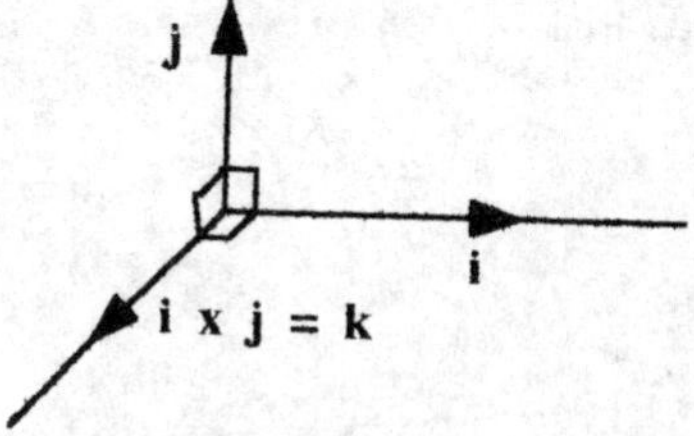

Fig. 8-I/55

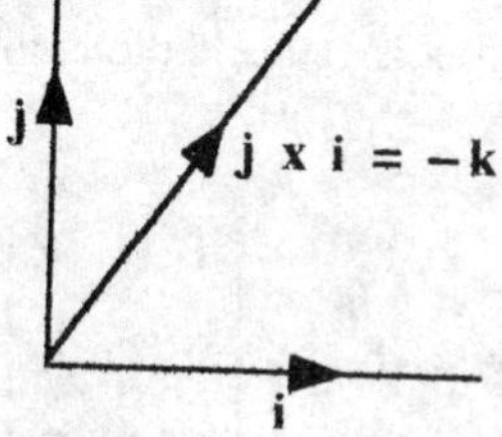

Fig. 8-I/56

$\mathbf{i} \times \mathbf{j} = \mathbf{k}$ $\qquad$ $\mathbf{j} \times \mathbf{i} = -\mathbf{k}$

$\mathbf{j} \times \mathbf{k} = \mathbf{i}$ $\qquad$ $\mathbf{k} \times \mathbf{j} = -\mathbf{i}$

$\mathbf{k} \times \mathbf{i} = \mathbf{j}$ $\qquad$ $\mathbf{i} \times \mathbf{k} = -\mathbf{j}$

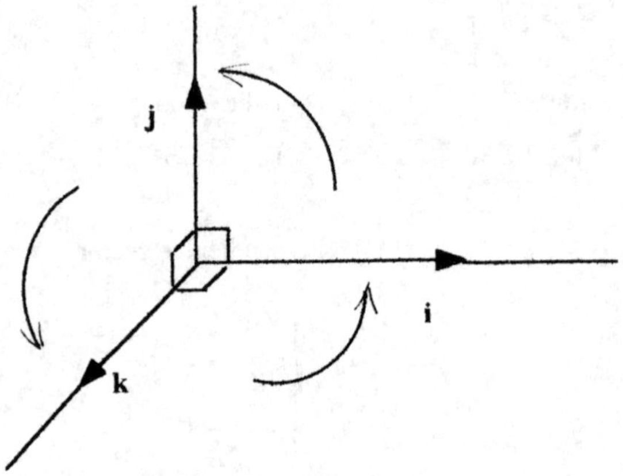

Fig. 8-I/57

Using the above and that the vector products are distributive we have

$$\mathbf{a} \times \mathbf{b} = (x_1\mathbf{i} + y_1\mathbf{j} + z_1\mathbf{k}) \times (x_2\mathbf{i} + y_2\mathbf{j} + z_2\mathbf{k})$$

$$= x_1x_2(\mathbf{i} \times \mathbf{i}) + x_1y_2(\mathbf{i} \times \mathbf{j}) + x_1z_2(\mathbf{i} \times \mathbf{k}) + y_1x_2(\mathbf{j} \times \mathbf{i}) + y_1y_2(\mathbf{j} \times \mathbf{j})$$

$$y_1z_2(\mathbf{j} \times \mathbf{k}) + z_1x_2(\mathbf{k} \times \mathbf{i}) + z_1y_2(\mathbf{k} \times \mathbf{j}) + z_1z_2(\mathbf{k} \times \mathbf{k})$$

$$= x_1y_2\mathbf{k} - x_1z_2\mathbf{j} - y_1x_2\mathbf{k} + y_1z_2\mathbf{i} + z_1x_2\mathbf{j} - z_1y_2\mathbf{i}$$

$$\mathbf{a} \times \mathbf{b} = (y_1z_2 - z_1y_2)\mathbf{i} + (z_1x_2 - x_1z_2)\mathbf{j} + (x_1y_2 - y_1x_2)\mathbf{k} \quad \text{or}$$

$$\mathbf{a} \times \mathbf{b} = (y_1z_2 - z_1y_2)\mathbf{i} - (x_1z_2 - z_1x_2)\mathbf{j} + (x_1y_2 - y_1x_2)\mathbf{k}$$

this is rather tedious to obtain, it is observed that

$$\mathbf{a} \times \mathbf{b} = \begin{vmatrix} \mathbf{i} & \mathbf{j} & \mathbf{k} \\ x_1 & y_1 & z_1 \\ x_2 & y_2 & z_2 \end{vmatrix}$$

$$= \mathbf{i}(y_1z_2 - y_2z_1) - \mathbf{j}(x_1z_2 - x_2z_1) + \mathbf{k}(x_1y_2 - x_2y_1)$$

$$\mathbf{a} \times \mathbf{b} = \left(|a|\,|b| \sin \theta\right) \hat{\mathbf{n}}$$

$$= (a_2 b_3 - a_3 b_2)\,\mathbf{i} + (a_3 b_1 - a_1 b_3)\,\mathbf{j} + (a_1 b_2 - a_2 b_1)\,\mathbf{k}$$ where $\hat{\mathbf{n}}$ is the unit vector perpendicular to both **a** and **b** such as **a**, **b**, **n** form a right-handed set.

WORKED EXAMPLE 44

Determine the vector products

(i) $\mathbf{a} \times \mathbf{b}$
(ii) $\mathbf{a} \times \mathbf{c}$
(iii) $\mathbf{b} \times \mathbf{c}$

where $\mathbf{a} = -\mathbf{i} + 2\mathbf{j} - 3\mathbf{k}$
$\mathbf{b} = 2\mathbf{i} + 3\mathbf{j} + 4\mathbf{k}$
$\mathbf{c} = 3\mathbf{i} - \mathbf{j} + 2\mathbf{k}$.

SOLUTION 44

(i) $$\mathbf{a} \times \mathbf{b} = \begin{vmatrix} \mathbf{i} & \mathbf{j} & \mathbf{k} \\ -1 & 2 & -3 \\ 2 & 3 & 4 \end{vmatrix}$$

$$= \mathbf{i}\left[2 \times 4 - (3)(-3)\right] - \mathbf{j}\left[(-1)(4) - (2)(-3)\right] + \mathbf{k}\left[(-1)(3) - 2 \times 2\right]$$

$$= 17\mathbf{i} - 2\mathbf{j} - 7\mathbf{k}$$

(ii) $$\mathbf{a} \times \mathbf{c} = \begin{vmatrix} \mathbf{i} & \mathbf{j} & \mathbf{k} \\ -1 & 2 & -3 \\ 3 & -1 & 2 \end{vmatrix}$$

$$= \mathbf{i}\,(4 - 3) - \mathbf{j}\,(-2 + 9) + \mathbf{k}\,(1 - 6)$$

$$= \mathbf{i} - 7\mathbf{j} - 5\mathbf{k}$$

(iii) $\mathbf{b} \times \mathbf{c} = \begin{vmatrix} \mathbf{i} & \mathbf{j} & \mathbf{k} \\ 2 & 3 & 4 \\ 3 & -1 & 2 \end{vmatrix}$

$= \mathbf{i}\,(6 + 4) - \mathbf{j}\,(4 - 12) + \mathbf{k}\,(-2 - 9)$

$= 10\mathbf{i} + 8\mathbf{j} - 11\mathbf{k}.$

Observe that $\mathbf{a} \times \mathbf{b}$, $\mathbf{a} \times \mathbf{c}$, $\mathbf{b} \times \mathbf{c}$ are vectors although $\mathbf{a} \cdot \mathbf{b}$, $\mathbf{a} \cdot \mathbf{c}$, $\mathbf{b} \cdot \mathbf{c}$ are scalars. Therefore the cross products are vectors the dot products are scalars.

WORKED EXAMPLE 45

Simplify the following cross products.

(i) $\mathbf{c} \times (\mathbf{c} + \mathbf{b})$ (ii) $(\mathbf{a} \times \mathbf{a}) \times (\mathbf{a} + \mathbf{b})$

(iii) $(\mathbf{a} + \mathbf{b}) \times (\mathbf{a} - \mathbf{b})$ (iv) $(\mathbf{a} \times \mathbf{b}) \cdot \mathbf{a}$.

SOLUTION 45

(i) $\mathbf{c} \times (\mathbf{c} + \mathbf{b}) = \mathbf{c} \times \mathbf{c} + \mathbf{c} \times \mathbf{b} = \mathbf{c} \times \mathbf{b}$ since $\mathbf{c} \times \mathbf{c} = 0$

(ii) $(\mathbf{a} \times \mathbf{a}) \times (\mathbf{a} + \mathbf{b}) = 0 \times (\mathbf{a} + \mathbf{b}) = 0$ since $\mathbf{a} \times \mathbf{a} = 0$

(iii) $(\mathbf{a} + \mathbf{b}) \times (\mathbf{a} - \mathbf{b}) = \mathbf{a} \times \mathbf{a} - \mathbf{a} \times \mathbf{b} + \mathbf{b} \times \mathbf{a} - \mathbf{b} \times \mathbf{b}$

$= -\mathbf{a} \times \mathbf{b} + \mathbf{b} \times \mathbf{a} = 2(\mathbf{b} \times \mathbf{a})$

since $\mathbf{a} \times \mathbf{a} = 0$ and $\mathbf{b} \times \mathbf{b} = 0$ but $\mathbf{a} \times \mathbf{b} = -\mathbf{b} \times \mathbf{a}$.

(iv) $\mathbf{a} \times \mathbf{b}$ is perpendicular to $\mathbf{a}$ and the scalar product $(\mathbf{a} \times \mathbf{b}) \cdot \mathbf{a}$ is zero

since $|\mathbf{a} \times \mathbf{b}|\,|\mathbf{a}| \cos 90° = 0$.

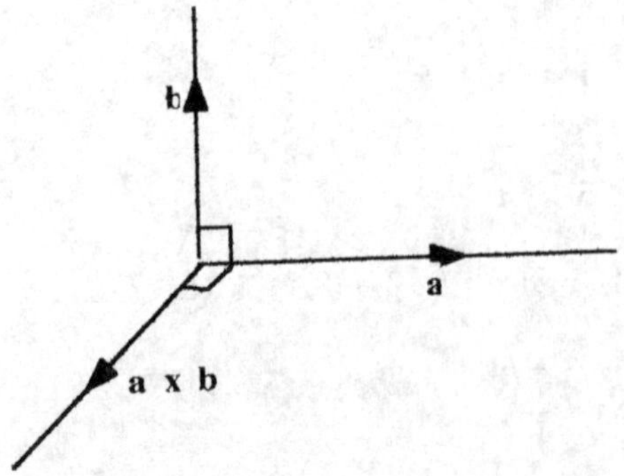

Fig. 8-I/58

WORKED EXAMPLE 46

If $\mathbf{a} = 2\mathbf{i} - 3\mathbf{j} + 5\mathbf{k}$, $\mathbf{b} = -3\mathbf{i} - 2\mathbf{k}$, $\mathbf{c} = \mathbf{i} + \mathbf{j} + \mathbf{k}$

find (i) $(\mathbf{a} \times \mathbf{b}) \times \mathbf{c}$ (ii) $\mathbf{a} \times (\mathbf{b} \times \mathbf{c})$ (iii) $\mathbf{a} \,.\, (\mathbf{b} \times \mathbf{c})$
(iv) $(\mathbf{a} \times \mathbf{b}) \,.\, \mathbf{c}$ (v) $\mathbf{a} \,.\, \mathbf{b} \,.\, \mathbf{c}$.

SOLUTION 46

(i) $$\mathbf{a} \times \mathbf{b} = \begin{vmatrix} \mathbf{i} & \mathbf{j} & \mathbf{k} \\ 2 & -3 & 5 \\ -3 & 0 & -2 \end{vmatrix} = \mathbf{i}\,(6) - \mathbf{j}\,(-4 + 15) + \mathbf{k}\,(-9)$$

$$= 6\mathbf{i} - 11\mathbf{j} - 9\mathbf{k}$$

$$(6\mathbf{i} - 11\mathbf{j} - 9\mathbf{k}) \times (\mathbf{i} + \mathbf{j} + \mathbf{k}) = \begin{vmatrix} \mathbf{i} & \mathbf{j} & \mathbf{k} \\ 6 & -11 & -9 \\ 1 & 1 & 1 \end{vmatrix}$$

$$= \mathbf{i}\,(-11 + 9) - \mathbf{j}\,(6 + 9) + \mathbf{k}\,(6 + 11)$$

$$= -2\mathbf{i} - 15\mathbf{j} + 17\mathbf{k}$$

$$(\mathbf{a} \times \mathbf{b}) \times \mathbf{c} = -2\mathbf{i} - 15\mathbf{j} + 17\mathbf{k}$$

(ii) $\mathbf{a} \times (\mathbf{b} \times \mathbf{c})$

$$\mathbf{b} \times \mathbf{c} = \begin{vmatrix} \mathbf{i} & \mathbf{j} & \mathbf{k} \\ -3 & 0 & -2 \\ 1 & 1 & 1 \end{vmatrix} = \mathbf{i}\,(2) - \mathbf{j}\,(-3 + 2) + \mathbf{k}\,(-3) = 2\mathbf{i} + \mathbf{j} - 3\mathbf{k}$$

$$\mathbf{a} \times (\mathbf{b} \times \mathbf{c}) = \begin{vmatrix} \mathbf{i} & \mathbf{j} & \mathbf{k} \\ 2 & -3 & 5 \\ 2 & 1 & -3 \end{vmatrix} = \mathbf{i}\,(9 - 5) - \mathbf{j}\,(-6 - 10) + \mathbf{k}\,(2 + 6)$$

$$= 4\mathbf{i} + 16\mathbf{j} + 8\mathbf{k}$$

(iii) $$\mathbf{a} \,.\, (\mathbf{b} \times \mathbf{c}) = \mathbf{a} \,.\, (2\mathbf{i} + \mathbf{j} - 3\mathbf{k})$$
$$= (2\mathbf{i} - 3\mathbf{j} + 5\mathbf{k}) \,.\, (2\mathbf{i} + \mathbf{j} - 3\mathbf{k})$$
$$= 4 - 3 - 15 = -14$$

(iv) $$(\mathbf{a} \times \mathbf{b}) \,.\, \mathbf{c} = (6\mathbf{i} - 11\mathbf{j} - 9\mathbf{k}) \,.\, (\mathbf{i} + \mathbf{j} + \mathbf{k})$$
$$= 6 - 11 - 9 = -14$$

(v) $\mathbf{a} \cdot \mathbf{b} \cdot \mathbf{c} = [(2\mathbf{i} - 3\mathbf{j} + 5\mathbf{k}) \cdot (-3\mathbf{i} - 2\mathbf{k})] \cdot (\mathbf{i} + \mathbf{j} + \mathbf{k})$

$= (-6 - 10) \cdot (\mathbf{i} + \mathbf{j} + \mathbf{k})$

$= -16(\mathbf{i} + \mathbf{j} + \mathbf{k})$.

WORKED EXAMPLE 47

Find the angle between the position vector $\overrightarrow{OP} = 3\mathbf{i} - 2\mathbf{j} + \mathbf{k}$ and $\overrightarrow{OQ} = -\mathbf{i} + \mathbf{j} + 4\mathbf{k}$ using the vector product formula.

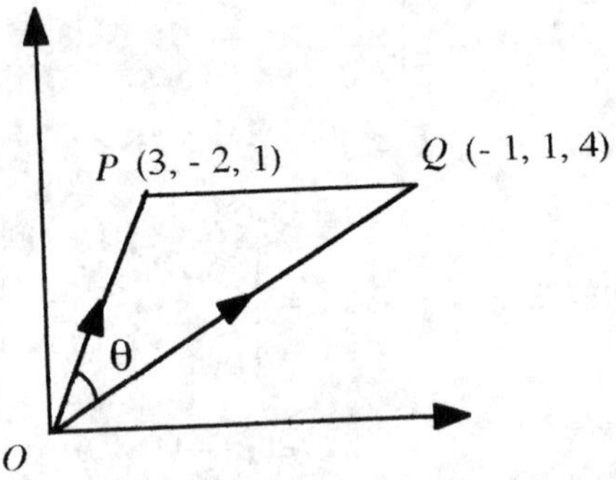

Fig. 8-I/59

SOLUTION 47

$$\frac{\left|\overrightarrow{OP} \times \overrightarrow{OQ}\right|}{\left|\overrightarrow{OP}\right| \left|\overrightarrow{OQ}\right|} = \sin\theta$$

$$\overrightarrow{OP} \times \overrightarrow{OQ} = (3\mathbf{i} - 2\mathbf{j} + \mathbf{k}) \times (-\mathbf{i} + \mathbf{j} + 4\mathbf{k})$$

$$= \begin{vmatrix} \mathbf{i} & \mathbf{j} & \mathbf{k} \\ 3 & -2 & 1 \\ -1 & 1 & 4 \end{vmatrix} = \mathbf{i}(-8 - 1) - \mathbf{j}(12 + 1) + \mathbf{k}(3 - 2)$$

$$= -9\mathbf{i} - 13\mathbf{j} + \mathbf{k}$$

$$\left|\overrightarrow{OP} \times \overrightarrow{OQ}\right| = \sqrt{9^2 + 13^2 + 1^2} = 15.8$$

$$\left|\overrightarrow{OP}\right| = \sqrt{3^2 + 2^2 + 1^2} = 3.74, \quad \left|\overrightarrow{OQ}\right| = \sqrt{1^2 + 1^2 + 4^2} = 4.2$$

$$\sin\theta = \frac{15.8}{3.74 \times 4.24} = 0.996367672$$

$\theta = 85.1°$.

6.2 THE PERPENDICULAR DISTANCE, d, OF A POINT $P(x_1, y_1, z_1)$ FROM A LINE WITH VECTOR EQUATION $\mathbf{r} = \mathbf{a} + \lambda\mathbf{b}$

The position vectors of the points A and P are $\mathbf{a}$ and $\mathbf{p}$ respectively

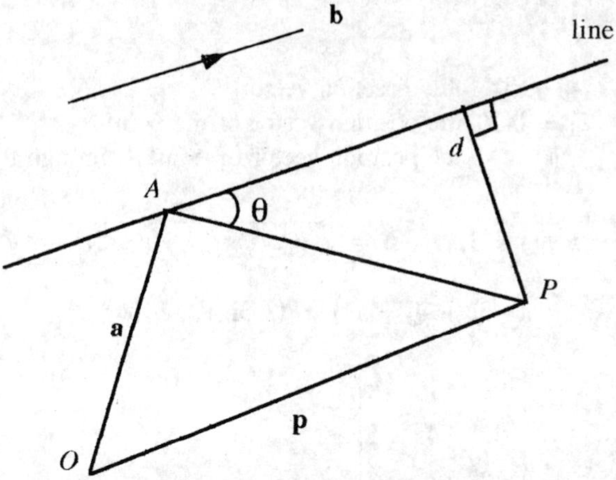

Fig. 8-I/60 The perpendicular distance from a line.

The vector product $= \mathbf{b} \times \overrightarrow{AP} = |\mathbf{b}|\,|\overrightarrow{AP}|\,\sin\theta\,\hat{\mathbf{n}}$

$$|\mathbf{b} \times \overrightarrow{AP}| = |\mathbf{b}|\,|\overrightarrow{AP}|\,\sin\theta$$

$$|\overrightarrow{AP}|\,\sin\theta = \frac{|\mathbf{b} \times \overrightarrow{AP}|}{|\mathbf{b}|}$$

$$\overrightarrow{AP} = \mathbf{p} - \mathbf{a}$$

$$\sin\theta = \frac{d}{\overrightarrow{AP}} \quad \Rightarrow \quad d = \overrightarrow{AP}\sin\theta$$

$$d = \frac{|\mathbf{b} \times \overrightarrow{AP}|}{|\mathbf{b}|}$$

$$\boxed{d = \frac{|\mathbf{b} \times (\mathbf{p} - \mathbf{a})|}{|\mathbf{b}|}}$$

WORKED EXAMPLE 48

Find the perpendicular distance of the point (− 1, 2, − 4) from the line whose vector equations is given **r** = (2**i** + **j** − **k**) + λ (− 3**i** + 4**j** − 5**k**).

SOLUTION 48

b = − 3**i** + 4**j** − 5**k** the direction vector
p = − **i** + 2**j** − 4**k** the position vector of the point
a = 2**i** + **j** − **k** the position vector of point A through the line

$$\mathbf{p} - \mathbf{a} = -3\mathbf{i} + \mathbf{j} - 3\mathbf{k}, \quad \mathbf{b} = \sqrt{(-3)^2 + 4^2 + (-5)^2} = \sqrt{50} = 7.07.$$

$$\mathbf{b} \times (\mathbf{p} - \mathbf{a}) = (-3\mathbf{i} + 4\mathbf{j} - 5\mathbf{k}) \times (-3\mathbf{i} + \mathbf{j} - 3\mathbf{k})$$

$$= \begin{vmatrix} \mathbf{i} & \mathbf{j} & \mathbf{k} \\ -3 & 4 & -5 \\ -3 & 1 & -3 \end{vmatrix}$$

$$= \mathbf{i}(-12 + 5) - \mathbf{j}(9 - 15) + \mathbf{k}(-3 + 12)$$

$$= -7\mathbf{i} + 6\mathbf{j} + 9\mathbf{k}, \quad \left|\mathbf{b} \times (\mathbf{p} - \mathbf{a})\right| = \sqrt{49 + 36 + 81}$$

$$= \sqrt{166} = 12.9$$

$$d = \frac{\left|\mathbf{b} \times (\mathbf{p} - \mathbf{a})\right|}{|\mathbf{b}|} = \frac{12.9}{7.07} = 1.82.$$

WORKED EXAMPLE 49

A line passes through two points A (1, 2, − 3) and B (− 2, − 3, 1) find the perpendicular distance from the origin to the line.

SOLUTION 49

The vector equation of the line is **r** = (**i** + 2**j** − 3**k**) + λ (− 3**i** − 5**j** + 4**k**).
The position vector is **i** + 2**j** − 3**k** the direction vector is − 3**i** − 5**j** + 4**k**.

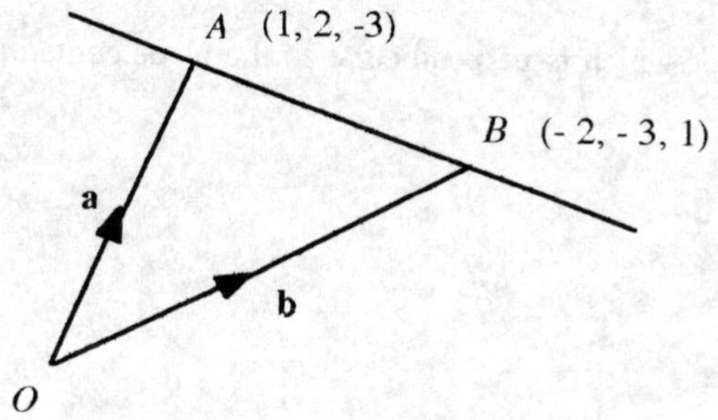

Fig. 8-I/61 Perpendicular distance from a point to the line

$$d = \frac{|\mathbf{b} \times (\mathbf{p} - \mathbf{a})|}{(\mathbf{b})}$$

where $d = \dfrac{\sqrt{75}}{\sqrt{50}} = 1.22$

$\mathbf{p} - \mathbf{a} = -\mathbf{i} - 2\mathbf{j} + 3\mathbf{k}$ where $\mathbf{p} = O$ (origin), $\mathbf{a} = \mathbf{i} + 2\mathbf{j} - 3\mathbf{k}$

$\mathbf{b} = -3\mathbf{i} - 5\mathbf{j} + 4\mathbf{k}$ the direction vector $= -2\mathbf{i} - 3\mathbf{j} + \mathbf{k} - (\mathbf{i} + 2\mathbf{j} - 3\mathbf{k})$

$= -3\mathbf{i} - 5\mathbf{j} + 4\mathbf{k}$

$$|\mathbf{b}| = \sqrt{(-3)^2 + (-5)^2 + 4^2} = \sqrt{9 + 25 + 16} = \sqrt{50}$$

$$\mathbf{b} \times (\mathbf{p} - \mathbf{a}) = (-3\mathbf{i} - 5\mathbf{j} + 4\mathbf{k}) \times (-\mathbf{i} - 2\mathbf{j} + 3\mathbf{k})$$

$$= \begin{vmatrix} \mathbf{i} & \mathbf{j} & \mathbf{k} \\ -3 & -5 & 4 \\ -1 & -2 & 3 \end{vmatrix} = \mathbf{i}\,(-15 + 8) - \mathbf{j}\,(-9 + 4) + \mathbf{k}\,(6 - 5)$$

$$= -7\mathbf{i} + 5\mathbf{j} + \mathbf{k}$$

$$|\mathbf{b} \times (\mathbf{p} - \mathbf{a})| = \sqrt{(-7)^2 + 5^2 + 1^2} = \sqrt{75}\,.$$

WORKED EXAMPLE 50

The coordinates of the vertices of a triangle *ABC* are given *A* (− 1, 2, 3), *B* (0, − 3, 1), *C* (2, 0, − 4). Determine (i) the angle between $\overrightarrow{AB}$ and $\overrightarrow{BC}$,

(ii) the angle between $\overrightarrow{AC}$ and $\overrightarrow{AB}$, (iii) the areas of the triangles

(a) OAB (b) OBC (c) ABC.

Find also a unit vector which is perpendicular to the plane containing the triangle ABC.

SOLUTION 50

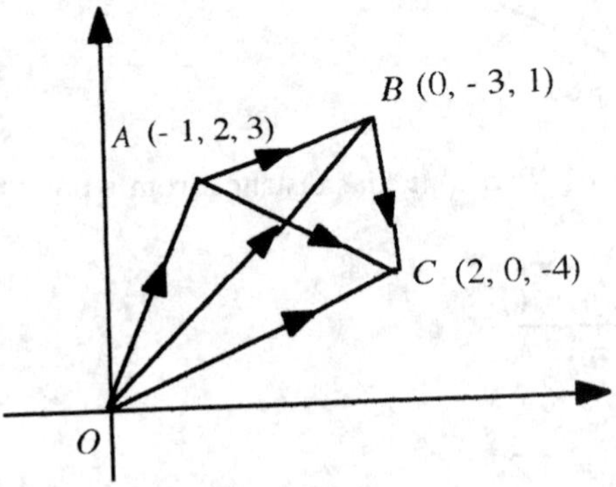

Fig. 8-I/62

(i) The position vectors of A, B, and C are:

$$\overrightarrow{OA} = -\mathbf{i} + 2\mathbf{j} + 3\mathbf{k}$$

$$\overrightarrow{OB} = -3\mathbf{j} + \mathbf{k}$$

$$\overrightarrow{OC} = 2\mathbf{i} - 4\mathbf{k}$$

$$\overrightarrow{AB} = \overrightarrow{OB} - \overrightarrow{OA} = -3\mathbf{j} + \mathbf{k} - (-\mathbf{i} + 2\mathbf{j} + 3\mathbf{k}) = \mathbf{i} - 5\mathbf{j} - 2\mathbf{k}$$

$$\overrightarrow{BC} = \overrightarrow{OC} - \overrightarrow{OB} = 2\mathbf{i} - 4\mathbf{k} - (-3\mathbf{j} + \mathbf{k}) = 2\mathbf{i} + 3\mathbf{j} - 5\mathbf{k}.$$

The vector product of $\overrightarrow{AB}$ and $\overrightarrow{BC}$ is given by

$$\left|\overrightarrow{AB} \times \overrightarrow{BC}\right| = \left|\overrightarrow{AB}\right| \left|\overrightarrow{BC}\right| \sin\theta$$

$$\sin\theta = \frac{\left|\overrightarrow{AB} \times \overrightarrow{BC}\right|}{\left|\overrightarrow{AB}\right| \left|\overrightarrow{BC}\right|}$$

$$\overrightarrow{AB} \times \overrightarrow{BC} = \begin{vmatrix} \mathbf{i} & \mathbf{j} & \mathbf{k} \\ 1 & -5 & -2 \\ 2 & 3 & -5 \end{vmatrix} = \mathbf{i}\,(25 + 6) - \mathbf{j}\,(-5 + 4) + \mathbf{k}\,(3 + 10)$$

$$= 31\mathbf{i} + \mathbf{j} + 13\mathbf{k}$$

$$\left|\overrightarrow{AB} \times \overrightarrow{BC}\right| = \sqrt{31^2 + 1^2 + 13^2} = 33.6$$

$$\left|\overrightarrow{AB}\right| = \left|\mathbf{i} - 5\mathbf{j} - 2\mathbf{k}\right| = \sqrt{1^2 + 5^2 + 2^2} = 5.48$$

$$\left|\overrightarrow{BC}\right| = \left|2\mathbf{i} + 3\mathbf{j} - 5\mathbf{k}\right| = \sqrt{2^2 + 3^2 + 5^2} = 6.16$$

$$\sin\theta = \frac{\left|\overrightarrow{AB} \times \overrightarrow{BC}\right|}{\left|\overrightarrow{AB}\right|\left|\overrightarrow{BC}\right|} = \frac{33.6}{5.48 \times 6.16} = 0.99535501$$

$$\theta = 84.5^\circ$$

(ii) $\overrightarrow{AC} = \overrightarrow{OC} - \overrightarrow{OA} = 2\mathbf{i} - 4\mathbf{k} - (-\mathbf{i} + 2\mathbf{j} + 3\mathbf{k}) = 3\mathbf{i} - 2\mathbf{j} - 7\mathbf{k}$

$\overrightarrow{AB} = \mathbf{i} - 5\mathbf{j} - 2\mathbf{k}.$

The vector product of $\overrightarrow{AC}$ and $\overrightarrow{AB}$ is

$$\overrightarrow{AC} \times \overrightarrow{AB} = (3\mathbf{i} - 2\mathbf{j} - 7\mathbf{k}) \times (\mathbf{i} - 5\mathbf{j} - 2\mathbf{k})$$

$$= \begin{vmatrix} \mathbf{i} & \mathbf{j} & \mathbf{k} \\ 3 & -2 & -7 \\ 1 & -5 & -2 \end{vmatrix} = \mathbf{i}\,(4 - 35) - \mathbf{j}\,(-6 + 7) + \mathbf{k}\,(-15 + 2)$$

$$= -31\mathbf{i} - \mathbf{j} - 13\mathbf{k}$$

$$\left|\overrightarrow{AC} \times \overrightarrow{AB}\right| = \sqrt{31^2 + 1^2 + 13^2} = 33.6$$

$$\overrightarrow{AC} = \overrightarrow{OC} - \overrightarrow{OA} = 2\mathbf{i} - 4\mathbf{k} - (-\mathbf{i} + 2\mathbf{j} + 3\mathbf{k}) = 3\mathbf{i} - 2\mathbf{j} - 7\mathbf{k}$$

$$\left|\overrightarrow{AC}\right| = \sqrt{3^2 + 2^2 + 7^2} = 7.87$$

$$\left|\overrightarrow{AB}\right| = \sqrt{1 + 5^2 + 2^2} = 5.48$$

$$\sin \phi = \frac{\left|\overrightarrow{AC} \times \overrightarrow{AB}\right|}{\left|\overrightarrow{AC}\right|\left|\overrightarrow{AB}\right|} = \frac{33.6}{(7.87)\ (5.48)} = 0.7791$$

$$\phi = 51.2^\circ$$

(iii) (a) Area $\Delta\ OAB = \sqrt{s(s-a)(s-b)(s-c)}$

$$\left|\overrightarrow{OA}\right| = \sqrt{1^2 + 2^2 + 3^2} = 3.74$$

$$\left|\overrightarrow{OB}\right| = \sqrt{(-3)^2 + 1^2} = 3.16$$

$$\left|\overrightarrow{AB}\right| = 5.48$$

$$s = \frac{3.74 + 3.16 + 5.48}{2} = 6.19$$

$$\text{Area } \Delta\ OAB = \sqrt{6.19\ (6.19 - 3.74)\ (6.19 - 3.16)\ (6.19 - 5.48)}$$

$$= \sqrt{6.19 \times 2.45 \times 3.03 \times 0.71} = 5.71 \text{ square units.}$$

(b) Area $\Delta\ OBC = \sqrt{s(s-a)(s-b)(s-c)}$

$$\left|\overrightarrow{OB}\right| = 3.16,$$

$$\left|\overrightarrow{OC}\right| = \sqrt{2^2 + 4^2} = \sqrt{20} = 4.47,$$

$$\left|\overrightarrow{BC}\right| = 6.16$$

$$s = \frac{3.16 + 4.47 + 6.16}{2} = 6.9$$

$$\text{Area } \Delta\ OBC = \sqrt{6.9 \times (6.9 - 3.16) \times (6.9 - 4.47) \times (6.9 - 6.15)}$$

$$= \sqrt{6.9 \times 3.74 \times 2.43 \times 0.75} = 6.86 \text{ square units.}$$

(c) Area $\Delta ABC = \sqrt{6.9 \times (6.9 - 3.16) \times (6.9 - 4.47) \times (6.9 - 6.15)}$

$$\left|\overrightarrow{AB}\right| = 5.48, \quad \left|\overrightarrow{BC}\right| = 6.16, \quad \left|\overrightarrow{AC}\right| = 7.87$$

$$s = \frac{5.48 + 6.16 + 7.87}{2} = 9.76$$

$$\text{Area } \Delta ABC = \sqrt{9.76 \times (9.76 - 5.48) \times (9.76 - 6.16) \times (9.76 - 7.87)}$$

$$= \sqrt{9.76 \times 4.28 \times 3.6 \times 1.89} = 16.9 \text{ square units}$$

To find the unit vector which is perpendicular to the plane containing the triangle ABC.

$\overrightarrow{AB} \times \overrightarrow{BC}$ is a vector which is perpendicular to both $\overrightarrow{AB}$ and $\overrightarrow{BC}$ and is therefore perpendicular to the plane of the triangle ABC.

$$\hat{\mathbf{n}} = \frac{\overrightarrow{AB} \times \overrightarrow{BC}}{\left|\overrightarrow{AB} \times \overrightarrow{BC}\right|} = \frac{31\mathbf{i} + \mathbf{j} + 13\mathbf{k}}{\sqrt{31^2 + 1^2 + 13^2}} = \frac{1}{33.6}(31\mathbf{i} + \mathbf{j} + 13\mathbf{k})$$

$$\hat{\mathbf{n}} = \frac{\overrightarrow{AC} \times \overrightarrow{AB}}{\left|\overrightarrow{AC} \times \overrightarrow{AB}\right|} = \frac{-31\mathbf{i} - \mathbf{j} - 13\mathbf{k}}{33.6} = -\frac{1}{33.6}(31\mathbf{i} + \mathbf{j} + 13\mathbf{k})$$

this is equal and opposite to the unit vector we found previously.

6.3 AREA OF TRIANGLE

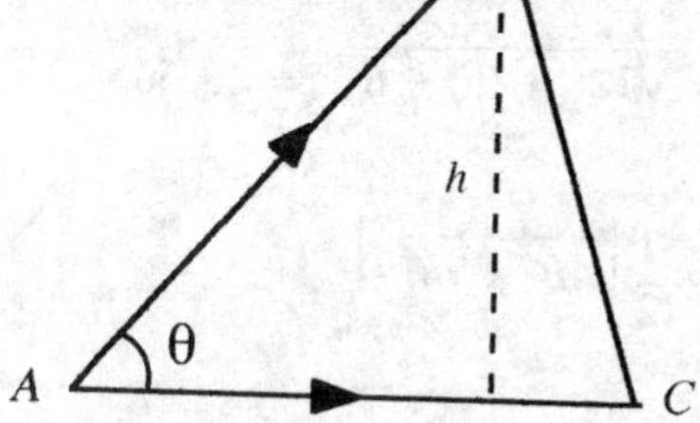

Fig. 8-I/63 $\sin\theta = \dfrac{\mathbf{h}}{\left|\overrightarrow{AB}\right|}$

The area of $\Delta ABC = \frac{1}{2}$ base $\times$ height

$$= \frac{1}{2}\left|\overrightarrow{AC}\right| \times h$$

$$= \frac{1}{2}\left|\overrightarrow{AC}\right| \times \left(\left|\overrightarrow{AB}\right| \sin\theta\right)$$

$$= \frac{1}{2}\left|\overrightarrow{AC} \times \overrightarrow{AB}\right|.$$

From the previous example

$$\text{Area } \Delta\, OAB = \frac{1}{2}\left|\overrightarrow{OA} \times \overrightarrow{OB}\right|$$

$$= \frac{1}{2}(11.45) = 5.71 \text{ square units}$$

since

$$\overrightarrow{OA} \times \overrightarrow{OB} = \begin{vmatrix} \mathbf{i} & \mathbf{j} & \mathbf{k} \\ -1 & 2 & 3 \\ 0 & -3 & 1 \end{vmatrix} = \mathbf{i}\,(2 + 9) - \mathbf{j}\,(-1) + \mathbf{k}\,(3)$$

$$= 11\mathbf{i} + \mathbf{j} + 3\mathbf{k}$$

$$\left|\overrightarrow{OA} \times \overrightarrow{OB}\right| = \sqrt{11^2 + 1^2 + 3^2} = 11.45$$

$$\text{Area } \Delta\, OBC = \frac{1}{2}\left|\overrightarrow{OB} \times \overrightarrow{OC}\right| = \frac{1}{2}(13.56) = 6.78 \text{ square units}$$

since

$$\overrightarrow{OB} \times \overrightarrow{OC} = \begin{vmatrix} \mathbf{i} & \mathbf{j} & \mathbf{k} \\ 0 & -3 & 1 \\ 2 & 0 & -4 \end{vmatrix} = \mathbf{i}\,(12) - \mathbf{j}\,(-2) + \mathbf{k}\,(6) = 12\mathbf{i} + 2\mathbf{j} + 6\mathbf{k}$$

$$\left|\overrightarrow{OB} \times \overrightarrow{OC}\right| = \sqrt{12^2 + 2^2 + 6^2} = 13.56$$

$$\text{Area } \Delta\, ABC = \frac{1}{2}\left|\overrightarrow{AB} \times \overrightarrow{BC}\right|$$

$$= \frac{1}{2}\left|31\mathbf{i} + \mathbf{j} + 13\mathbf{k}\right| = \frac{1}{2} \times 33.6 = 16.8 \text{ square units.}$$

WORKED EXAMPLE 51

Two sides of a triangle are given by the vector $\mathbf{a} = 2\mathbf{i} + 3\mathbf{j} - \mathbf{k}$, $\mathbf{b} = -\mathbf{i} + 4\mathbf{j} + 2\mathbf{k}$. Find the area of the triangle using the vector product.

SOLUTION 51

$$\text{Area } \Delta = \frac{1}{2}|\mathbf{a} \times \mathbf{b}|$$

$$= \frac{1}{2}|10\mathbf{i} - 3\mathbf{j} + 11\mathbf{k}| = \frac{1}{2}\sqrt{10^2 + 3^2 + 11^2} = \frac{15.2}{2} = 7.6$$

$$\text{where } \mathbf{a} \times \mathbf{b} = \begin{vmatrix} \mathbf{i} & \mathbf{j} & \mathbf{k} \\ 2 & 3 & -1 \\ -1 & 4 & +2 \end{vmatrix} = \mathbf{i}(6 + 4) - \mathbf{j}(4 - 1) + \mathbf{k}(8 + 3)$$

$$= 10\mathbf{i} - 3\mathbf{j} + 11\mathbf{k}.$$

WORKED EXAMPLE 52

Prove the sine rule of a triangle ABC, $\frac{a}{\sin A} = \frac{b}{\sin B} = \frac{c}{\sin C}$ using vector products.

SOLUTION 52

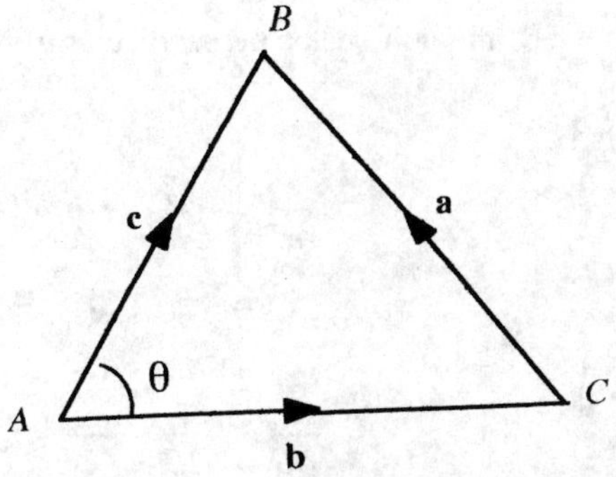

Fig. 8-I/64

$$\text{Area of } \Delta\, ABC = \frac{1}{2}|\mathbf{a} \times \mathbf{b}| = \frac{1}{2}|\mathbf{a}|\,|\mathbf{b}| \sin C$$

Area of $\Delta\, ABC = \frac{1}{2}|\mathbf{b} \times \mathbf{c}| = \frac{1}{2}\, |\mathbf{b}|\, |\mathbf{c}| \sin A$

Area of $\Delta\, ABC = \frac{1}{2}|\mathbf{a} \times \mathbf{c}| = \frac{1}{2}\, |\mathbf{a}|\, |\mathbf{c}|\, \sin B$

$$\frac{1}{2}\, |\mathbf{a}|\, |\mathbf{b}|\, \sin C = \frac{1}{2}\, |\mathbf{b}|\, |\mathbf{c}|\, \sin A = \frac{1}{2}\, |\mathbf{a}|\, |\mathbf{c}|\, \sin B$$

$|\mathbf{a}| \sin C = |\mathbf{c}| \sin A$ $\qquad$ $|\mathbf{b}| \sin A = |\mathbf{a}| \sin B$

$$\frac{|\mathbf{a}|}{\sin A} = \frac{|\mathbf{c}|}{\sin C} \qquad \frac{|\mathbf{a}|}{\sin A} = \frac{|\mathbf{b}|}{\sin B}$$

therefore $\dfrac{|\mathbf{a}|}{\sin A} = \dfrac{|\mathbf{b}|}{\sin B} = \dfrac{|\mathbf{c}|}{\sin C}$.

WORKED EXAMPLE 53

The position vectors of the points A, B, C are respectively

$\overrightarrow{OA} = \mathbf{a} = -\,2\mathbf{i} - 3\mathbf{j} + \mathbf{k}$

$\overrightarrow{OB} = \mathbf{b} = 5\mathbf{i} + 2\mathbf{j} - 2\mathbf{k}$

$\overrightarrow{OC} = \mathbf{c} = 3\mathbf{i} - \mathbf{j} - 2\mathbf{k}$.

Find (a) $\overrightarrow{AB} \times \overrightarrow{AC}$ (b) $\overrightarrow{AB} \,.\, \overrightarrow{AC}$ (c) $\sin A$ (d) the area of $\Delta\, ABC$,

(e) $\cos A$, (f) the unit vector perpendicular to both $\overrightarrow{AB}$ and $\overrightarrow{AC}$.

SOLUTION 53

(a)

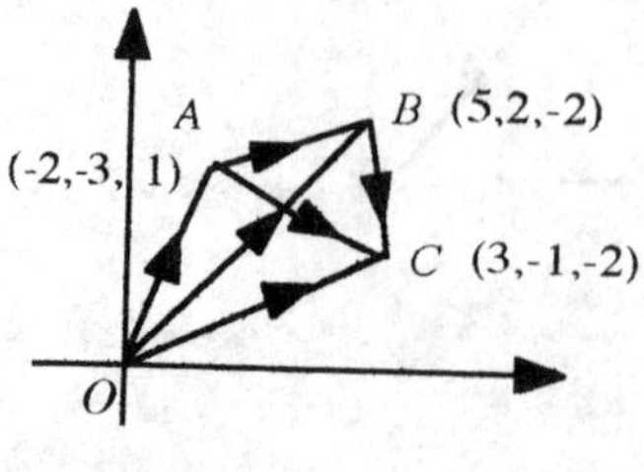

Fig. 8-I/65

$\overrightarrow{AB} = \overrightarrow{OB} - \overrightarrow{OA}$

$= (5\mathbf{i} + 2\mathbf{j} - 2\mathbf{k}) - (-\,2\mathbf{i} - 3\mathbf{j} + \mathbf{k})$

$= 7\mathbf{i} + 5\mathbf{j} - 3\mathbf{k}$

$\overrightarrow{AC} = \overrightarrow{OC} - \overrightarrow{OA}$

$= (3\mathbf{i} - \mathbf{j} - 2\mathbf{k}) - (-\,2\mathbf{i} - 3\mathbf{j} + \mathbf{k})$

$= 5\mathbf{i} + 2\mathbf{j} - 3\mathbf{k}$

$$\overrightarrow{AB} \times \overrightarrow{AC} = \begin{vmatrix} \mathbf{i} & \mathbf{j} & \mathbf{k} \\ 7 & 5 & -3 \\ 5 & 2 & -3 \end{vmatrix} = \mathbf{i}\,(-15+6) - \mathbf{j}\,(-21+15) + \mathbf{k}\,(14-25)$$

$$= -9\mathbf{i} + 6\mathbf{j} - 11\mathbf{k}$$

(b) $\overrightarrow{AB} \, . \, \overrightarrow{AC} = (7\mathbf{i} + 5\mathbf{j} - 3\mathbf{k}) \, . \, (5\mathbf{i} + 2\mathbf{j} - 3\mathbf{k}) = 35 + 10 + 9 = 54.$

(c) $\mathbf{a} \times \mathbf{b} = \left(|\mathbf{a}| \; |\mathbf{b}| \; \sin\theta\right) \hat{\mathbf{n}}$

$$|\mathbf{a} \times \mathbf{b}| = |\mathbf{a}| \; |\mathbf{b}| \; \sin\theta \; |\hat{\mathbf{n}}|$$

$$\left|\overrightarrow{AB} \times \overrightarrow{AC}\right| = |7\mathbf{i} + 5\mathbf{j} - 3\mathbf{k}| \, |5\mathbf{i} + 2\mathbf{j} - 3\mathbf{k}| \sin A \quad (1)$$

$$|-9\mathbf{i} + 6\mathbf{j} - 11\mathbf{k}| = \sqrt{7^2 + 5^2 + 3^2}\,\sqrt{5^2 + 2^2 + 3^2} \sin A$$

$$\sqrt{9^2 + 6^2 + 11^2} = \sqrt{83}\,\sqrt{38} \sin A = \sqrt{238} = 15.43$$

$$\sin A = \frac{15.43}{9.11 \times 6.16} = 0.275$$

(d) Area of the triangle $ABC = \frac{1}{2}\left|\left(\overrightarrow{AB} \times \overrightarrow{AC}\right)\right|$

$$= \frac{1}{2}\, 15.43 = 7.72 \text{ square units.}$$

(e) $\overrightarrow{AB} \, . \, \overrightarrow{AC} = \left|\overrightarrow{AB}\right| \left|\overrightarrow{AC}\right| \cos A$

$$54 = \sqrt{83}\,\sqrt{38} \cos A$$

$$\cos A = \frac{54}{56} = 0.962$$

(f) $\hat{\mathbf{n}} = \dfrac{-9\mathbf{i} + 6\mathbf{j} - 11\mathbf{k}}{15.43}$

$$= -\frac{9}{15.43}\mathbf{i} + \frac{6}{15.43}\mathbf{j} - \frac{11}{15.43}\mathbf{k}$$

$$\hat{\mathbf{n}} = -0.583\mathbf{i} + 0.389\mathbf{j} - 0.713\mathbf{k}.$$

6.4 VOLUME OF A TETRAHEDRON

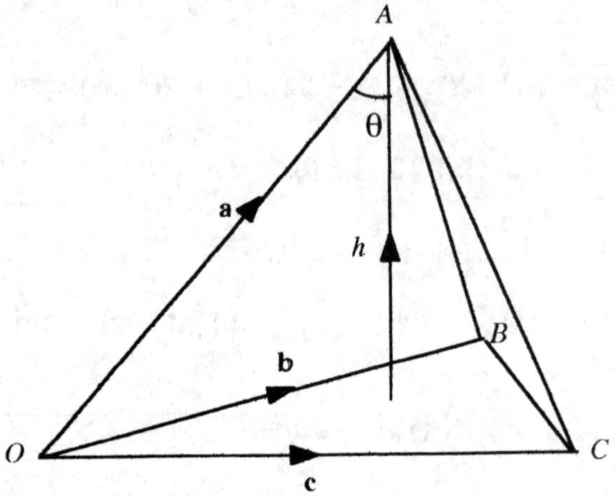

Fig. 8-I/66

Referring to a fixed point O, the position vectors of the point A, B and C are $\mathbf{a}$, $\mathbf{b}$ and $\mathbf{c}$ respectively.

$$\text{Volume of a tetrahedron} = \frac{1}{3}\,(\text{area of base}) \times \text{height}$$

$$= \frac{1}{3}\left(\frac{1}{2}\text{ area of } \Delta\, OBC\right) \times \text{height}$$

$$= \frac{1}{6}\left|\mathbf{b} \times \mathbf{c}\right| \left|\mathbf{a}\right| \cos\theta = \frac{1}{6}\left|(\mathbf{b} \times \mathbf{c}) \cdot \mathbf{a}\right|$$

WORKED EXAMPLE 54

The position vectors of the points A, B and C are $\mathbf{a} = -2\mathbf{i} + 3\mathbf{j} - 5\mathbf{k}$, $\mathbf{b} = \mathbf{i} + 4\mathbf{j} + 7\mathbf{k}$ and $\mathbf{c} = 3\mathbf{i} - 2\mathbf{j} + 2\mathbf{k}$. Determine the volume of the tetrahedron with the base $\Delta\, OBC$ and vertex A.

SOLUTION 54

$$V = \frac{1}{6}\left|(\mathbf{b} \times \mathbf{c}) \cdot \mathbf{a}\right|$$

$$\mathbf{b} \times \mathbf{c} = \begin{vmatrix} \mathbf{i} & \mathbf{j} & \mathbf{k} \\ 1 & 4 & 7 \\ 3 & -2 & 2 \end{vmatrix} = \mathbf{i}\,(8+14) - \mathbf{j}\,(2 - 21) + \mathbf{k}\,(-2 - 12)$$

$$= 22\mathbf{i} + 19\mathbf{j} - 14\mathbf{k}$$

$$V = \frac{1}{6}\left|(22\mathbf{i} + 19\mathbf{j} - 14\mathbf{k}).(-2\mathbf{i} + 3\mathbf{j} - 5\mathbf{k})\right|$$

$$V = \frac{1}{6}\left|-44 + 57 + 70\right|$$

$$V = \frac{1}{6}(83) = 13.8 \text{ cubic units.}$$

6.5 VOLUME OF A PARALLELEPIPED

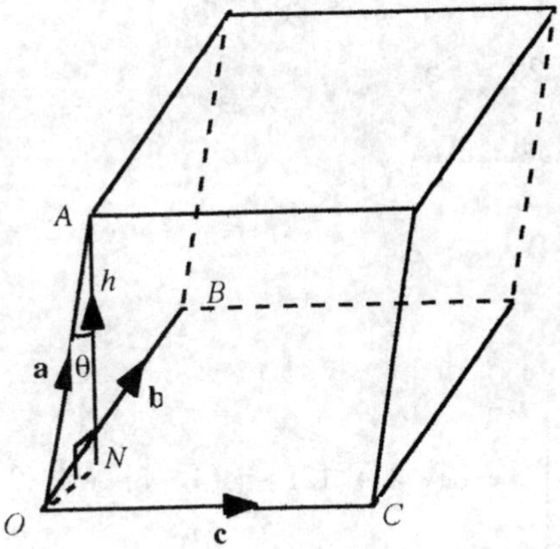

$$\cos\theta = \frac{h}{\mathbf{a}}$$

Fig. 8-I/67

The position vectors of the points A, B and C with reference to a fixed point O, the origin, are **a**, **b** and **c** respectively.

The volume of a parallelepiped $= \text{area of base} \times \text{height}$

$$= |\mathbf{b} \times \mathbf{c}|\,h = |\mathbf{b} \times \mathbf{c}|\ |\mathbf{a}|\cos\theta$$

where θ is the angle between **a** and **h**

$$\boxed{V = \left|(\mathbf{b} \times \mathbf{c}).\mathbf{a}\right|}$$

WORKED EXAMPLE 55

Find the volume of a parallelepiped where O is the origin and A, B and C are the points $(-3, 2, 4)$, $(2, -3, -1)$ and $(3, -1, 2)$ respectively.

SOLUTION 55

$\mathbf{a} = -3\mathbf{i} + 2\mathbf{j} + 4\mathbf{k}, \quad \mathbf{b} = 2\mathbf{i} - 3\mathbf{j} - \mathbf{k}, \quad \mathbf{c} = 3\mathbf{i} - \mathbf{j} + 2\mathbf{k}$

$V = \left|(\mathbf{b} \times \mathbf{c}) . \mathbf{a}\right|$

$$\mathbf{b} \times \mathbf{c} = \begin{vmatrix} \mathbf{i} & \mathbf{j} & \mathbf{k} \\ 2 & -3 & -1 \\ 3 & -1 & 2 \end{vmatrix} = \mathbf{i}(-6-1) - \mathbf{j}(4+3) + \mathbf{k}(-2+9)$$

$$= -7\mathbf{i} - 7\mathbf{j} + 7\mathbf{k}.$$

$$\mathbf{b} \times \mathbf{c} . \mathbf{a} = (-7\mathbf{i} - 7\mathbf{j} + 7\mathbf{k}) . (-3\mathbf{i} + 2\mathbf{j} + 4\mathbf{k})$$

$$= 21 - 14 + 28 = 35$$

$V = \left|\mathbf{b} \times \mathbf{c} . \mathbf{a}\right| = 35$ cubic units.

Alternatively

$V = \left| (\mathbf{a} \times \mathbf{b}) . \mathbf{c} \right|$

$$\mathbf{a} \times \mathbf{b} = \begin{vmatrix} \mathbf{i} & \mathbf{j} & \mathbf{k} \\ -3 & 2 & 4 \\ 2 & -3 & -1 \end{vmatrix} = \mathbf{i}(-2+12) - \mathbf{j}(3-8) + \mathbf{k}(9-4)$$

$$= 10\mathbf{i} + 5\mathbf{j} + 5\mathbf{k}$$

$$\mathbf{a} \times \mathbf{b} . \mathbf{c} = (10\mathbf{i} + 5\mathbf{j} + 5\mathbf{k}) . (3\mathbf{i} - \mathbf{j} + 2\mathbf{k})$$

$$= 30 - 5 + 10 = 35 \text{ cubic units.}$$

therefore $\mathbf{b} \times \mathbf{c} . \mathbf{a} = \mathbf{a} \times \mathbf{b} . \mathbf{c}$.

6.6 TRIPLE SCALAR PRODUCT

$\mathbf{a} \times \mathbf{b} . \mathbf{c}$ is called a triple scalar product.

The volume of a parallelepiped $= \mathbf{a} \times \mathbf{b} . \mathbf{c}$ or

$= \mathbf{b} \times \mathbf{c} . \mathbf{a}$

therefore $\mathbf{a} \times \mathbf{b} . \mathbf{c} = \mathbf{b} \times \mathbf{c} . \mathbf{a}$.

Note: Do the cross product first and then dot product.

$$\mathbf{b} \times \mathbf{c} . \mathbf{a} = \mathbf{a} . \mathbf{b} \times \mathbf{c} = -\mathbf{b} \times \mathbf{a} . \mathbf{c}.$$

WORKED EXAMPLE 56

Show that the following pairs of lines are skew:

(i) $\mathbf{r} = \mathbf{i} + \mathbf{k} + \lambda(\mathbf{i} + 3\mathbf{j} + 4\mathbf{k})$
$\mathbf{r} = 2\mathbf{i} + 3\mathbf{j} + \mu(4\mathbf{i} - \mathbf{j} + \mathbf{k})$

(ii) $\mathbf{r} = \mathbf{i} + \mathbf{j} + \lambda(2\mathbf{i} - \mathbf{j} + \mathbf{k})$
$\mathbf{r} = 2\mathbf{i} + \mathbf{j} - \mathbf{k} + \mu(3\mathbf{i} - 5\mathbf{j} + 2\mathbf{k})$

SOLUTION 56

(i) $$(a_1 - a_2) . b_1 \times b_2 = (\mathbf{i} + \mathbf{k} - 2\mathbf{i} - 3\mathbf{j}).(\mathbf{i} + 3\mathbf{j} + 4\mathbf{k}) \times (4\mathbf{i} - \mathbf{j} + \mathbf{k})$$

$$= (-\mathbf{i} - 3\mathbf{j} + \mathbf{k}).(7\mathbf{i} + 15\mathbf{j} - 13\mathbf{k})$$

$$= -7 - 45 - 13 = -65$$

$$(\mathbf{i} + 3\mathbf{j} + 4\mathbf{k}) \times (4\mathbf{i} - \mathbf{j} + \mathbf{k}) = \begin{vmatrix} \mathbf{i} & \mathbf{j} & \mathbf{k} \\ 1 & 3 & 4 \\ 4 & -1 & 1 \end{vmatrix}$$

$$= \mathbf{i}(3 + 4) - \mathbf{j}(1 - 16) + \mathbf{k}(-1 - 12)$$

$$= 7\mathbf{i} + 15\mathbf{j} - 13\mathbf{k}$$

the lines do not intersect since $(a_1 - a_2) . b_1 \times b_2$ is not equal to zero and the lines are not parallel since the direction ratios of the lines are different $1 : 3 : 4$ and $4 : -1 : 1$. Therefore the lines are skew.

(ii) $$(a_1 - a_2) . b_1 \times b_2 = (\mathbf{i} + \mathbf{j} - 2\mathbf{i} - \mathbf{j} + \mathbf{k}) . b_1 \times b_2 = (-\mathbf{i} + \mathbf{k}) . b_1 \times b_2$$

$$b_1 \times b_2 = (2\mathbf{i} - \mathbf{j} + \mathbf{k}) \times (3\mathbf{i} - 5\mathbf{j} + 2\mathbf{k})$$

$$= \begin{vmatrix} \mathbf{i} & \mathbf{j} & \mathbf{k} \\ 2 & -1 & 1 \\ 3 & -5 & 2 \end{vmatrix} = \mathbf{i}(-2 + 5) - \mathbf{j}(4 - 3) + \mathbf{k}(-10 + 3)$$

$$= 3\mathbf{i} - \mathbf{j} - 7\mathbf{k}$$

$$(a_1 - a_2) . b_1 \times b_2 = (-\mathbf{i} + \mathbf{k}) . (3\mathbf{i} - \mathbf{j} - 7\mathbf{k}) = -3 - 7 = -10$$

the lines do not intersect.

$x = 1 + 2\lambda$

$y = 1 - \lambda$ $\qquad \dfrac{x - 1}{2} = \dfrac{y - 1}{1} = \dfrac{z}{1} = \lambda$

$z = \lambda$

$x = 2 + 3\mu$

$y = 1 - 5\mu$ $\qquad \dfrac{x - 2}{3} = \dfrac{y - 1}{-5} = \dfrac{z + 1}{2} = \mu$

$z = -1 + 2\mu$

$2 : -1 : 1$, $3 : -5 : 2$ the direction ratios are not the same, therefore the lines are not parallel. The lines are skew.

Consider the example.

WORKED EXAMPLE 57

Find the perpendicular distance of a point C (1, 2, 3) from the line with a vector equation $\mathbf{r} = (2\mathbf{i} + 3\mathbf{j} + 4\mathbf{k}) + t(-3\mathbf{i} + 4\mathbf{j} - \mathbf{k})$.

SOLUTION 57

$$d = \frac{|\mathbf{b} \times (\mathbf{c} - \mathbf{a})|}{|\mathbf{b}|}$$

$\mathbf{b} = -3\mathbf{i} + 4\mathbf{j} - \mathbf{k}$ the direction vector

$\mathbf{a} = 2\mathbf{i} + 3\mathbf{j} + 4\mathbf{k}$ the position vector

$\mathbf{c} = \mathbf{i} + 2\mathbf{j} + 3\mathbf{k}$ the position vector of the point C

$$|\mathbf{b}| = \sqrt{3^2 + 4^2 + 1^2} = \sqrt{26}$$

$$\mathbf{c} - \mathbf{a} = \mathbf{i} + 2\mathbf{j} + 3\mathbf{k} - 2\mathbf{i} - 3\mathbf{j} - 4\mathbf{k} = -\mathbf{i} - \mathbf{j} - \mathbf{k}$$

$$\mathbf{b} \times (\mathbf{c} - \mathbf{a}) = (-3\mathbf{i} + 4\mathbf{j} - \mathbf{k}) \times (-\mathbf{i} - \mathbf{j} - \mathbf{k})$$

$$= \begin{vmatrix} \mathbf{i} & \mathbf{j} & \mathbf{k} \\ -3 & 4 & -1 \\ -1 & -1 & -1 \end{vmatrix} = \mathbf{i}(-4 - 1) - \mathbf{j}(3 - 1) + \mathbf{k}(3 + 4)$$

$$= -5\mathbf{i} - 2\mathbf{j} + 7\mathbf{k}$$

$$d = \frac{|-5\mathbf{i} - 2\mathbf{j} + 7\mathbf{k}|}{\sqrt{26}} = \frac{\sqrt{25 + 4 + 49}}{\sqrt{26}} = \sqrt{3}$$

6.7 THE SHORTEST DISTANCE BETWEEN TWO SKEW LINES

Let the vector equations of two skew lines be $l_1 : \mathbf{r}_1 = a_1 + \lambda b_1$

$l_2 : \mathbf{r}_2 = a_2 + \mu b_2$

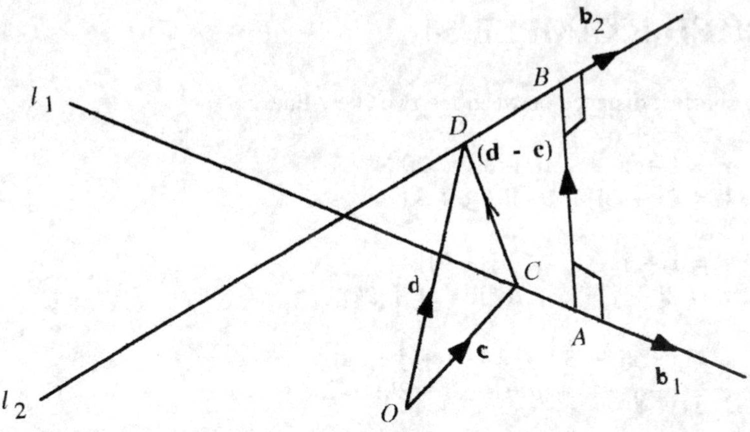

Fig. 8-I/68

The shortest distance between the two lines must be perpendicular to the lines, let this be $\overrightarrow{AB}$ as shown, the cross product of the positive direction vectors $\mathbf{b}_1 \times \mathbf{b}_2$ is parallel to $\overrightarrow{AB}$.

The unit vector, $\hat{\mathbf{n}}$, in the direction of $\overrightarrow{AB}$ is $\dfrac{\mathbf{b}_1 \times \mathbf{b}_2}{|\mathbf{b}_1 \times \mathbf{b}_2|}$.

If the angle between $\overrightarrow{CD}$ and $\overrightarrow{AB}$ is θ

$|\overrightarrow{AB}| = |\overrightarrow{CD}| \cos\theta = \left|\overrightarrow{CD} \cdot \hat{\mathbf{n}}\right|$

since $\overrightarrow{CD} \cdot \hat{\mathbf{n}} = |\overrightarrow{CD}|\ |\hat{\mathbf{n}}| \cos\theta$ where $|\hat{\mathbf{n}}| = 1$

Therefore, $|\overrightarrow{AB}| = \left|\overrightarrow{CD} \cdot \hat{\mathbf{n}}\right|$ and $\overrightarrow{CD} = \mathbf{d} - \mathbf{c}$.

$$d = \left|(\mathbf{d} - \mathbf{c}) \cdot \frac{\mathbf{b}_1 \times \mathbf{b}_2}{|\mathbf{b}_1 \times \mathbf{b}_2|}\right|$$

the shortest distance between two skew lines.
If the lines intersect then $d = 0$

$$\boxed{(\mathbf{d} - \mathbf{c}) \cdot \mathbf{b}_1 \times \mathbf{b}_2 = 0}$$

WORKED EXAMPLE 58

Find the shortest distance between the two skew lines.

(i) $l_1 : \mathbf{r} = \mathbf{i} + \mathbf{k} + \lambda (\mathbf{i} + 3\mathbf{j} + 4\mathbf{k})$
$l_2 : \mathbf{r} = 2\mathbf{i} + 3\mathbf{j} + \mu (4\mathbf{i} - \mathbf{j} + \mathbf{k})$

(ii) $l_1 : \mathbf{r} = \mathbf{i} + \mathbf{j} + \lambda (2\mathbf{i} - \mathbf{j} + \mathbf{k})$
$l_2 : \mathbf{r} = 2\mathbf{i} + \mathbf{j} - \mathbf{k} + \mu (3\mathbf{i} - 5\mathbf{j} + 2\mathbf{k})$

(iii) $l_1 : \mathbf{r} = \mathbf{i} - 2\mathbf{j} + 3\mathbf{k} + \lambda (-\mathbf{i} + \mathbf{j} - 2\mathbf{k})$
$l_2 : \mathbf{r} = \mathbf{i} - \mathbf{j} - \mathbf{k} + \mu (\mathbf{i} + 2\mathbf{j} - 2\mathbf{k})$

(iv) $l_1 : \mathbf{r} = -3\mathbf{i} + \mathbf{j} + \lambda (2\mathbf{i} + \mathbf{j} + 2\mathbf{k})$
$l_2 : \mathbf{r} = 8\mathbf{i} + 3\mathbf{j} + 15\mathbf{k} + \mu (3\mathbf{i} + 2\mathbf{j} + 5\mathbf{k})$

SOLUTION 58

(i) $$d = \left| (\mathbf{d} - \mathbf{c}) \cdot \frac{\mathbf{b}_1 \times \mathbf{b}_2}{|\mathbf{b}_1 \times \mathbf{b}_2|} \right| \text{ where}$$

d is the shortest distance between two skew lines. Referring to Fig. 8-I/68, $\mathbf{d} = \mathbf{i} + \mathbf{k}$, the position vector of l_1, $\mathbf{b}_2 = \mathbf{i} + 3\mathbf{j} + 4\mathbf{k}$ the direction vector of l_1; $\mathbf{c} = 2\mathbf{i} + 3\mathbf{j}$, the position vector of l_2 and $\mathbf{b}_1 = 4\mathbf{i} - \mathbf{j} + \mathbf{k}$, the direction vector of l_2.

$\mathbf{d} = \mathbf{i} + \mathbf{k}$, $\mathbf{c} = 2\mathbf{i} + 3\mathbf{j}$, $\mathbf{b}_2 = \mathbf{i} + 3\mathbf{j} + 4\mathbf{k}$, $\mathbf{b}_1 = 4\mathbf{i} - \mathbf{j} + \mathbf{k}$

$$\mathbf{d} = \left| (\mathbf{i} + \mathbf{k} - 2\mathbf{i} - 3\mathbf{j}) \cdot \frac{(4\mathbf{i} - \mathbf{j} + \mathbf{k}) \times (\mathbf{i} + 3\mathbf{j} + 4\mathbf{k})}{|(4\mathbf{i} - \mathbf{j} + \mathbf{k}) \times (\mathbf{i} + 3\mathbf{j} + 4\mathbf{k})|} \right|$$

$$(4\mathbf{i} - \mathbf{j} + \mathbf{k}) \times (\mathbf{i} + 3\mathbf{j} + 4\mathbf{k}) = \begin{vmatrix} \mathbf{i} & \mathbf{j} & \mathbf{k} \\ 4 & -1 & 1 \\ 1 & 3 & 4 \end{vmatrix}$$

$$= \mathbf{i}(-4 - 3) - \mathbf{j}(16 - 1) + \mathbf{k}(12 + 1)$$
$$= -7\mathbf{i} - 15\mathbf{j} + 13\mathbf{k}.$$

$$|(4\mathbf{i} - \mathbf{j} + \mathbf{k}) \times (\mathbf{i} + 3\mathbf{j} + 4\mathbf{k})| = |-7\mathbf{i} - 15\mathbf{j} + 13\mathbf{k}|$$

$$= \sqrt{49 + 225 + 169} = 21.1$$

$$\mathbf{d} = \left|\frac{(-\mathbf{i} - 3\mathbf{j} + \mathbf{k}).(-7\mathbf{i} - 15\mathbf{j} + 13\mathbf{k})}{21.1}\right| = \frac{7 + 45 + 13}{21.1} = 3.08 \text{ units}$$

(ii) $\mathbf{d} = \mathbf{i} + \mathbf{j}$, $\mathbf{c} = 2\mathbf{i} + \mathbf{j} - \mathbf{k}$, $\mathbf{b}_2 = 2\mathbf{i} - \mathbf{j} + \mathbf{k}$, $\mathbf{b}_1 = (3\mathbf{i} - 5\mathbf{j} + 2\mathbf{k})$

$$\mathbf{d} = \left|(\mathbf{d} - \mathbf{c}) \, . \, \frac{\mathbf{b}_1 \times \mathbf{b}_2}{|\mathbf{b}_1 \times \mathbf{b}_2|}\right|$$

$$\mathbf{b}_1 \times \mathbf{b}_2 = \begin{vmatrix} \mathbf{i} & \mathbf{j} & \mathbf{k} \\ 3 & -5 & 2 \\ 2 & -1 & 1 \end{vmatrix} = \mathbf{i}\,(-5 + 2) - \mathbf{j}\,(3 - 4) + \mathbf{k}\,(-3 + 10)$$

$$= -3\mathbf{i} + \mathbf{j} + 7\mathbf{k}$$

$$|\mathbf{b}_1 \times \mathbf{b}_2| = |-3\mathbf{i} + \mathbf{j} + 7\mathbf{k}| = \sqrt{9 + 1 + 49} = \sqrt{59} = 7.68.$$

$$\mathbf{d} = \left|\frac{(-\mathbf{i} + \mathbf{k}).(-3\mathbf{i} + \mathbf{j} + 7\mathbf{k})}{7.68}\right| = \frac{3 + 7}{7.58} = \frac{10}{7.58} = 1.30$$

(iii) $\mathbf{d} = \mathbf{i} - 2\mathbf{j} + 3\mathbf{k}$, $\mathbf{c} = \mathbf{i} - \mathbf{j} - \mathbf{k}$, $\mathbf{b}_2 = -\mathbf{i} + \mathbf{j} - 2\mathbf{k}$, $\mathbf{b}_1 = \mathbf{i} + 2\mathbf{j} - 2\mathbf{k}$

$$\mathbf{d} - \mathbf{c} = \mathbf{i} - 2\mathbf{j} + 3\mathbf{k} - \mathbf{i} + \mathbf{j} + \mathbf{k} = -\mathbf{j} + 4\mathbf{k}$$

$$\mathbf{b}_1 \times \mathbf{b}_2 = \begin{vmatrix} \mathbf{i} & \mathbf{j} & \mathbf{k} \\ 1 & 2 & -2 \\ -1 & 1 & -2 \end{vmatrix} = \mathbf{i}\,(-4 + 2) - \mathbf{j}\,(-2 - 2) + \mathbf{k}\,(1 + 2)$$

$$= -2\mathbf{i} + 4\mathbf{j} + 3\mathbf{k}$$

$$|\mathbf{b}_1 \times \mathbf{b}_2| = |-2\mathbf{i} + 4\mathbf{j} + 3\mathbf{k}| = \sqrt{4 + 16 + 9} = \sqrt{29}$$

$$\mathbf{d} = \left|\frac{(-\mathbf{j} + 4\mathbf{k}) \, . \, (-2\mathbf{i} + 4\mathbf{j} + 3\mathbf{k})}{\sqrt{29}}\right| = \frac{-4 + 12}{\sqrt{29}} = \frac{8}{\sqrt{29}} = 1.49$$

(iv) $\mathbf{d} = -3\mathbf{i} + \mathbf{j}$, $\mathbf{c} = 8\mathbf{i} + 3\mathbf{j} + 15\mathbf{k}$, $\mathbf{b}_2 = 2\mathbf{i} + \mathbf{j} + 2\mathbf{k}$, $\mathbf{b}_1 = 3\mathbf{i} + 2\mathbf{j} + 5\mathbf{k}$

$$\mathbf{d} - \mathbf{c} = -3\mathbf{i} + \mathbf{j} - 8\mathbf{i} - 3\mathbf{j} - 15\mathbf{k} = -11\mathbf{i} - 2\mathbf{j} - 15\mathbf{k}$$

$$\mathbf{b}_1 \times \mathbf{b}_2 = \begin{vmatrix} \mathbf{i} & \mathbf{j} & \mathbf{k} \\ 3 & 2 & 5 \\ 2 & 1 & 2 \end{vmatrix} = \mathbf{i}\,(4 - 5) - \mathbf{j}\,(6 - 10) + \mathbf{k}\,(3 - 4)$$

$$= -\mathbf{i} + 4\mathbf{j} - \mathbf{k}$$

$$|\mathbf{b}_1 \times \mathbf{b}_2| = |-\mathbf{i} + 4\mathbf{j} - \mathbf{k}| = \sqrt{1 + 16 + 1} = \sqrt{18} = 4.24$$

$$d = \left| \frac{(-11\mathbf{i} - 2\mathbf{j} - 15\mathbf{k}) \cdot (-\mathbf{i} + 4\mathbf{j} - \mathbf{k})}{4.24} \right| = \frac{11 - 8 + 15}{4.24} = \frac{18}{4.24} = 4.25.$$

6.8 FORMULAE (SUMMARY) PLANES

$$\boxed{ax + by + cz = d}$$

the cartesian equation of a plane where $a : b : c$ are the direction ratios of a normal to the plane

$$\boxed{\frac{ax_1 + by_1 + cz_1 - d}{\sqrt{a^2 + b^2 + c^2}}}$$

the perpendicular distance of the point $A\,(x_1, y_1, z_1)$ from the plane $ax + by + cz = d$, where the direction cosines are $l : m : n$, or

$$\frac{a}{\sqrt{a^2 + b^2 + c^2}} : \frac{b}{\sqrt{a^2 + b^2 + c^2}} : \frac{c}{\sqrt{a^2 + b^2 + c^2}}, \text{ or } \cos\alpha : \cos\beta : \cos\gamma.$$

$$\boxed{\mathbf{a} \times \mathbf{b} = (|\mathbf{a}|\,|\mathbf{b}|\,\sin\theta)\,\hat{\mathbf{n}}}$$

the vector product of **a** and **b** in a direction perpendicular to the plane containing **a** and **b** in the sense a right-handed screw turned from **a** to **b**.

$$\boxed{\mathbf{a} \times \mathbf{b} = -\mathbf{b} \times \mathbf{a}}$$

the vector product is <u>not</u> commutative.

$$\mathbf{a} \times \mathbf{b} = \begin{vmatrix} \mathbf{i} & \mathbf{j} & \mathbf{k} \\ x_1 & y_1 & z_1 \\ x_2 & y_2 & z_2 \end{vmatrix} \quad \mathbf{a} = x_1\mathbf{i} + y_1\mathbf{j} + z_1\mathbf{k}, \qquad \mathbf{b} = x_2\mathbf{i} + y_2\mathbf{j} + z_2\mathbf{k}.$$

$$\boxed{|\mathbf{a} \times \mathbf{b}| = |\mathbf{a}|\,|\mathbf{b}| \sin\theta}$$

$$\boxed{\text{AREA OF A TRIANGLE } ABC = \frac{1}{2}|\mathbf{a} \times \mathbf{b}|}$$ where **a** and **b** are two sides.

$\boxed{\mathbf{r} \cdot \mathbf{n} = d}$ the standard form of the vector equation of a plane.

$$\boxed{p = \mathbf{a} \cdot \hat{\mathbf{n}} - D}$$

perpendicular distance of a point from a plane, the point P and the origin O are on opposite side of the plane Π.

$$\boxed{\cos\theta = \hat{\mathbf{n}}_1 \cdot \hat{\mathbf{n}}_2}$$

the angle between two planes Π_1 and Π_2.

$$\boxed{\hat{\mathbf{n}}_1 = \hat{\mathbf{n}}_2}$$

the planes Π_1 and Π_2 are parallel.

$$\boxed{\hat{\mathbf{n}}_1 \cdot \hat{\mathbf{n}}_2 = 0}$$

the planes Π_1 and Π_2 are perpendicular.

$$\boxed{\sin\theta = \frac{\mathbf{b} \cdot \hat{\mathbf{n}}}{|\mathbf{b}|}}$$

the angle between a line and a plane Π, where **b** is the direction vector of a line.

$$\boxed{\mathbf{r}\,.\,(\hat{\mathbf{n}}_1 - k\hat{\mathbf{n}}_2) = D_1 - kD_2}$$

the equation of the plane passing through the intersections of two planes Π_1 and Π_2 with vector equations $\mathbf{r}\,.\,\hat{\mathbf{n}}_1 = D_1$ and $\mathbf{r}\,.\,\hat{\mathbf{n}}_2 = D_2$.

$$\boxed{\mathbf{r} = \mathbf{a} + s\,\mathbf{b} + t\,\mathbf{c}}$$

the vector equation of a plane through the point with position vector **a** and parallel to **b** and **c**.

Volume of a tetrahedron $\boxed{V = \frac{1}{6}\left|(\mathbf{b} \times \mathbf{c})\,.\,\mathbf{a}\right|}$

where **b** and **c** are any two sides of the base and **a** is the position vector of the

vertex. Alternatively $\boxed{V = \frac{1}{6}\left|\mathbf{a} \times \mathbf{b}\,.\,\mathbf{c}\right|}$

Volume of a parallelepiped $\boxed{V = \left|\mathbf{b} \times \mathbf{c}\,.\,\mathbf{a}\right| = \left|\mathbf{a} \times \mathbf{b}\,.\,\mathbf{c}\right|}$

Condition that two lines intersect with vector equations $\mathbf{r}_1 = \mathbf{a}_1 + \lambda\mathbf{b}_1$, $\mathbf{r}_2 = \mathbf{a}_2 + \mu\mathbf{b}_2$

$$\boxed{(\mathbf{a}_1 - \mathbf{a}_2)\,.\,\mathbf{b}_1 \times \mathbf{b}_2 = 0}$$

EXERCISES 6

1. Verify the anti commutative property for the vectors

$$\mathbf{u} = 3\mathbf{i} + 3\mathbf{j} + 5\mathbf{k}$$
$$\mathbf{v} = -2\mathbf{i} + 4\mathbf{j} + \mathbf{k}$$

(i) $\mathbf{u} \times \mathbf{v}$ and (ii) $\mathbf{v} \times \mathbf{u}$.

2. Verify the anti commutative property for the following pairs of vectors:

(a) $\mathbf{u} = \mathbf{i} + \mathbf{j} + \mathbf{k}$ $\quad \mathbf{v} = -2\mathbf{i} - \mathbf{j} + \mathbf{k}$

$\mathbf{u} \times \mathbf{v}$ and $\mathbf{v} \times \mathbf{u}$

(b) $\mathbf{u} = \begin{pmatrix} 3 \\ -5 \\ 3 \end{pmatrix}, \quad \mathbf{v} = \begin{pmatrix} -5 \\ 3 \\ 1 \end{pmatrix}$

$\mathbf{u} \times \mathbf{v}$ and $\mathbf{v} \times \mathbf{u}$.

(c) $\mathbf{v} = \begin{pmatrix} -3 \\ -4 \\ +5 \end{pmatrix}, \quad \mathbf{w} = \begin{pmatrix} 1 \\ 1 \\ 1 \end{pmatrix}$

$\mathbf{v} \times \mathbf{w}$ and $\mathbf{w} \times \mathbf{v}$.

3. Show that (i) $(\mathbf{a} \times \mathbf{b}) \,.\, \mathbf{a}$

(ii) $(\mathbf{a} \times \mathbf{b}) \,.\, \mathbf{b}$

are orthogonal.

4. Show that **a** is parallel to **b** if and only if

$$\mathbf{a} \times \mathbf{b} = \mathbf{o}.$$

5. Find $\mathbf{u} \times \mathbf{v}$.

(i) $\mathbf{u} = \mathbf{i} + 2\mathbf{j} + 3\mathbf{k}$, $\quad \mathbf{v} = -\mathbf{i} + 2\mathbf{j} + \mathbf{k}$

(ii) $\mathbf{u} = 4\mathbf{i} + 3\mathbf{k}$, $\quad \mathbf{v} = 3\mathbf{j} - \mathbf{k}$

(iii) $\mathbf{u} = 2\mathbf{i} + \mathbf{j} + 2\mathbf{k}$, $\quad \mathbf{v} = \mathbf{i} - \mathbf{j} + 2\mathbf{k}$.

6. Show that (i) $\mathbf{i} \times \mathbf{j} = \mathbf{k}$

(ii) $\mathbf{i} \times \mathbf{k} = -\mathbf{j}$

(iii) $\mathbf{j} \times \mathbf{k} = \mathbf{i}$

(iv) $\mathbf{k} \times \mathbf{i} = \mathbf{j}$

(v) $\mathbf{i} \times \mathbf{j} \times \mathbf{k} = \mathbf{j} \times \mathbf{k} \times \mathbf{i} = \mathbf{k} \times \mathbf{i} \times \mathbf{j}$.

7. Find an equation of the plane through the three points P, Q and R given by the position vectors $\mathbf{p} = \mathbf{i} + 2\mathbf{j} - 5\mathbf{k}$, $\mathbf{q} = -3\mathbf{i} + 4\mathbf{j} - \mathbf{k}$, $\mathbf{r} = 3\mathbf{j} + 5\mathbf{k}$.

8. Find an equation of the plane through the three points P, Q and R given by the position vectors $\mathbf{p} = \mathbf{i} + 2\mathbf{j} - 5\mathbf{k}$, $\mathbf{q} = -3\mathbf{i} + 4\mathbf{j} - \mathbf{k}$, $\mathbf{r} = 3\mathbf{i} + 5\mathbf{k}$.

9. Find the perpendicular distance of a point A (4, 5, 6) from the line with a vector equation $\mathbf{r} = \mathbf{i} + \mathbf{j} + \mathbf{k} + \lambda(-2\mathbf{i} + 3\mathbf{j} - \mathbf{k})$.

10. Find the perpendicular distance of a point A (2, − 1, 3) from the line with a vector equation $\mathbf{r} = -2\mathbf{i} + \mathbf{j} - \mathbf{k} + \lambda(5\mathbf{i} - \mathbf{j} - \mathbf{k})$.

11. Prove that the perpendicular distance of a point $C\,(x_1, y_1, z_1)$ from the line with a vector equation $\mathbf{r} = \mathbf{a} + \lambda\mathbf{b}$ is given by $d = \dfrac{|\mathbf{b} \times (\mathbf{c} - \mathbf{a})|}{|\mathbf{b}|}$.

12. Show that the area of $\Delta\, ABC$ is given $\frac{1}{2}\,|\mathbf{a} \times \mathbf{b}|$.

13. Show that the volume of a tetrahedron is given by $V = \frac{1}{6}\left|(\mathbf{b} \times \mathbf{c}) \,.\, \mathbf{a}\right|$ where **b** and **c** are any two sides of the base and **a** is the position vector or the vertex.

14. Show that the volume of a paralleliped is given by $V = \left|(\mathbf{b} \times \mathbf{c}) \,.\, \mathbf{a}\right|$ where **a**, **b** and **c** are the position vectors.

15. The position vectors of the vertices of a tetrahedron $ABCD$ given as follows:

$$\begin{aligned} \mathbf{a} &= \mathbf{i} - 2\mathbf{j} + 6\mathbf{k} \\ \mathbf{b} &= 2\mathbf{i} + 3\mathbf{j} - \mathbf{k} \\ \mathbf{c} &= 5\mathbf{i} - 4\mathbf{j} - 3\mathbf{k} \\ \mathbf{d} &= -3\mathbf{i} + 2\mathbf{j} + 2\mathbf{k} \end{aligned}$$

(i) Determine the angle between the faces ABC and BCD.
(ii) Determine the angle between the faces ACD and ABD.

16. The position vector of the points P, Q and R are $2\mathbf{i} - 3\mathbf{j} + 2\mathbf{k}$, $-3\mathbf{i} + \mathbf{j} + 4\mathbf{k}$, and $3\mathbf{i} + 2\mathbf{j} - 3\mathbf{k}$ respectively.

(a) Find $\overrightarrow{PQ} \times \overrightarrow{PR}$.
(b) Hence calculate the area of $\Delta\, PQR$.
(c) Determine the equation of the plane PQR in the form $\mathbf{r} \,.\, \mathbf{n} = d$.

17. The position vectors of the points A, B and C are $4\mathbf{j} - 5\mathbf{k}$, $2\mathbf{i} - \mathbf{j} + \mathbf{k}$, and $-3\mathbf{i} + \mathbf{j} + 7\mathbf{k}$ respectively

(a) Find $\overrightarrow{AB} \times \overrightarrow{AC}$.

(b) Hence calculate the area of $\Delta\, ABC$.

(c) Determine the equation of the plane ABC in the form $\mathbf{r} \,.\, \mathbf{n} = d$.

18. Show from first principles that the vector product $\mathbf{a} \times \mathbf{b}$ is given by the

determinant $\begin{vmatrix} \mathbf{i} & \mathbf{j} & \mathbf{k} \\ a_1 & a_2 & a_3 \\ b_1 & b_2 & b_3 \end{vmatrix}$.

19. Determine the perpendicular distances from the point $P\ (1,\ 1,\ 1)$ to the following lines:

(i) $\mathbf{r} = (2 + 3\lambda)\,\mathbf{i} + (1 - 2\lambda)\,\mathbf{j} + (3 + \lambda)\,\mathbf{k}$

(ii) $\mathbf{r} = (1 - t\,)\,\mathbf{i} + (1 + t\,)\,\mathbf{j} + (1 - 2t\,)\,\mathbf{k}$

(iii) $\mathbf{i} + \mathbf{j} - 3\mathbf{k} + t\,(-2\mathbf{i} + 3\mathbf{j} + 4\mathbf{k})$.

20. Find the distance of the point $P\ (-1,\ -2,\ -4)$ from the line $\mathbf{r} = -\mathbf{i} + 7\mathbf{k} + \mu\,(\mathbf{i} - 2\mathbf{j} - 3\mathbf{k})$.

21. Find the distance of the point $P\ (5,\ 8,\ 9)$ from the line $\mathbf{r} = 2\mathbf{i} + 5\mathbf{k} + V\,(3\mathbf{i} + 4\mathbf{j} + 8\mathbf{k})$.

22. Find the vector equation of the line which passes through the point $P\ (1,\ 2,\ -1)$ and which is perpendicular to the plane containing the vectors $\mathbf{v} = (1,\ -1,\ 1)$, $\mathbf{w}\ (2,\ 1,\ 3)$.

8. VECTORS IN TWO AND THREE DIMENSIONS

SOLUTIONS 1

1. See text.
2. See text.
3. See text.
4. See text.
5. See text.
6.

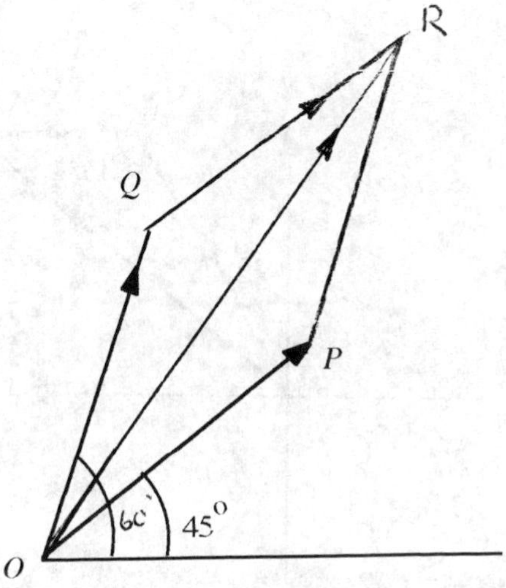

Fig. 8-II/1 The parallelogram.

$\left|\overrightarrow{OP}\right| = 100$ N $\qquad \left|\overrightarrow{OQ}\right| = 250$ N

PR is drawn parallel to *OQ* and equal
QR is drawn parallel to *OP* and equal.

$\overrightarrow{OR}$ is the resultant, *OPRQ* is the parallelogram of forces.

$O\hat{P}R = 180° - 15° = 165°$. Applying the cosine rule

$$(OR)^2 = (OP)^2 + (PR)^2 - 2(OP)(PR)\cos O\hat{P}R$$

$$= 100^2 + 250^2 - 2(100)(250)\cos 165° = 72500 + 48296.291$$

$\boxed{OR = 348 \text{ N}}$ to three significant figures.

Applying the sine rule

$$\frac{PR}{\sin R\hat{O}P} = \frac{OR}{\sin 165^\circ}$$

$$\sin R\hat{O}P = \frac{(PR) \sin 165^\circ}{OR} = \frac{250 \sin 165^\circ}{348} = 0.1859332$$

$$R\hat{O}P = 10.7^\circ.$$

Therefore the direction of OR with the horizontal is $45 + 10.7 = 55.7^\circ$.

7.

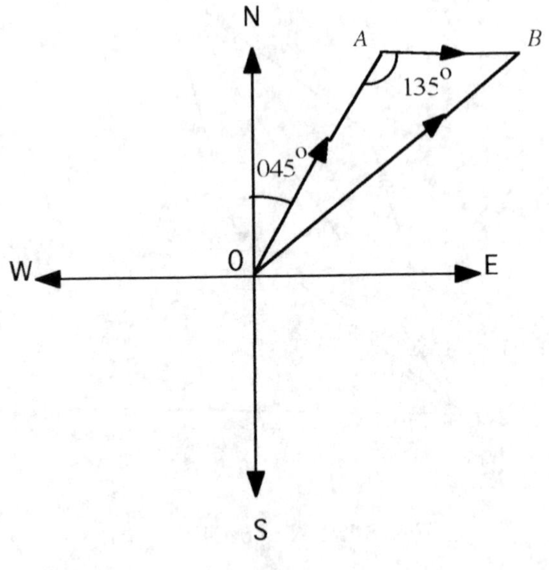

Fig. 8-II/2 The cardinals and the bearings.

Using the cosine rule

$$\begin{aligned}(OB)^2 &= (OA)^2 + (AB)^2 - 2(OA)(AB) \cos 135^\circ \\ &= 25^2 + 5^2 - 2(25)(5)(-0.707) \\ &= 625 + 25 + 176.75 = 826.75\end{aligned}$$

$OB = 28.8$ km/h.

Using the sine rule

$$\frac{AB}{\sin B\hat{O}A} = \frac{OB}{\sin 135^\circ}$$

$$\sin B\hat{O}A = \frac{AB \sin 135^\circ}{OB} = \frac{5 \times 0.707}{28.8} = 0.122743$$

$$B\hat{O}A = 7.05^\circ.$$

The bearing of the yacht is 052.05°.

8.

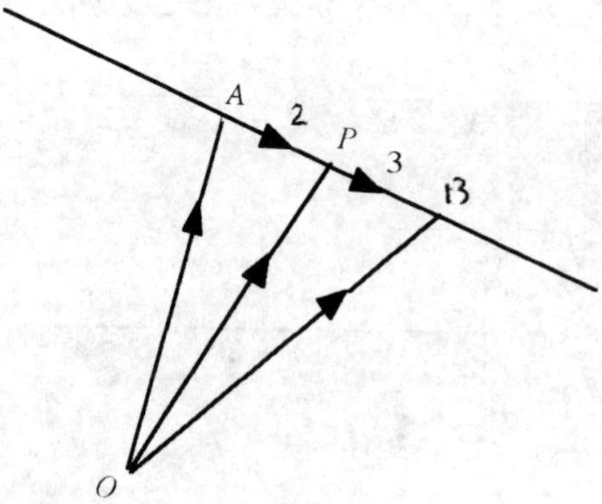

Fig. 8-II/3

$$\overrightarrow{OP} = \overrightarrow{OA} + \overrightarrow{AP} = \overrightarrow{OA} + \frac{2}{5}\overrightarrow{AB} = \overrightarrow{OA} + \frac{2}{5}\left(\overrightarrow{OB} - \overrightarrow{OA}\right)$$

$$\overrightarrow{OP} = \overrightarrow{OA} + \frac{2}{5}\overrightarrow{OB} - \frac{2}{5}\overrightarrow{OA} = \frac{3}{5}\overrightarrow{OA} + \frac{2}{5}\overrightarrow{OB}.$$

$$\overrightarrow{OP} = \frac{3}{5}\overrightarrow{OA} + \frac{2}{5}\overrightarrow{OB}.$$

SOLUTIONS 2

1. (i) $\mathbf{i} + 2\mathbf{j} + 3\mathbf{k}$ (ii) $-\mathbf{i} + 2\mathbf{j} - 3\mathbf{k}$ (iii) $3\mathbf{j} + 5\mathbf{k}$

   (ii) $-4\mathbf{i} + 2\mathbf{j} + \mathbf{k}$ (v) $3\mathbf{i} + 4\mathbf{k}$.

2. $A\ (2, 3, -1)$, $B\ (-1, 2, -4)$, $C\ (-3, 1, 1)$.

3. (a) $|\mathbf{u}| = \sqrt{(1)^2 + (-2)^2 + \left(\sqrt{20}\right)^2} = \sqrt{1 + 4 + 20} = 5$

   (b) $|\mathbf{v}| = \sqrt{(-3)^2 + 7^2 + 4^2} = \sqrt{9 + 49 + 16} = \sqrt{74} = 8.60.$

4. $\left|\overrightarrow{OP}\right| = \sqrt{3^2 + 4^2 + 5^2} = 7.07$

   $\left|\overrightarrow{OQ}\right| = \sqrt{(-2)^2 + (-1)^2 + 1^2} = \sqrt{6} = 2.45$

   $\left|\overrightarrow{OR}\right| = \sqrt{2^2 + (-3)^2 + 5^2} = \sqrt{4 + 9 + 25} = \sqrt{38} = 6.16.$

5. (i) $|\mathbf{a}| = \sqrt{1^2 + 2^2 + 3^2} = 3.74$

   (ii) $|\mathbf{b} - \mathbf{a}| = \sqrt{(2-1)^2 + (2-2)^2 + (2-3)^2} = \sqrt{1 + 1}$

   $= \sqrt{2} = 1.414$

   (iii) $\left|2\mathbf{c} - \frac{1}{2}\mathbf{a}\right| = \left|6\mathbf{i} + 10\mathbf{k} - \frac{1}{2}\mathbf{i} - \mathbf{j} - \frac{3}{2}\mathbf{k}\right| = |5.5\mathbf{i} - \mathbf{j} + 8.5\mathbf{k}|$

   $= \sqrt{5.5^2 + (-1)^2 + 8.5^2} = \sqrt{103.5} = 10.17$

6.

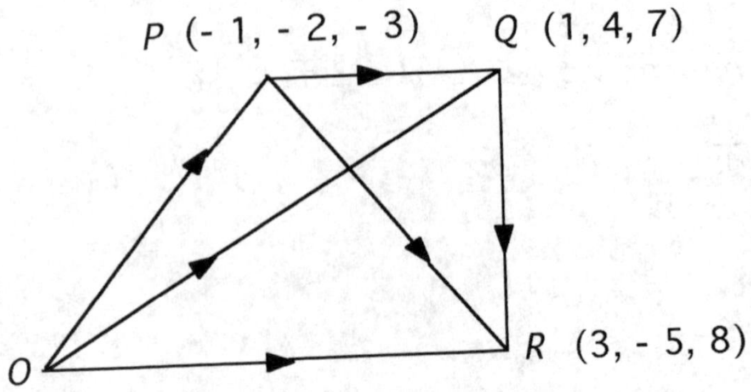

Fig. 8-II/4

$$\overrightarrow{PQ} = \overrightarrow{OQ} - \overrightarrow{OP} = [1 - (-1)]\,\mathbf{i} + [4 - (-2)]\,\mathbf{j} + [7 - (-3)]\,\mathbf{k}$$

$$= 2\mathbf{i} + 6\mathbf{j} + 10\mathbf{k}$$

$$\overrightarrow{PR} = [3 - (-1)]\,\mathbf{i} + [-5 - (-2)]\,\mathbf{j} + [8 - (-3)]\,\mathbf{k} = 4\mathbf{i} - 3\mathbf{j} + 11\mathbf{k}$$

$$\overrightarrow{QR} = \overrightarrow{OR} - \overrightarrow{OQ} = (3 - 1)\,\mathbf{i} + (-5 - 4)\,\mathbf{j} + (8 - 7)\,\mathbf{k} = 2\mathbf{i} - 9\mathbf{j} + \mathbf{k}$$

$$\left|\overrightarrow{PQ}\right| = \sqrt{2^2 + 6^2 + 10^2} = 11.8$$

$$\left|\overrightarrow{PR}\right| = \sqrt{4^2 + (-3)^2 + 11^2} = 12.1$$

$$\left|\overrightarrow{QR}\right| = \sqrt{2^2 + (-9)^2 + 1^2} = 9.27.$$

7. (i) $1 : -3 : 5$ are the direction ratios of $\mathbf{u} = \mathbf{i} - 3\mathbf{j} + 5\mathbf{k}$

$$\frac{1}{\sqrt{1^2 + (-3)^2 + 5^2}} : -\frac{3}{\sqrt{1^2 + (-3)^2 + 5^2}} : \frac{5}{\sqrt{1^2 + (-3)^2 + 5^2}}$$

are the direction cosines of the vector $\left(\frac{1}{\sqrt{35}} : -\frac{3}{\sqrt{35}} : \frac{5}{\sqrt{35}}\right)$

(ii) $-2 : 4 : -6$ are the direction ratios of $\mathbf{v} = -2\mathbf{i} + 4\mathbf{j} - 6\mathbf{k}$ and the corresponding direction cosines are

$$\frac{-2}{\sqrt{(-2)^2 + (4)^2 + (-6)^2}} : \frac{4}{\sqrt{56}} : \frac{-6}{\sqrt{56}}.$$

(iii) $3 : -7 : 11$ are the direction ratios of $\mathbf{w} = 3\mathbf{i} - 7\mathbf{j} + 11\mathbf{k}$ and the corresponding direction cosines are

$$\frac{3}{\sqrt{3^2 + (-7)^2 + 11^2}} : \frac{-7}{\sqrt{3^2 + (-7)^2 + 11^2}} : \frac{11}{\sqrt{3^2 + (-7)^2 + 11^2}} \text{ or}$$

$$\frac{3}{\sqrt{179}} : -\frac{7}{\sqrt{179}} : \frac{11}{\sqrt{179}}$$

$0.224 : -0.523 : 0.822.$

8. Let α, β and γ be the angles that the vector is making with respect to x, y and z respectively.

$$\cos\alpha = \frac{5}{7}, \quad \cos = \frac{4}{7}, \quad \cos\gamma = \frac{2\sqrt{2}}{7}$$

$\alpha = 44.4°$, $\beta = 55.2°$, $\gamma = 66.2°$ and using the calculator

$\cos^2 44.4° + \cos^2 55.2° + \cos^2 66.2° = 1.$

9. $\cos^2\alpha + \cos^2\beta + \cos^2\gamma = 1$

$\cos^2 45° + \cos^2 67.5° + \cos^2\gamma = 1$

$\cos^2\gamma = 1 - \cos^2 45° - \cos^2 67.5° = 1 - 0.5 - 0.146 = 0.354,$

$\cos\gamma = 0.595, \ \gamma = 53.5°.$

10. See text.

11. See text.

12. $\cos\alpha = \dfrac{2\sqrt{10}}{9} \quad \Rightarrow \quad \alpha = 45.4°$

$\cos\beta = \dfrac{5}{9} \quad \Rightarrow \quad \beta = 56.3°$

$\cos\gamma = \dfrac{4}{9} \quad \Rightarrow \quad \gamma = 63.6°.$

13. $\overrightarrow{OP} = \dfrac{\mathbf{a}\mu + \mathbf{b}\lambda}{\lambda + \mu}$

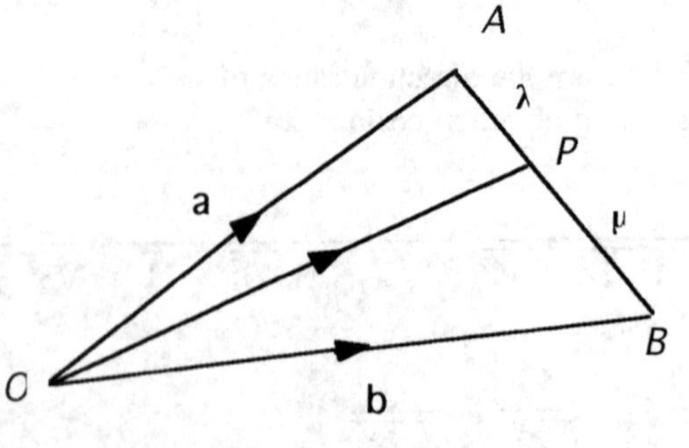

Fig. 8-II/5

P divides the line *AB* in the ratio $\lambda : \mu$ therefore the points *A*, *P* and *B* are collinear.

14. The direction cosines are proportional to $(l - a, m - b, n - c)$. The actual direction cosines are

$$\frac{l - a}{\sqrt{(l - a)^2 + (m - b)^2 + (n - c)^2}} : \frac{m - b}{\sqrt{(l - a)^2 + (m - b)^2 + (n - c)^2}} :$$

$$\frac{n - c}{\sqrt{(l - a)^2 + (m - b)^2 + (n - c)^2}}.$$

15. The direction cosines are proportional to $(3 - 1, - 4 - 2, 5 - 3)$ or $(2, - 6, 2)$. The actual direction cosines are

$$\frac{2}{\sqrt{2^2 + (-6)^2 + 2^2}} : \frac{-6}{\sqrt{2^2 + (-6)^2 + 2^2}} : \frac{2}{\sqrt{2^2 + (-6)^2 + 2^2}} \text{ or}$$

$$\frac{2}{\sqrt{44}} : - \frac{6}{\sqrt{44}} : \frac{2}{\sqrt{44}} \text{ or } 0.302 : - 0.905 : 0.302.$$

16. Let $3m$, $7m$, $11m$ be the actual direction cosines, since

$$(3m)^2 + (7m)^2 + (11m)^2 = 1$$

$$m^2 = \frac{1}{3^2 + 7^2 + 11^2} = \frac{1}{9 + 49 + 121} = \frac{1}{179} \text{ then}$$

$$m = \frac{1}{\sqrt{179}}.$$

The actual direction cosines are

$$\frac{3}{\sqrt{179}}, \frac{7}{\sqrt{179}}, \frac{11}{\sqrt{179}} \text{ or } 0.224, 0.523, 0.822.$$

17. $\cos^2 \alpha + \cos^2 \beta + \cos^2 \gamma = 1$

$\cos^2 70^\circ + \cos^2 \beta + \cos^2 80^\circ = 1$

$\cos^2 \beta = 1 - \cos^2 70^\circ - \cos^2 80^\circ$

$= 1 - 0.1169777 - 0.0301536 = 0.8528686$

$\cos \beta = 0.9235088$

$$\boxed{\beta = 22.6^\circ}$$

18. $\cos^2 \alpha + \cos^2 \beta + \cos^2 \gamma = 1$

let $\alpha = \beta = \gamma$

$3 \cos^2 \alpha = 1$

$$\cos \alpha = \pm \frac{1}{\sqrt{3}}$$

$$\frac{1}{\sqrt{3}} : \frac{1}{\sqrt{3}} : \frac{1}{\sqrt{3}} \text{ or } -\frac{1}{\sqrt{3}} : -\frac{1}{\sqrt{3}} : -\frac{1}{\sqrt{3}} .$$

19. $\cos^2 \alpha + \cos^2 \beta + \cos^2 \gamma = 1$

$\cos^2 \alpha + \cos^2 \alpha + \cos^2 2\alpha = 1$

$\cos 2\alpha = 2 \cos^2 \alpha - 1$

$\cos^2 2\alpha = 4 \cos^4 \alpha - 4 \cos^2 \alpha + 1$

$2 \cos^2 \alpha + 4 \cos^4 \alpha - 4 \cos^2 \alpha + 1 = 1$

$4 \cos^4 \alpha - 2 \cos^2 \alpha = 0$

$2 \cos^2 \alpha \left(2 \cos^2 \alpha - 1\right) = 0$

$\cos \alpha = 0$ (undefined)

$$\text{or } \cos \alpha = \pm \frac{1}{\sqrt{2}} .$$

The direction cosines are

$$\frac{1}{\sqrt{2}} : \frac{1}{\sqrt{2}} : 0 \text{ or } -\frac{1}{\sqrt{2}} : -\frac{1}{\sqrt{2}} : 0 .$$

20.

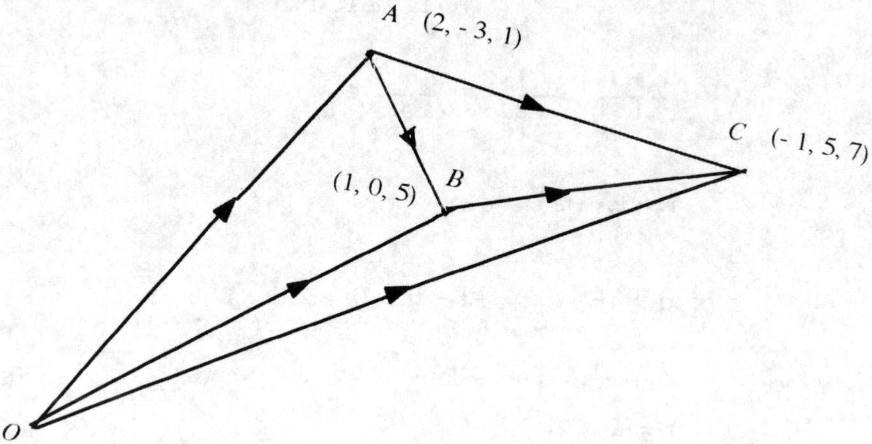

Fig. 8-II/6

$\overrightarrow{AB} = -\mathbf{i} + 3\mathbf{j} + 4\mathbf{k}$

$\overrightarrow{BC} = -2\mathbf{i} + 5\mathbf{j} + 2\mathbf{k}$

$\overrightarrow{AC} = -3\mathbf{i} + 8\mathbf{j} + 6\mathbf{k}$

$\left|\overrightarrow{AB}\right| = \sqrt{(-1)^2 + 3^2 + 4^2} = \sqrt{26} = 5.10 = a$

$\left|\overrightarrow{BC}\right| = \sqrt{(-2)^2 + 5^2 + 2^2} = \sqrt{33} = 5.74 = b$

$\left|\overrightarrow{AC}\right| = \sqrt{(-3)^2 + 8^2 + 6^2} = \sqrt{109} = 10.4 = c.$

The perimeter $2s = 5.1 + 5.74 + 10.4 = 21.24$

$s = 10.62$ the semi-perimeter

$$A = \sqrt{s(s-a)(s-b)(s-c)}$$

$$= \sqrt{10.62 \times (10.62 - 5.10) \times (10.62 - 5.74) \times (10.62 - 10.4)}$$

$$= \sqrt{10.62 \times 5.52 \times 4.88 \times 0.22} = 7.93 \text{ square units.}$$

SOLUTIONS 3

1. (a) $\dfrac{x+1}{1} = \dfrac{y+2}{2} = \dfrac{z+3}{3} = \lambda$

$x = \lambda - 1$
$y = 2\lambda - 2$
$z = 3\lambda - 3$

$x\mathbf{i} + y\mathbf{j} + z\mathbf{k} = -\mathbf{i} - 2\mathbf{j} - 3\mathbf{j} + \lambda(\mathbf{i} + 2\mathbf{j} + 3\mathbf{k})$
$\mathbf{r} = (-\mathbf{i} - 2\mathbf{j} - 3\mathbf{j}) + \lambda(\mathbf{i} + 2\mathbf{j} + 3\mathbf{k})$

this vector is of the form

$\mathbf{r} = \mathbf{a} + \lambda\mathbf{b}$

where $\mathbf{a} = -\mathbf{i} - 2\mathbf{j} - 3\mathbf{j}$ is the position vector and
$\mathbf{b} = \mathbf{i} + 2\mathbf{j} + 3\mathbf{j}$ is the direction vector.

(b) $\dfrac{x-1}{2} = \dfrac{y-2}{-3} = \dfrac{z-3}{4} = t$

$x = 2t + 1$
$y = -3t + 2$
$z = 4t + 3$

$x\mathbf{i} + y\mathbf{j} + z\mathbf{k} = \mathbf{i} + 2\mathbf{j} + 3\mathbf{k} + t(2\mathbf{i} - 3\mathbf{j} + 4\mathbf{k})$

this vector is of the form

$\mathbf{r} = \mathbf{a} + t\,\mathbf{b}$

where $\mathbf{a} = \mathbf{i} + 2\mathbf{j} + 3\mathbf{k}$ the position vector and
$\mathbf{b} = 2\mathbf{i} - 3\mathbf{j} + 4\mathbf{k}$ the direction vector.

(c) $\dfrac{x}{3} = \dfrac{y+3}{-4} = \dfrac{z-1}{2} = \mu$

$x = 3\mu$
$y = -4\mu - 3$
$z = 2\mu + 1$

$x\,\mathbf{i} + y\mathbf{j} + z\mathbf{k} = -3\mathbf{j} + \mathbf{k} + \mu(3\mathbf{i} - 4\mathbf{j} + 2\mathbf{k})$

this vector is of the form

$\mathbf{r} = \mathbf{a} + \mu\mathbf{b}$

where $\mathbf{a} = -3\mathbf{j} + \mathbf{k}$ the position vector and
$\mathbf{b} = 3\mathbf{i} - 4\mathbf{j} + 2\mathbf{k}$ the direction vector.

(d) $\dfrac{x+a}{p} = \dfrac{y+b}{q} = \dfrac{z+c}{r} = s$

$x = sp - a$
$y = qs - b$
$z = rs - c$

$x\mathbf{i} + y\mathbf{j} + z\mathbf{k} = (-a\mathbf{i} - b\mathbf{j} - c\mathbf{k}) + s\,(p\mathbf{i} + q\mathbf{j} + r\mathbf{k})$

this vector is of the form

$\mathbf{r} = \mathbf{a} + s\mathbf{b}$
where $\mathbf{a} = -a\mathbf{i} - b\mathbf{j} - c\mathbf{k}$ is the position vector and
$\mathbf{b} = = p\mathbf{i} + q\mathbf{j} + r\mathbf{k}$ is the direction vector.

2. (a) The direction vector is $\mathbf{i} + 2\mathbf{j} + 3\mathbf{k}$
the direction ratios $1 : 2 : 3$

the direction cosines $\dfrac{1}{\sqrt{14}} : \dfrac{2}{\sqrt{14}} : \dfrac{3}{\sqrt{14}}$

where $|\mathbf{i} + 2\mathbf{j} + 3\mathbf{k}| = \sqrt{14}$.

(b) The direction vector is $2\mathbf{i} - 3\mathbf{j} + 4\mathbf{k}$
the direction ratios $2 : -3 : 4$

the direction cosines $\dfrac{2}{\sqrt{29}} : \dfrac{-3}{\sqrt{29}} : \dfrac{4}{\sqrt{29}}$

where $|2\mathbf{i} - 3\mathbf{j} + 4\mathbf{k}| = \sqrt{2^2 + (-3)^2 + 4^2} = \sqrt{29}$.

(c) The direction vector is $3\mathbf{i} - 4\mathbf{j} + 2\mathbf{k}$
the direction ratios $3 : -4 : 2$

the direction cosines $\dfrac{3}{\sqrt{29}} : \dfrac{-4}{\sqrt{29}} : \dfrac{2}{\sqrt{29}}$

where $|3\mathbf{i} - 4\mathbf{j} + 2\mathbf{k}| = \sqrt{3^2 + (-4)^2 + 2^2} = \sqrt{29}$.

(d) The direction vector is $p\mathbf{i} + q\mathbf{j} + r\mathbf{k}$
the direction ratios $p : q : r$

the direction cosines $\dfrac{p}{\sqrt{p^2+q^2+r^2}} : \dfrac{q}{\sqrt{p^2+q^2+r^2}} : \dfrac{r}{\sqrt{p^2+q^2+r^2}}$

where $|p\mathbf{i} + q\mathbf{j} + r\mathbf{k}| = \sqrt{p^2 + q^2 + r^2}$.

3. $l = 1, m = 2, n = 3$ since the lines are parallel and hence the direction ratios are the same.

$$\frac{x + a}{1} = \frac{y + b}{2} = \frac{z + c}{3}$$ which passes through the point

$(-3, -4, -5)$, therefore $a = 3$, $b = 4$ and $c = 5$.

4. The line $\frac{x + a}{-3} = \frac{y + b}{-4} = \frac{z + c}{-5}$ is parallel to the line

$$\frac{x - 1}{l} = \frac{y - 2}{m} = \frac{z - 3}{n}$$ therefore the direction ratios are the same

$l : m : n$ is $-3 : -4 : -5$ $\quad$ $l = -3, m = -4, n = -5$. The line

$$\frac{x + a}{-3} = \frac{y + b}{-4} = \frac{z + c}{-5}$$ passes through the point $(2, 2, 2)$, therefore

$a = -2$, $b = -2$, and $c = -2$.

5. The direction vectors of question 1 are:
   (a) $\mathbf{i} + 2\mathbf{j} + 3\mathbf{k}$
   (b) $2\mathbf{i} - 3\mathbf{j} + 4\mathbf{k}$
   (c) $3\mathbf{i} - 4\mathbf{j} + 2\mathbf{k}$
   (d) $p\mathbf{i} + q\mathbf{j} + r\mathbf{k}$.

The corresponding unit vectors are:

(a) $$\hat{\mathbf{a}} = \frac{\mathbf{a}}{|\mathbf{a}|} = \frac{\mathbf{i} + 2\mathbf{j} + 3\mathbf{k}}{\sqrt{1^2 + 2^2 + 3^2}} = \frac{1}{\sqrt{14}}\mathbf{i} + \frac{2}{\sqrt{14}}\mathbf{j} + \frac{3}{\sqrt{14}}\mathbf{k}$$

(b) $$\hat{\mathbf{a}} = \frac{2\mathbf{i} - 3\mathbf{j} + 4\mathbf{k}}{\sqrt{2^2 + 3^2 + 4^2}} = \frac{2}{\sqrt{29}}\mathbf{i} - \frac{3}{\sqrt{29}}\mathbf{j} + \frac{4}{\sqrt{29}}\mathbf{k}$$

(c) $$\hat{\mathbf{a}} = \frac{3\mathbf{i} - 4\mathbf{j} + 2\mathbf{k}}{\sqrt{3^2 + 4^2 + 2^2}} = \frac{3}{\sqrt{29}}\mathbf{i} - \frac{4}{\sqrt{29}}\mathbf{j} + \frac{2}{\sqrt{29}}\mathbf{k}$$

(d) $$\hat{\mathbf{a}} = \frac{p\mathbf{i} + q\mathbf{j} + r\mathbf{k}}{\sqrt{p^2 + q^2 + r^2}}$$

$$= \frac{p}{\sqrt{p^2 + q^2 + r^2}}\mathbf{i} + \frac{q}{\sqrt{p^2 + q^2 + r^2}}\mathbf{j} + \frac{r}{\sqrt{p^2 + q^2 + r^2}}\mathbf{k}.$$

6. $\mathbf{r} = \mathbf{a} + \lambda\mathbf{b}$
$\mathbf{r} = (-\mathbf{i} + 2\mathbf{j} + 5\mathbf{k}) + \lambda\,(2\mathbf{i} - 3\mathbf{j} + 7\mathbf{k})$.

7. $\mathbf{r} = \mathbf{a} + \lambda\mathbf{b}$
$\mathbf{r} = (\mathbf{i} - \mathbf{j} + 3\mathbf{k}) + \mu\,(2\mathbf{i} + 3\mathbf{j} - 5\mathbf{k})$.

8. $\mathbf{r} = \mathbf{a} + \lambda\mathbf{b}$

$\mathbf{r} = \left(a_1\mathbf{i} + a_2\mathbf{j} + a_3\mathbf{k}\right) + t\left(b_1\mathbf{i} + b_2\mathbf{j} + b_3\mathbf{k}\right)$.

9. $\mathbf{r} = \mathbf{a} + \lambda\,(\mathbf{b} - \mathbf{a})$
$\mathbf{r} = (\mathbf{i} - 2\mathbf{j} + 3\mathbf{k}) + \lambda\,(-3\mathbf{i} + 6\mathbf{j} + 4\mathbf{k})$.

10. $\mathbf{r} = \mathbf{w} + \lambda\,(\mathbf{u} - \mathbf{w})$.

11. $\mathbf{r} = (2\mathbf{i} + 2\mathbf{j} + 2\mathbf{k}) + \lambda\,(\mathbf{i} + \mathbf{j} + \mathbf{k})$.

12. $\mathbf{r} = \mathbf{a} + \lambda\mathbf{b}$ this is the vector equation of a line with position vector **a** and it is parallel to the direction vector **b**.

$\mathbf{r} = \mathbf{a} + \lambda\,(\mathbf{b} - \mathbf{a})$ this is the vector equation of a line passing through two points with position vectors **a** and **b** respectively, the direction vector is $\mathbf{b} - \mathbf{a}$.

13. $$\mathbf{r}_1 = \begin{pmatrix} 1 \\ -3 \\ 2 \end{pmatrix} + \lambda \begin{pmatrix} -2 \\ 3 \\ -4 \end{pmatrix}$$

$$\mathbf{r}_2 = \begin{pmatrix} 2 \\ 1 \\ -1 \end{pmatrix} + \mu \begin{pmatrix} 1 \\ 7 \\ -1 \end{pmatrix}$$

$$\mathbf{r}_3 = \begin{pmatrix} 1 \\ 1 \\ 1 \end{pmatrix} + \nu \begin{pmatrix} 2 \\ 2 \\ -3 \end{pmatrix}.$$

14. (a) For $t = 1$, $3\mathbf{j} - 5\mathbf{k} + 2\mathbf{i} - 3\mathbf{j} + 7\mathbf{k} = 2\mathbf{i} + 2\mathbf{k}$
$A\,(2, 0, 2)$

For $t = 2$, $3\mathbf{j} - 5\mathbf{k} + 4\mathbf{i} - 6\mathbf{j} + 14\mathbf{k} = 4\mathbf{i} - 3\mathbf{j} + 9\mathbf{k}$
$B\,(4, -3, 9)$

For $t = -3$, $3\mathbf{j} - 5\mathbf{k} - 6\mathbf{i} + 9\mathbf{j} - 21\mathbf{k} = -6\mathbf{i} + 12\mathbf{j} - 26\mathbf{k}$
$C\,(-6, 12, -26)$.

(b) For $\mu = 0$, $\mathbf{i} - \mathbf{j} + 7\mathbf{k}$
$A\,(1, -1, 7)$.

For $\mu = -2$, $\quad$ **i** − **j** + 7**k** − 2**i** − 6**j** − 8**k** = − **i** − 7**j** − **k**
$B(-1, -7, -1)$.

For $\mu = 1$, $\quad$ **i** − **j** + 7**k** + **i** + 3**j** + 4**k** = 2**i** + 2**j** + 11**k**
$C(2, 2, 11)$.

(c) For $\lambda = -2$, $\quad$ − 2**i** + **j** − 4**k** + 6**i** − 10**j** − 2**k** = 4**i** − 9**j** − 6**k**
$A(4, -9, -6)$.

For $\lambda = -1$, $\quad$ − 2**i** + **j** − 4**k** + 3**i** − 5**j** − **k** = **i** − 4**j** − 5**k**
$B(1, -4, -5)$.

For $\lambda = 4$, $\quad$ (− 2**i** + **j** − 4**k**) − 12**i** + 20**j** + 4**k** = − 14**i** + 21**j**
$C(-14, 21, 0)$.

15. $\mathbf{r} = 5\mathbf{i} - \mathbf{j} + 7\mathbf{k} + \lambda(-2\mathbf{i} + 3\mathbf{j} + 3\mathbf{k})$
$x\mathbf{i} + y\mathbf{j} + z\mathbf{k} = 5\mathbf{i} - \mathbf{j} + 7\mathbf{k} + \lambda(-2\mathbf{i} + 3\mathbf{j} + 3\mathbf{k})$
$x = 5 - 2\lambda,\ y = -1 + 3\lambda,\ z = 7 + 3\lambda$

$$\lambda = \frac{5 - x}{2} = \frac{y + 1}{3} = \frac{z - 7}{3}$$

$x = 1, \qquad y = 5, \qquad z = 13$

$$\lambda = \frac{5 - 1}{2} = 2, \qquad \lambda = \frac{5 + 1}{3} = 2, \qquad \lambda = \frac{13 - 7}{3} = 2.$$

Therefore the point (1, 5, 13) lies on the line l.

16. $\mathbf{r} = (5\mathbf{j} + 7\mathbf{k}) + \mu(3\mathbf{i} - 7\mathbf{j} - 3\mathbf{k})$

$x\mathbf{i} + y\mathbf{j} + z\mathbf{k} = (5\mathbf{j} + 7\mathbf{k}) + \mu(3\mathbf{i} - 7\mathbf{j} - 3\mathbf{k})$

$x = 3\mu$	$y = 5 - 7\mu$	$z = 7 - 3\mu$
$x = 3$	$y = -2$	$z = 4$
$3 = 3\mu$	$-2 - 5 = -7\mu$	$4 - 7 = -3\mu$
$\mu = 1$	$\mu = 1$	$\mu = 1.$

Therefore the point (3, − 2, 4) lies on the line l.

17. $\mathbf{r} = (-2\mathbf{i} + 4\mathbf{j} - 5\mathbf{k}) + \lambda(3\mathbf{i} + 5\mathbf{j} + \mathbf{k})$
$A(-2, 4, -5)$

$x = -2 + 3\lambda = -2 \quad \Rightarrow \lambda = 0$
$y = 4 + 5\lambda = 4 \quad \Rightarrow \lambda = 0$
$z = -5 + \lambda = -5 \quad \Rightarrow \lambda = 0$

$\boxed{\lambda = 0}$

$B\ (-5, -1, -6)$

$$x = -2 + 3\lambda = -5 \quad \Rightarrow \lambda = -1$$
$$y = 4 + 5\lambda = -1 \quad \Rightarrow \lambda = -1$$
$$z = -5 + \lambda = -6 \quad \Rightarrow \lambda = -1$$

$$\boxed{\lambda = -1}$$

$C\ (4, 14, -3)$

$$x = -2 + 3\lambda = 4 \quad \Rightarrow \lambda = 2$$
$$y = 4 + 5\lambda = 14 \quad \Rightarrow \lambda = 2$$
$$z = -5 + \lambda = -3 \quad \Rightarrow \lambda = 2$$

$$\boxed{\lambda = 2}$$

SOLUTIONS 4

1. Let the position vector be $\mathbf{a} = -\mathbf{i} + 3\mathbf{j} + 5\mathbf{k}$ and the direction vector be $\mathbf{b} = 2\mathbf{i} + 3\mathbf{j} - \mathbf{k}$, then the vector equation $\mathbf{r} = \mathbf{a} + s\mathbf{b}$ where s is a scalar parameter.

$\mathbf{r} = (-\mathbf{i} + 3\mathbf{j} + 5\mathbf{k}) + s\,(2\mathbf{i} + 3\mathbf{j} - \mathbf{k})$

$l_1 : x\mathbf{i} + y\mathbf{j} + z\mathbf{k} = (-\mathbf{i} + 3\mathbf{j} + 5\mathbf{k}) + s\,(2\mathbf{i} + 3\mathbf{j} - \mathbf{k}) \quad \ldots (1)$

$l_2 : x\mathbf{i} + y\mathbf{j} + z\mathbf{k} = (2\mathbf{i} + 3\mathbf{j} + 4\mathbf{k}) + \lambda\,(-\mathbf{i} + 2\mathbf{j} + 5\mathbf{k}) \quad \ldots (2)$

From (1) $x = -1 + 2s, \quad y = 3 + 3s, \quad z = 5 - s$

$$s = \frac{x+1}{2}, \quad s = \frac{y-3}{3}, \quad s = 5 - z.$$

From (2) $x = 2 - \lambda, \quad y = 3 + 2\lambda, \quad z = 4 + 5\lambda$

$$\lambda = 2 - x, \quad \lambda = \frac{y-3}{2}, \quad \lambda = \frac{z-4}{5}$$

$\frac{2-x}{1} = \frac{y-3}{2} = \frac{z-4}{5} = \lambda$ the direction ratios are $-1 : 2 : 5$

$\frac{x+1}{2} = \frac{y-3}{3} = \frac{5-z}{1} = s$ the direction ratios are $2 : 3 : -1$.

Since the direction ratios are not equal the lines are not parallel.

$2 - \lambda = -1 + 2s, \quad \lambda = 3 - 2s \quad \ldots (4)$

$3 + 3s = 3 + 2\lambda, \quad \lambda = \frac{3}{2}s \quad \ldots (5)$

$5 - s = 4 + 5\lambda, \quad \lambda = \frac{1-s}{5} \quad \ldots (6)$

Solving (4) and (5) $\frac{3}{2}s = 3 - 2s, \ \frac{7}{2}s = 3, \ s = \frac{6}{7}$

Solving (5) and (6) $\frac{3}{2}s = \frac{1-s}{5}, \ \frac{3}{2}s + \frac{s}{5} = \frac{1}{5}, \ \frac{17}{10}s = \frac{1}{5}, \ s = \frac{2}{17}$

the lines do not intersect.

2. $\mathbf{b} + \mathbf{c} = 4\mathbf{i} - \mathbf{j} + \mathbf{k}$

$$\mathbf{a} \,.\, \mathbf{b} = (2\mathbf{i} + 3\mathbf{j} + 4\mathbf{k}) \,.\, (\mathbf{i} - 2\mathbf{j} + 3\mathbf{k})$$
$$= 2 - 6 + 12 = 8$$

$$\mathbf{a} \,.\, \mathbf{c} = 6 + 3 - 8 = 1$$

$$\mathbf{a} \,.\, (\mathbf{b} + \mathbf{c}) = (2\mathbf{i} + 3\mathbf{j} + 4\mathbf{k}) \,.\, (4\mathbf{i} - \mathbf{j} + \mathbf{k})$$
$$= 8 - 3 + 4 = 9$$

$$\mathbf{a} \,.\, (\mathbf{b} + \mathbf{c}) = \mathbf{a} \,.\, \mathbf{b} + \mathbf{a} \,.\, \mathbf{c}$$
$$= 8 + 1 = 9$$ distriburtive.

3.

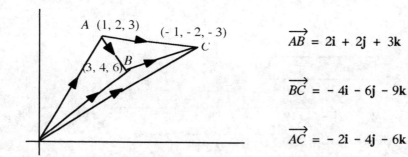

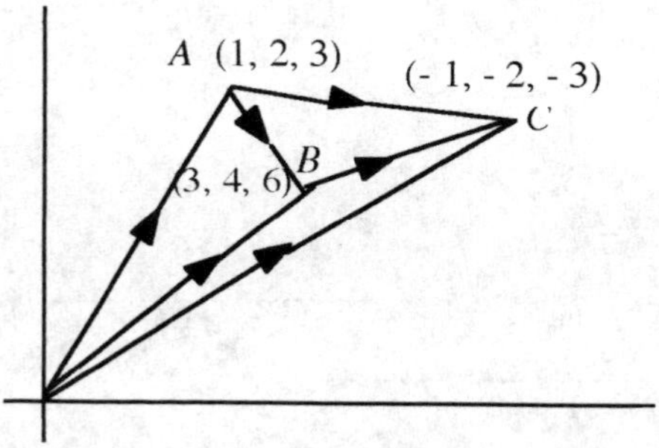

$$\overrightarrow{AB} = 2\mathbf{i} + 2\mathbf{j} + 3\mathbf{k}$$

$$\overrightarrow{BC} = -4\mathbf{i} - 6\mathbf{j} - 9\mathbf{k}$$

$$\overrightarrow{AC} = -2\mathbf{i} - 4\mathbf{j} - 6\mathbf{k}$$

Fig. 8-II/7

$$\left|\overrightarrow{AB}\right| = \sqrt{2^2 + 2^2 + 3^2} = \sqrt{17} = 4.123$$

$$\left|\overrightarrow{BC}\right| = \sqrt{16 + 36 + 81} = \sqrt{133} = 11.5$$

$$\left|\overrightarrow{AC}\right| = \sqrt{4 + 16 + 36} = \sqrt{56} = 7.48$$

$$s = \frac{4.123 + 11.5 + 7.48}{2} = 11.6$$

$$\text{Area} = \sqrt{11.6 \times (11.6 - 4.123)(11.6 - 11.5)(11.6 - 7.48)}$$

$$= \sqrt{11.6 \times 7.48 \times 0.1 \times 4.12}$$

$= 5.98$ square units.

4. $\cos^2 \alpha + \cos^2 \beta + \cos \gamma = 1$

$\cos^2 30 + \cos^2 60 + \cos^2 \gamma = 1$

$\cos^2 \gamma = 1 - 0.75 - 0.25 = 0$

$\gamma = 90°.$

5. (a) $\mathbf{a} . \mathbf{b} = |\mathbf{a}|\ |\mathbf{b}| \cos \theta$

$\cos 90° = 0$

$\mathbf{a} . \mathbf{b} = 0$

$(t\,\mathbf{i} + \mathbf{j} + 3\mathbf{k}) . (-2\mathbf{i} + \lambda\mathbf{j} + 3\mathbf{k}) = -2t + \lambda + 9 = 0$

$\boxed{\lambda = 2t - 9}$

(b) If **a** is parallel to **b**, their direction ratios are equal $t = -2$ and $\lambda = 1$.

6. (a) $(7\mathbf{i} + 2\lambda\mathbf{j} - 9\mathbf{k}) . (7\mathbf{i} + 4\mathbf{j} + \mu\mathbf{k}) = 0$

$49 + 8\lambda - 9\mu = 0$

$\boxed{8\lambda = -49 + 9\mu}$

(b) $\lambda = -1, \mu = 2$

$(7\mathbf{i} - 2\mathbf{j} - 9\mathbf{k}) . (7\mathbf{i} + 4\mathbf{j} + 2\mathbf{k}) = \sqrt{49 + 4 + 81}\ \sqrt{49 + 16 + 4}\ \cos \theta$

$49 - 8 - 18 = \sqrt{7^2 + 4 + 81}\ \sqrt{49 + 16 + 4}\ \cos \theta$

$23 = (11.6)(8.31) \cos \theta$

$$\cos \theta = \frac{23}{11.6 \times 8.31} = 0.238696$$

$\theta \approx 76.2°.$

(c) The direction ratios are the same

$2\lambda = 4, \boxed{\lambda = 2}$ $\boxed{\mu = -9}$

7.

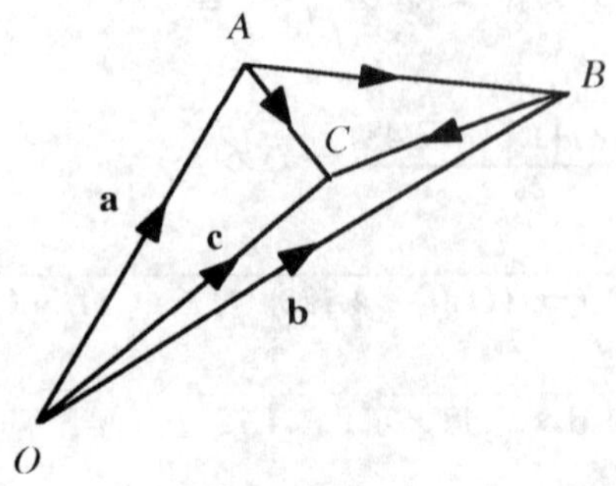

Fig. 8-II/8

(a) $\overrightarrow{AB} = \mathbf{b} - \mathbf{a} = -3\mathbf{i} - 2\mathbf{j} + 4\mathbf{k} - 2\mathbf{i} - 5\mathbf{j} + 7\mathbf{k}$

$$\boxed{\overrightarrow{AB} = -5\mathbf{i} - 7\mathbf{j} + 11\mathbf{k}}$$

$\overrightarrow{AC} = \mathbf{c} - \mathbf{a} = \mathbf{i} + 6\mathbf{j} + 11\mathbf{k} - 2\mathbf{i} - 5\mathbf{j} + 7\mathbf{k}$

$$\boxed{\overrightarrow{AC} = -\mathbf{i} + \mathbf{j} + 18\mathbf{k}}$$

$\overrightarrow{BC} = \mathbf{c} - \mathbf{b} = \mathbf{i} + 6\mathbf{j} + 11\mathbf{k} + 3\mathbf{i} + 2\mathbf{j} - 4\mathbf{k}$

$$\boxed{\overrightarrow{BC} = 4\mathbf{i} + 8\mathbf{j} + 7\mathbf{k}}$$

(b). (i) $\left|\overrightarrow{AB}\right| = \sqrt{(-5)^2 + (-7)^2 + 11^2} = 13.96$

$\left|\overrightarrow{AC}\right| = \sqrt{(-1)^2 + 1^2 + 18^2} = 18.06$

$\left|\overrightarrow{BC}\right| = \sqrt{4^2 + 8^2 + 7^2} = 11.36$

$(AC)^2 = (AB)^2 + (BC)^2 - 2 \times AB \times BC \cos \angle ABC$

$326 = 195 + 129 - 2 \times 13.96 \times 11.36 \cos \angle ABC$

$$\cos \angle ABC = \frac{324 - 326}{2 \times 13.96 \times 11.36}$$

$$= -\frac{2}{2 \times 13.96 \times 11.36} \Rightarrow \angle ABC = 90.4^\circ$$

the acute angle $\angle ABC = 89.6^\circ$

(ii) $\overrightarrow{AB} . \overrightarrow{BC} = \left|\overrightarrow{AB}\right| \left|\overrightarrow{BC}\right| \cos \angle ABC$

$(-5\mathbf{i} - 7\mathbf{j} + 11\mathbf{k}) . (4\mathbf{i} + 8\mathbf{j} + 7\mathbf{k}) = 13.96 \times 11.36 \cos \angle ABC$

$$\cos \angle ABC = \frac{-20 - 56 + 77}{13.96 \times 11.36} = \frac{1}{13.96 \times 11.36}$$

$\angle ABC = 89.6^\circ$

8. (a)

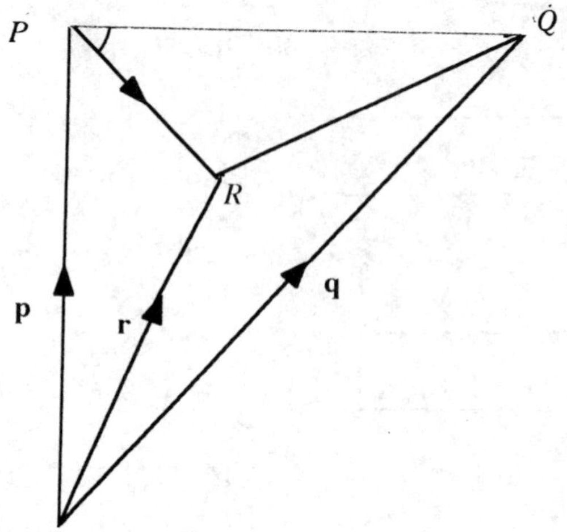

Fig. 8-II/9

$\overrightarrow{PQ} = \mathbf{q} - \mathbf{p} = \mathbf{i} + 2\mathbf{j} + 3\mathbf{k} \quad \left|\overrightarrow{PQ}\right| = \sqrt{1^2 + 2^2 + 3^2} = \sqrt{14}$

$\overrightarrow{PR} = \mathbf{r} - \mathbf{p} = -6\mathbf{i} + 3\mathbf{j} - 4\mathbf{k} \quad \left|\overrightarrow{PR}\right| = \sqrt{36 + 9 + 16} = \sqrt{61}$

$\overrightarrow{RQ} = \mathbf{q} - \mathbf{r} = 7\mathbf{i} - \mathbf{j} + 7\mathbf{k} \quad \left|\overrightarrow{RQ}\right| = \sqrt{49 + 1 + 49} = \sqrt{99}$.

(b) $\angle RPQ$ (i) $(RQ)^2 = (PR)^2 + (PQ)^2 - 2(PR)(PQ)\cos\angle RPQ$

$$= \frac{61 + 14 - 99}{2\sqrt{61}\sqrt{14}} = \frac{-24}{2\sqrt{61}\sqrt{14}}$$

$$= -0.4106315 \Rightarrow \angle RPQ = 114.24^\circ$$

$\angle RPQ = 65.76^\circ$ the acute angle.

(ii) $\overrightarrow{PR} \cdot \overrightarrow{PQ} = (-6\mathbf{i} + 3\mathbf{j} - 4\mathbf{k}) \cdot (\mathbf{i} + 2\mathbf{j} + 3\mathbf{k})$

$$= -6 + 6 - 12$$

$$= \sqrt{36 + 9 + 16}\sqrt{1 + 4 + 9}\cos\angle RPQ$$

$$\cos\angle RPQ = \frac{-12}{\sqrt{61}\sqrt{14}} = -0.4106315$$

$\angle RPQ = 65.76^\circ$ the acute angle.

9.

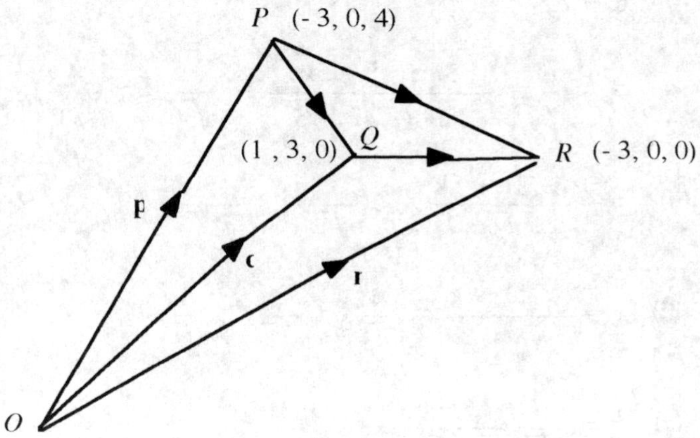

Fig. 8-II/10

(a) $\overrightarrow{PQ} = \mathbf{q} - \mathbf{p} = 4\mathbf{i} + 3\mathbf{j} - 4\mathbf{k}$

$\overrightarrow{PR} = \mathbf{r} - \mathbf{p} = -4\mathbf{k}$

$\overrightarrow{QR} = \mathbf{r} - \mathbf{q} = -4\mathbf{i} - 3\mathbf{j}$

$\left|\overrightarrow{PQ}\right| = \sqrt{4^2 + 3^2 + 4^2} = \sqrt{41}$

$\left|\overrightarrow{PR}\right| = 4$

$\left|\overrightarrow{QR}\right| = \sqrt{4^2 + 3^2} = 5$

(b) (i) $\mathbf{a} = 3\mathbf{i} - 4\mathbf{j} + 5\mathbf{k}$

$|\mathbf{a}| = a = \sqrt{(3)^2 + (-4)^2 + 5^2} = \sqrt{50}$

(ii) $|\mathbf{b}| = b = \sqrt{(-3)^2 + 5^2} = \sqrt{34}$

(iii) $|\mathbf{r}| = r = \sqrt{1^2 + 1^2 + 1^2} = \sqrt{3}$

(iv) $|\mathbf{r}| = r = \sqrt{a^2 + b^2 + c^2}$

(v) $|\mathbf{p}| = p = \sqrt{x^2 + y^2 + z^2}$

(i) $\mathbf{a} = a\hat{\mathbf{a}}$

$$\hat{\mathbf{a}} = \frac{\mathbf{a}}{a} = \frac{3\mathbf{i} - 4\mathbf{j} + 5\mathbf{k}}{\sqrt{3^2 + (-4)^2 + 5^2}} = \frac{3}{\sqrt{50}}\mathbf{i} - \frac{4}{\sqrt{50}}\mathbf{j} + \frac{5}{\sqrt{50}}\mathbf{k}$$

(ii) $$\hat{\mathbf{b}} = \frac{-3\mathbf{i} + 5\mathbf{k}}{\sqrt{34}} = -\frac{3}{\sqrt{34}}\mathbf{i} + \frac{5}{\sqrt{34}}\mathbf{k}$$

(iii) $$\hat{\mathbf{r}} = \frac{\mathbf{i} + \mathbf{j} + \mathbf{k}}{\sqrt{3}} = \frac{1}{\sqrt{3}}\mathbf{i} + \frac{1}{\sqrt{3}}\mathbf{j} + \frac{1}{\sqrt{3}}\mathbf{k}$$

(iv) $$\hat{\mathbf{r}} = \frac{a\mathbf{i} + b\mathbf{j} + c\mathbf{k}}{\sqrt{a^2 + b^2 + c^2}}$$

(v) $$\hat{\mathbf{p}} = \frac{x\mathbf{i} + y\mathbf{j} + z\mathbf{k}}{\sqrt{x^2 + y^2 + z^2}}.$$

10. (a) $\mathbf{u} \cdot \mathbf{v} = |\mathbf{u}|\,|\mathbf{v}| \cos\theta$

$$(2\mathbf{i} - 3\mathbf{j} + 4\mathbf{k}) \cdot (-\mathbf{i} + \mathbf{j} - \mathbf{k}) = \sqrt{4 + 9 + 16}\,\sqrt{1 + 1 + 1}\,\cos\theta$$

$$\cos\theta = \frac{-2 - 3 - 4}{\sqrt{29}\,\sqrt{3}} = -\frac{9}{\sqrt{29}\,\sqrt{3}}$$

the acute angle $\theta = 15.2^\circ$

(b) $\mathbf{u} = (1, 2, 3)$ and $\mathbf{v} = (-1, -2, -3)$

$\mathbf{u} \cdot \mathbf{v} = (\mathbf{i} + 2\mathbf{j} + 3\mathbf{k}) \cdot (-\mathbf{i} - 2\mathbf{j} - 3\mathbf{k}) = -1 - 4 - 9$

$$= \sqrt{1 + 4 + 9}\,\sqrt{1 + 4 + 9}\,\cos\theta$$

$$\cos\theta = \frac{14}{\sqrt{14}\,\sqrt{14}}$$ the acute angle

$$\boxed{\theta = 0^\circ}$$

the vectors are parallel.

11. (i) $3\mathbf{j}$ (ii) $-\mathbf{i} + 2\mathbf{j} + 3\mathbf{k}$ (iii) $-\mathbf{i} - 4\mathbf{j} - 9\mathbf{k}$ (iv) $4\mathbf{k}$ (v) $-4\mathbf{i} + 5\mathbf{k}$.

12. $(-7, 0, 7)$, $(0, 2, -3)$, $(0, 0, -1)$

13. (i) $|\mathbf{u}| = \sqrt{2^2 + 2^2 + 1} = 3$ (ii) $|\mathbf{v}| = \sqrt{5^2 + 5^2 + 6^2} = \sqrt{86}$

(iii) $|\mathbf{w}| = \sqrt{1^2 + 1^2 + 2^2} = \sqrt{6}$.

14. $\left|\overrightarrow{OP}\right| = \sqrt{1^2 + 4^2 + 5^2} = \sqrt{42}$,

$\left|\overrightarrow{OQ}\right| = \sqrt{1^2 + 2^2 + 5^2} = \sqrt{30}$

$\left|\overrightarrow{OR}\right| = \sqrt{2^2 + 4^2 + 6^2} = \sqrt{4 + 16 + 36} = \sqrt{56}$.

15. (i) $|\mathbf{a}| = \sqrt{4^2 + 5^2 + 6^2} = \sqrt{16 + 25 + 36} = \sqrt{77} = 8.78$

(ii) $|\mathbf{a}-\mathbf{c}| = |3\mathbf{i} - 8\mathbf{j} + 6\mathbf{k}| = \sqrt{9 + 64 + 36} = \sqrt{109} = 10.44$

(iii) $|\mathbf{b} + \mathbf{a} + \mathbf{c}| = |7\mathbf{i} - 5\mathbf{j} + 11\mathbf{k}| = \sqrt{7^2 + 5^2 + 11^2}$

$= \sqrt{195} = 13.96$

16. (i) $\mathbf{u} \cdot \mathbf{v} = (3\mathbf{i} - \mathbf{j} - 5\mathbf{k}) \cdot (-2\mathbf{i} + 5\mathbf{j} + 4\mathbf{k}) = -6 - 5 - 20$

$= \sqrt{9 + 1 + 25}\,\sqrt{4 + 25 + 16}\,\cos\theta$

$$\cos\theta = \frac{31}{\sqrt{35}\,\sqrt{45}} = 0.7811265$$

$$\boxed{\theta = 38.6^\circ}$$

(ii) $\mathbf{a} \cdot \mathbf{b} = (3\mathbf{j} + \mathbf{k}) \cdot (\mathbf{i} - \mathbf{k}) = -1$

$= \sqrt{9 + 1}\,\sqrt{1 + 1}\,\cos\theta$

$$\cos\theta = \frac{1}{\sqrt{10}\,\sqrt{2}} = 0.2236068$$

$$\boxed{\theta = 77.1^\circ}$$

(iii) $\mathbf{w} \cdot \mathbf{z} = (\mathbf{i} - \mathbf{j} - 7\mathbf{k}) \cdot (-2\mathbf{i} + 2\mathbf{j} + \mathbf{k}) = -2 - 2 - 7 = -11$

$$= \sqrt{1 + 1 + 49}\ \sqrt{4 + 4 + 1}\ \cos\theta$$

$$\cos\theta = \frac{11}{3\sqrt{51}} = 0.513436$$

$$\boxed{\theta = 59.1^\circ}$$

17. $|\mathbf{a}| = 1, \ |\mathbf{b}| = 2$

$\mathbf{a} \cdot \mathbf{b} = |\mathbf{a}|\ |\mathbf{b}| \cos 30^\circ = 0.866 \times 1 \times 2$

$= 1.732$ the scalar product.

18. (i) $\mathbf{i} \cdot \mathbf{j} \cdot \mathbf{k} = 0$ (ii) $\mathbf{i} \cdot \mathbf{i} = \mathbf{j} \cdot \mathbf{j} = \mathbf{k} \cdot \mathbf{k} = 1$

(iii) $\mathbf{i} \cdot \mathbf{i} \cdot \mathbf{i} = \mathbf{i}$ (iv) $\mathbf{i} \cdot \mathbf{j} = \mathbf{j} \cdot \mathbf{k} = \mathbf{k} \cdot \mathbf{i} = 0.$

19. (a) $\mathbf{a} \cdot \mathbf{b} = (2\mathbf{i} - 3\mathbf{j} - 5\mathbf{k}) \cdot (\mathbf{i} + 2\mathbf{j} + \mathbf{k}) = 2 - 6 - 5 = -9$

(b) $\mathbf{a} \cdot \mathbf{b} = (-\mathbf{j} - \mathbf{k}) \cdot (\mathbf{i} + \mathbf{j} + \mathbf{k}) = -1 - 1 = -2$

(c) $\mathbf{a} \cdot \mathbf{b} = (3\mathbf{i} + 4\mathbf{j} + 5\mathbf{k}) \cdot (-\mathbf{i} - \mathbf{j} - \mathbf{k}) = -3 - 4 - 5 = -12$

(d) $\mathbf{a} \cdot \mathbf{b} = (2\mathbf{i} + 2\mathbf{j} + 2\mathbf{k}) \cdot (2\mathbf{i} + 2\mathbf{j} + 2\mathbf{k}) = 4 + 4 + 4 = 12.$

20. (a) $\mathbf{u} \cdot \mathbf{v} = 0$

$(3t\,\mathbf{i} + 2t^2\mathbf{j} + \mathbf{k}) \cdot [(1 - t)\mathbf{i} + 3\mathbf{j} - \mathbf{k}] = 0$

$3t\,(1 - t) + 2t^2 3 - 1 = 0$

$3t - 3t^2 + 6t^2 - 1 = 0$

$3t^2 + 3t - 1 = 0$

$$t = \frac{-3 \pm \sqrt{9 + 12}}{6} = \frac{-3 \pm 4.58}{6}$$

$t = 0.264$ or $t = -1.264$

(b) $\mathbf{u} \cdot \mathbf{v} = [3(-2)\mathbf{i} + 2(4)\mathbf{j} + \mathbf{k}] \cdot [3\mathbf{i} + 3\mathbf{j} - \mathbf{k}]$

$$= (-6\mathbf{i} + 8\mathbf{j} + \mathbf{k}) \cdot (3\mathbf{i} + 3\mathbf{j} - \mathbf{k})$$

$$= -18 + 24 - 1$$

$$= 5 = \sqrt{6^2 + 8^2 + 1}\ \sqrt{3^2 + 3^2 + 1}\ \cos\theta$$

$$\cos\theta = \frac{5}{\sqrt{101}\ \sqrt{19}} = 0.1141385$$

$$\boxed{\theta = 83.5^\circ}$$

21. $\mathbf{a} \cdot \mathbf{b} = 0 = \left[2t^2\mathbf{i} + (1 - 2t)\mathbf{j} + t\mathbf{k}\right] \cdot \left[2t\mathbf{i} - 2t\mathbf{j} - 4t^2\mathbf{k}\right]$

$$= 4t^3 + (1 - 2t)(-2t) + t\left(-4t^2\right)$$

$$= 4t^3 - 2t + 4t^2 - 4t^3$$

$$= 4t^2 - 2t = 2t(2t - 1) = 0$$

$t = 0$ or $t = \dfrac{1}{2}$.

22. $\mathbf{p} \cdot \mathbf{q} = (3\mathbf{i} - 5\mathbf{j} + \mathbf{k}) \cdot (-2\mathbf{i} - \mathbf{j} + 2\mathbf{k}) = -6 + 5 + 2$

$$= 1 = \sqrt{3^2 + 5^2 + 1}\ \sqrt{2^2 + 1 + 2^2}\ \cos\theta$$

$$\cos\theta = \frac{1}{3\sqrt{35}} = 0.0563436$$

$$\boxed{\theta = 86.8^\circ}$$

23. $\mathbf{a} \cdot \mathbf{b} = (\mathbf{i} + 3\mathbf{j} + \mathbf{k}) \cdot (2\mathbf{i} - 2\mathbf{j} - 3\mathbf{k}) = 2 - 6 - 3 = -7$

$$= \sqrt{1 + 9 + 1}\ \sqrt{4 + 4 + 9}\ \cos\theta$$

$$\cos\theta = \frac{-7}{\sqrt{17}\ \sqrt{11}}$$

$$\cos\theta = \frac{7}{\sqrt{187}}$$

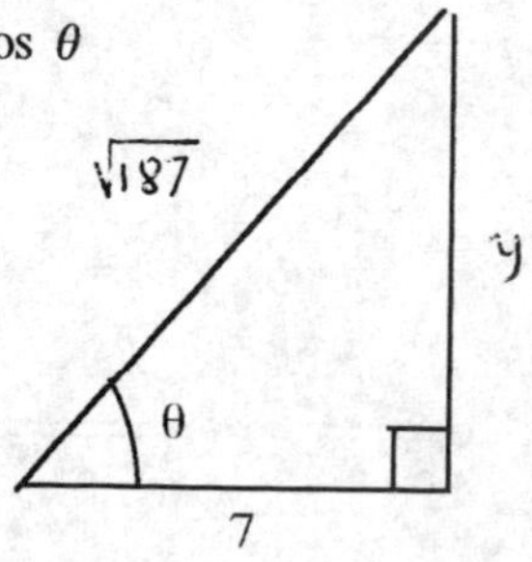

Fig. 8-II/11

$$y = \sqrt{187 - 7^2} = \sqrt{138} = 11.74734$$

$$\tan\theta = \frac{\sqrt{138}}{7} = 1.68.$$

24. (a) (i) $2\mathbf{a} - 3\mathbf{e} = 6\mathbf{j} - 10\mathbf{k} - 9\mathbf{i} - 12\mathbf{j} - 15\mathbf{k} = -9\mathbf{i} - 6\mathbf{j} - 25\mathbf{k}$

(ii) $\mathbf{b} + 3\mathbf{d} + \mathbf{e} = \mathbf{i} + 2\mathbf{j} - 3\mathbf{k} + 9\mathbf{i} + 6\mathbf{j} + 3\mathbf{k} + 3\mathbf{i} + 4\mathbf{j} + 5\mathbf{k}$

$$= 13\mathbf{i} + 12\mathbf{j} + 5\mathbf{k}$$

(iii) $2\mathbf{b} - 4\mathbf{d} + 2\mathbf{e} = 2\mathbf{i} + 4\mathbf{j} - 6\mathbf{k} - 12\mathbf{i} - 8\mathbf{j} - 4\mathbf{k} + 6\mathbf{i} + 8\mathbf{j} + 10\mathbf{k}$

$$= -4\mathbf{i} + 4\mathbf{j}$$

(b) (i) $|\mathbf{b} \,.\, \mathbf{e}| = |(\mathbf{i} + 2\mathbf{j} - 3\mathbf{k}) \,.\, (3\mathbf{i} + 4\mathbf{j} + 5\mathbf{k})|$

$$= |3 + 8 - 15| = 4$$

(ii) $|\mathbf{a} - \mathbf{e}| = |3\mathbf{j} - 5\mathbf{k} - 3\mathbf{i} - 4\mathbf{j} - 5\mathbf{k}| = |-3\mathbf{i} - \mathbf{j} - 10\mathbf{k}|$

$$= \sqrt{9 + 1 + 100} = \sqrt{110} = 10.5$$

(iii) $|\mathbf{d} - \mathbf{a}| = |3\mathbf{i} + 2\mathbf{j} + \mathbf{k} - 3\mathbf{j} + 5\mathbf{k}| = |3\mathbf{i} - \mathbf{j} + 6\mathbf{k}|$

$$= \sqrt{9 + 1 + 36} = \sqrt{46} = 6.78$$

(iv) $|\mathbf{d} \,.\, \mathbf{e}| = |(3\mathbf{i} + 2\mathbf{j} + \mathbf{k}) \,.\, (3\mathbf{i} + 4\mathbf{j} + 5\mathbf{k})| = 9 + 8 + 5 = 22$

(v) $|(\mathbf{a} \,.\, \mathbf{b}) \,.\, \mathbf{c}| = |[(3\mathbf{j} - 5\mathbf{k}) \,.\, (\mathbf{i} + 2\mathbf{j} - 3\mathbf{k})] \,.\, (-2\mathbf{i} - \mathbf{j} + \mathbf{k})|$

$$= |(6 + 15)(-2\mathbf{i} - \mathbf{j} + \mathbf{k})|$$

$$= |-42\mathbf{i} - 21\mathbf{j} + 21\mathbf{k}|$$

$$= \sqrt{42^2 + 21^2 + 21^2} = \sqrt{2646} = 51.4$$

(c) $0 : \dfrac{3}{\sqrt{3^2 + 5^2}} : \dfrac{-5}{\sqrt{3^2 + 5^2}}$ or $0 : 0.515 : -0.858$

$$\frac{1}{\sqrt{1 + 4 + 9}} : \frac{2}{\sqrt{14}} : -\frac{3}{\sqrt{14}}$$

$$\frac{-2}{\sqrt{2^2+1+1}} : \frac{-1}{\sqrt{6}} : \frac{1}{\sqrt{6}}$$

$$\frac{3}{\sqrt{3^2+2^2+1^2}} : \frac{2}{\sqrt{14}} : \frac{1}{\sqrt{14}}$$

$$\frac{3}{\sqrt{3^2+4^2+5^2}} : \frac{4}{\sqrt{50}} : \frac{5}{\sqrt{50}}.$$

(d) (i) $\mathbf{a} \,.\, \mathbf{e} = (3\mathbf{j} - 5\mathbf{k}) \,.\, (3\mathbf{i} + 4\mathbf{j} + 5\mathbf{k}) = 12 - 25 = -13$

$$= \sqrt{3^2+5^2}\sqrt{3^2+4^2+5^2}\cos\theta$$

$$\cos\theta = \frac{-13}{\sqrt{34}\sqrt{50}} \Rightarrow \theta = 71.6^\circ$$

(ii) $2\mathbf{a} \,.\, \mathbf{d} = (6\mathbf{j} - 10\mathbf{k}) \,.\, (3\mathbf{i} + 2\mathbf{j} + \mathbf{k}) = 12 - 10 = 2$

$$= \sqrt{36+100}\sqrt{9+4+1}\cos\theta$$

$$\cos\theta = \frac{2}{\sqrt{14}\sqrt{136}} \Rightarrow \theta = 87.4^\circ.$$

(iii) $\mathbf{c} \,.\, 2\mathbf{e} = (-2\mathbf{i} - \mathbf{j} + \mathbf{k}) \,.\, (6\mathbf{i} + 8\mathbf{j} + 10\mathbf{k})$

$$= -12 - 8 + 10 = -10$$

$$= \sqrt{4+1+1}\sqrt{36+64+100}\cos\theta$$

$$\cos\theta = \frac{10}{\sqrt{6}\sqrt{200}} \Rightarrow \boxed{\theta = 73.2^\circ}.$$

25. $l_1 : \mathbf{r} = 2\mathbf{i} + 3\mathbf{j} + 4\mathbf{k} + \lambda\,(2\mathbf{i} - 3\mathbf{j} + 5\mathbf{k})$

$x = 2 + 2\lambda, y = 3 - 3\lambda, z = 4 + 5\lambda$

$$\lambda = \frac{x-2}{2} = \frac{y-3}{-3} = \frac{z-4}{5}$$

$l_2 : \mathbf{r} = 2\mathbf{i} - 5\mathbf{j} + \mathbf{k} + \mu\,(4\mathbf{i} - 6\mathbf{j} + 10\mathbf{k})$

$x = 2 + 4\mu, y = -5 - 6\mu, z = 1 + 10\mu$

$$\mu = \frac{x-2}{4} = \frac{y+5}{-6} = \frac{z-1}{10}$$

$l_3 : \mathbf{r} = -\mathbf{i} + \mathbf{j} + 3\mathbf{k} + v(\mathbf{i} - \mathbf{j} + 2\mathbf{k})$

$x = -1 + v, y = 1 - v, z = 3 + 2v$

$$\frac{x+1}{1} = v = \frac{y-1}{-1} = \frac{z-3}{2}$$

l_1 and l_2 are parallel
since the direction ratios are the same

$2 : -3 : 5$ or $4 : -6 : 10$

check l_1 and l_3

$$\frac{x-2}{2} = \frac{y-3}{-3} \text{ and } x + 1 = \frac{y-1}{-1}$$

$$-3x + 6 = 2y - 6 \Rightarrow -3x - 2y = -12 \quad \dots (1)$$
$$x + 1 = -y + 1 \Rightarrow x + y = 0 \quad \dots (2)$$

$x = -y, -3x + 2x = -12,$ $\boxed{x = 12}$

$\boxed{y = -12}$

$$\lambda = \frac{12-2}{2} = \frac{-12-3}{-3} = 5 = \frac{z-4}{5} \Rightarrow z = 29$$

$$v = \frac{12+1}{1} = \frac{-12-1}{-1} = 13 = \frac{z-3}{2} \Rightarrow z = 29$$

l_1 and l_3 intersect and their point of intersection is $(12, -12, 29)$ for $\lambda = 5$ and $v = 13$.
Check l_2 and l_3

$$\mu = \frac{x-2}{4} = \frac{y+5}{-6} = \frac{z-1}{10}$$

$$v = \frac{x+1}{1} = \frac{y-1}{-1} = \frac{z-3}{2}$$

$$\frac{x-2}{4} = \frac{y+5}{-6} \Rightarrow -6x + 12 = 4y + 20 \Rightarrow 4y + 6x = -8$$

or $\boxed{2y + 3x = -4}$ ... (1)

$x + 1 = -y + 1 \Rightarrow x + y = 0 \Rightarrow x = -y$

$2y - 3y = -4 \quad \Rightarrow -y = -4 \Rightarrow$

$$\boxed{y = 4} \qquad \boxed{x = -4}$$

$$v = \frac{-4+1}{1} = \frac{4-1}{-1} = -3 = \frac{z-3}{2}$$

$$z = -6 + 3 = -3$$

$$\mu = \frac{-4-2}{4} = \frac{4+5}{-6}$$

$$\mu = -\frac{3}{2} = \frac{z-1}{10} \Rightarrow -15 = z - 1 \Rightarrow z = -14$$

inconsistent

therefore l_2 and l_3 are skew lines.

26.

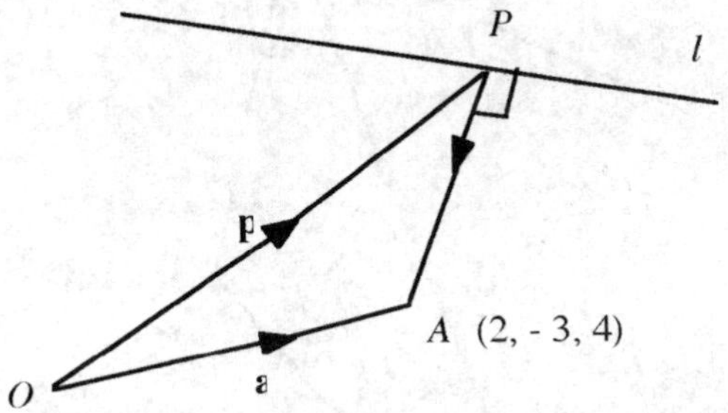

Fig. 8-II/12

Let P be the point the perpendicular from the point A meets the line l. Since P is a point on the l for which $\lambda = \mu$, then

$$\overrightarrow{OP} = \mathbf{p} = -\mathbf{i} + 2\mathbf{j} + 4\mathbf{k} + \mu(2\mathbf{i} - 3\mathbf{j} + 5\mathbf{k})$$
$$= (-1 + 2\mu)\mathbf{i} + (2 - 3\mu)\mathbf{j} + (4 + 5\mu)\mathbf{k}$$

$$\overrightarrow{PA} = \mathbf{a} - \mathbf{p} = (2\mathbf{i} - 3\mathbf{j} + 4\mathbf{k}) - [(-1 + 2\mu)\mathbf{i} + (2 - 3\mu)\mathbf{j} + (4 + 5\mu)\mathbf{k}]$$
$$= (2 + 1 - 2\mu)\mathbf{i} + (-3 - 2 + 3\mu)\mathbf{j} + (4 - 4 - 5\mu)\mathbf{k}$$
$$= (3 - 2\mu)\mathbf{i} + (-5 + 3\mu)\mathbf{j} - 5\mu\mathbf{k}$$

$\overrightarrow{PA}$ is perpendicular to l and l is parallel to 2i − 3j + 5k, the direction vector,

therefore $(3 - 2\mu) \cdot 2 + (-5 + 3\mu) \cdot (-3) - 5\mu(5) = 0$

$$6 - 4\mu + 15 - 9\mu - 25\mu = 0$$

$$-38\mu = -21$$

$$\mu = \frac{21}{38}$$

therefore $\overrightarrow{PA} = \left(3 - 2 \times \frac{21}{38}\right)\mathbf{i} + \left(-5 + 3 \times \frac{21}{38}\right)\mathbf{j} - 5\left(\frac{21}{38}\right)\mathbf{k}$

$$= \frac{1}{38}(72\mathbf{i} - 127\mathbf{j} - 105\mathbf{k})$$

$$\left|\overrightarrow{PA}\right| = \frac{1}{38}\sqrt{72^2 + 127^2 + 105^2} = 4.73 \text{ units.}$$

27.

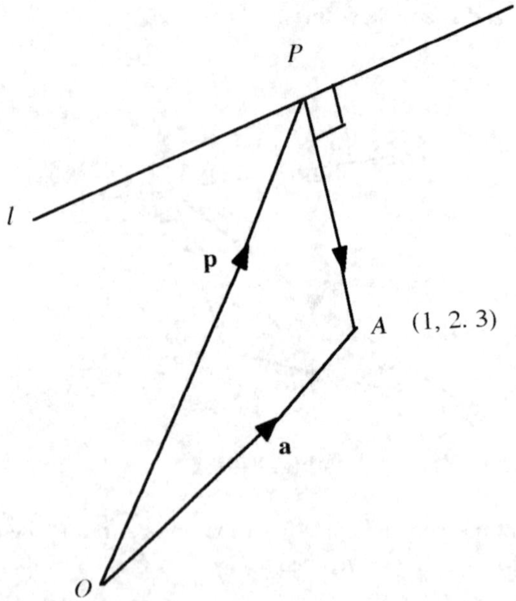

Fig. 8-II/13 Perpendicular distance from the point A (1, 2, 3) to the line with vector equation

$\mathbf{r} = \mathbf{i} + 3\mathbf{j} + 5\mathbf{k} + \mu(4\mathbf{i} + 3\mathbf{j} + 2\mathbf{k})$

$\overrightarrow{OP} = \mathbf{p} = \mathbf{i} + 3\mathbf{j} + 5\mathbf{k} + \mu(4\mathbf{i} + 3\mathbf{j} + 2\mathbf{k})$

$$= \mathbf{i}(1 + 4\mu) + \mathbf{j}(3 + 3\mu) + \mathbf{k}(5 + 2\mu)$$

$$\overrightarrow{PA} = \mathbf{a} - \mathbf{p} = \mathbf{i} + 2\mathbf{j} + 3\mathbf{k} - [\mathbf{i}\,(1 + 4\mu) + \mathbf{j}\,(3 + 3\mu) + \mathbf{k}\,(5 + 2\mu)]$$

$$= [\mathbf{i}\,(1 - 1 - 4\mu) + \mathbf{j}\,(2 - 3 - 3\mu) + \mathbf{k}\,(3 - 5 - 2\mu)]$$

$$= -4\mu\mathbf{i} + \mathbf{j}\,(-1 - 3\mu) + \mathbf{k}\,(-2 - 2\mu)$$

$\overrightarrow{PA}$ = is perpendicular to l and l is parallel to the direction vector, $4\mathbf{i} + 3\mathbf{j} + 2\mathbf{k}$ therefore

$$(4\mathbf{i} + 3\mathbf{j} + 2\mathbf{k}) \cdot [-4\mu\mathbf{i} + \mathbf{j}\,(-1 - 3\mu) + \mathbf{k}\,(-2 - 2\mu)] = 0$$

$$-16\mu - 3\,(1 + 3\mu) + 2\,(-2 - 2\mu) = 0$$

$$-16\mu - 3 - 9\mu - 4 - 4\mu = 0$$

$$-29\mu - 7 = 0$$

$$\mu = -\frac{7}{29}$$

therefore

$$\overrightarrow{PA} = -4\left(-\frac{7}{29}\right)\mathbf{i} + \left(-1 + \frac{3 \times 7}{29}\right)\mathbf{j} + \left(-2 + \frac{14}{29}\right)\mathbf{k}$$

$$= \frac{28}{29}\mathbf{i} - \frac{8}{29}\mathbf{j} - \frac{44}{29}\mathbf{k}$$

$$\left|\overrightarrow{PA}\right| = \frac{\sqrt{28^2 + 8^2 + 44^2}}{29} = 1.82 \text{ units.}$$

28. $\mathbf{r} = x_1\mathbf{i} + y_1\mathbf{j} + z_1\mathbf{k} + \lambda(a\mathbf{i} + b\mathbf{j} + c\mathbf{k})$

$$x = x_1 + a\lambda,\ y = y_1 + b\lambda,\ z = z_1 + c\lambda$$

$$\lambda = \frac{x - x_1}{a} = \frac{y - y_1}{b} = \frac{z - z_1}{c}.$$

29. See text.

30.

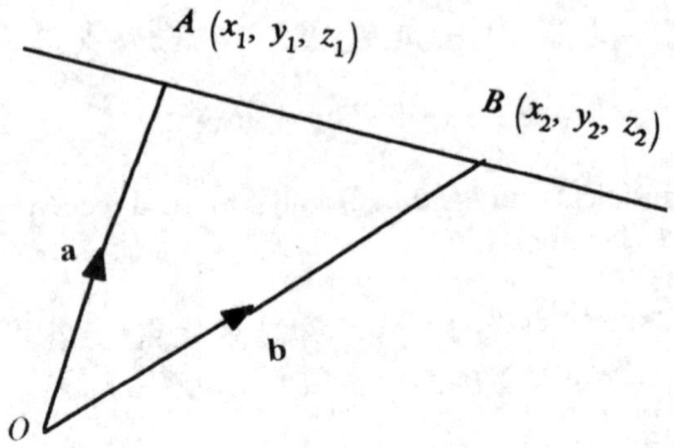

Fig. 8-II/14

$$\mathbf{r} = \mathbf{a} + \lambda(\mathbf{b} - \mathbf{a})$$

$$\mathbf{r} = (x_1\mathbf{i} + y_1\mathbf{j} + z_1\mathbf{k}) + \lambda\left[(x_2 - x_1)\mathbf{i} + (y_2 - y_1)\mathbf{j} + (z_2 - z_1)\mathbf{k}\right]$$

31. (i) $\dfrac{x+1}{1} = \dfrac{y-2}{2} = \dfrac{z+3}{3}$

$$\mathbf{r} = (-\mathbf{i} + 2\mathbf{j} - 3\mathbf{k}) + \lambda(\mathbf{i} + 2\mathbf{j} + 3\mathbf{k})$$

(ii) $\dfrac{x-3}{-3} = \dfrac{y+1}{5} = \dfrac{z-5}{7}$

$$\mathbf{r} = (3\mathbf{i} - \mathbf{j} + 5\mathbf{k}) + \lambda(-3\mathbf{i} + 5\mathbf{j} + 7\mathbf{k})$$

(iii) $\dfrac{x-2}{-1} = \dfrac{y-1}{-2} = \dfrac{z-4}{3}$

$$\mathbf{r} = (2\mathbf{i} + \mathbf{j} + 4\mathbf{k}) + \lambda(-\mathbf{i} - 2\mathbf{j} + 3\mathbf{k})$$

(iv) $\dfrac{x-1}{0} = \dfrac{y-2}{0} = \dfrac{z}{2}$

$$\mathbf{r} = \mathbf{i} + 2\mathbf{j} + \lambda\, 2\mathbf{k}$$

32. $l_1 : \mathbf{r} = (2\mathbf{i} - 3\mathbf{j} + 4\mathbf{k}) + \lambda(-\mathbf{i} - 3\mathbf{j} + 2\mathbf{k})$ ... (1)

$l_2 : \mathbf{r} = (3\mathbf{i} + 2\mathbf{k}) + \mu(\mathbf{i} - 2\mathbf{j} - 3\mathbf{k})$ ... (2)

From (1)

$x = 2 - \lambda, y = -3 - 3\lambda, z = 4 + 2\lambda$

$$\lambda = \frac{x-2}{-1} = \frac{y+3}{-3} = \frac{z-4}{2} \quad \text{... (3)}$$

From (2)

$x = 3 + \mu, y = -2\mu, \ z = 2 - 3\mu$

$$\mu = \frac{x-3}{1} = \frac{y}{-2} = \frac{z-2}{-3} \ \ldots (4)$$

Solving (3) and (4) for consistency

$$\frac{x-2}{-1} = \frac{y+3}{-3} \Rightarrow -3x + 6 = -y - 3 \Rightarrow \boxed{-3x + y = -9}$$

$$\frac{x-3}{1} = \frac{y}{-2} \Rightarrow -2x + 6 = y \Rightarrow \boxed{2x + y = 6}$$

Solving $-3x + y = -9 \quad \ldots (5)$

$2x + y = 6 \quad \ldots (6)$

$$5x = 15 \Rightarrow \boxed{x = 3}$$

$$-9 + y = -9 \Rightarrow \boxed{y = 0}$$

$$\lambda = \frac{3-2}{-1} = \frac{y+3}{-3} = \frac{z-4}{2} = -1 \Rightarrow \boxed{z = 2}$$

$$\mu = \frac{3-3}{1} = \frac{0}{-2} = \frac{2-2}{-3} \Rightarrow \boxed{\mu = 0}.$$

The lines intersect. The position vector of the point of intersection is

$\boxed{\overrightarrow{OP} = 3\mathbf{i} + 2\mathbf{k}}$

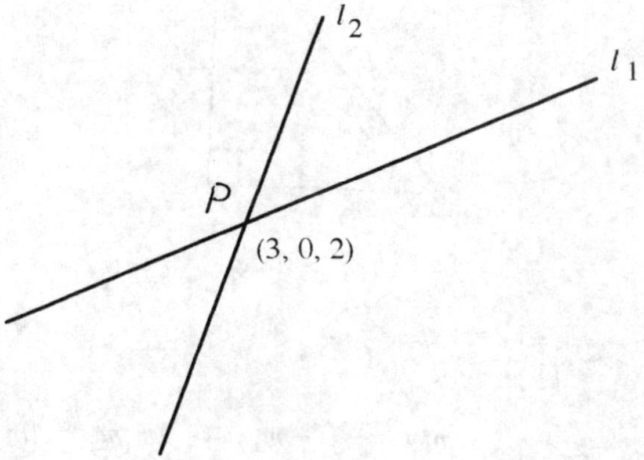

Fig. 8-II/15

33. $y = m_1 x + c_1$ ... (1) $\quad y = m_2 x + c_2$ ... (2)

The straight line equation (1) passes through the point $(0,\ c_1)$ and is parallel to m_1.

The vector equation of this line is

$$\mathbf{r} = \mathbf{j}c_1 + \lambda(\mathbf{i} + m_1\mathbf{j}) \quad \text{... (3)}$$

The straight line equation (2) passes through the point $(0,\ c_2)$ and is parallel to m_2.

The vector equation of this line is

$$\mathbf{r} = \mathbf{j}c_2 + \mu(\mathbf{i} + m_2\mathbf{j}) \quad \text{... (4)}$$

$$\mathbf{r} = \mathbf{j}c_2 + \mu(\mathbf{i} + m_2\mathbf{j})$$

$$\mathbf{r} = \mathbf{j}c_1 + \lambda(\mathbf{i} + m_1\mathbf{j}).$$

The angle between these lines can be found by taking the scalar product of the direction vectors.

$$(\mathbf{i} + m_2\mathbf{j}).(\mathbf{i} + m_1\mathbf{j}) = 1 + m_1 m_2$$

$$= \sqrt{1 + m_2^2}\,\sqrt{1 + m_1^2}\,\cos\theta$$

$$\cos\theta = \frac{1 + m_1 m_2}{\sqrt{1 + m_2^2}\,\sqrt{1 + m_1^2}}$$

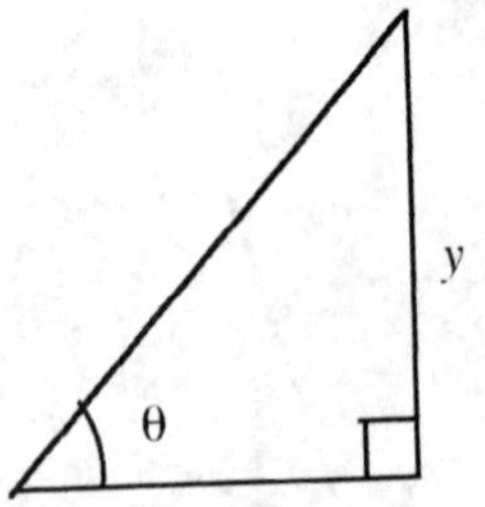

Fig. 8-II/16

$$y^2 = (1 + m_2^2)(1 + m_1^2) - (1 + m_1 m_2)^2$$

$$y^2 = 1 + m_2^2 + m_1^2 + m_1^2 m_2^2 - 1 - m_1^2 m_2^2 - 2m_1 m_2 = (m_1 - m_2)^2$$

$$y = m_1 - m_2$$

$$\tan\theta = \frac{m_1 - m_2}{1 + m_1 m_2}$$

$$\boxed{\theta = \tan^{-1}\frac{m_1 - m_2}{1 + m_1 m_2}}$$

34. The vector equation of the line $ax + by + c = 0$ is required in the form $\mathbf{r} = \mathbf{a} + \lambda\,(\mathbf{b} - \mathbf{a})$ where two points are considered.

When $x = 0, y = -\frac{c}{b}$, when $x = b$, $ab + by + c = 0, y = -\frac{ab}{b} - \frac{c}{b}$

the position vector is $-\mathbf{j}\frac{c}{b}$ and the vector equation

$\mathbf{r} = \mathbf{i}x + \mathbf{j}y = -\mathbf{j}\frac{c}{b} + \lambda(\mathbf{i}b - \mathbf{j}a)$ since the two points are $\left(0, \frac{c}{b}\right)$

and $\left(b, -a - \frac{c}{a}\right)$.

The direction vector of the general equation of the line is $\mathbf{i}b - \mathbf{j}a$

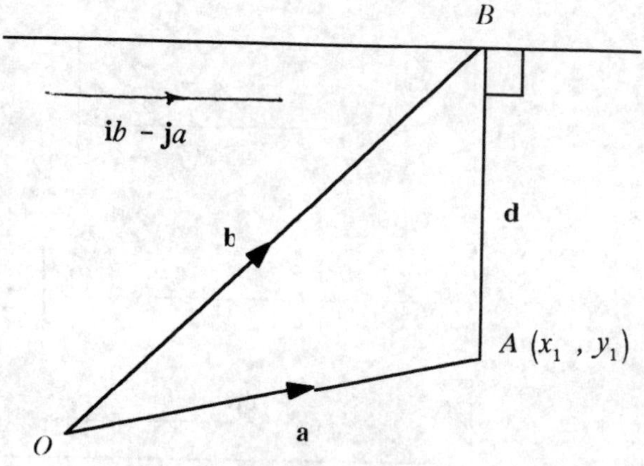

Fig. 8-II/17

$$\overrightarrow{OB} = \mathbf{b} = -\mathbf{j}\frac{c}{b} + \lambda(+\,\mathbf{i}b - \mathbf{j}a)$$

$$= \mathbf{i}b\lambda - \mathbf{j}\left(\frac{c}{b} + \lambda a\right)$$

$$\overrightarrow{BA} = \mathbf{a} - \mathbf{b} = \mathbf{i}x_1 + \mathbf{j}y_1 - \mathbf{i}b\lambda + \mathbf{j}\left(\frac{c}{b} + \lambda a\right)$$

$$= \mathbf{i}(x_1 - b\lambda) + \mathbf{j}\left(y_1 + \frac{c}{b} + \lambda a\right)$$

$\overrightarrow{BA}$ is perpendicular to l and l is parallel to $\mathbf{i}b - \mathbf{j}a$ therefore

$$(\mathbf{i}b - \mathbf{j}a) . \left[\mathbf{i}(x_1 - b\lambda) + \mathbf{j} \left(y_1 + \frac{c}{b} + a\lambda \right) \right]$$

$$b(x_1 - b\lambda) - a\left(y_1 + \frac{c}{b} + \lambda a \right) = 0$$

$$bx_1 - b^2\lambda - ay_1 - \frac{ac}{b} - \lambda a^2 = 0$$

$$(b^2 + a^2)\lambda = bx_1 - ay_1 - \frac{ac}{b}$$

$$\lambda = \frac{bx_1 - ay_1 - \frac{ac}{b}}{a^2 + b^2} \text{ at } B$$

therefore $$\overrightarrow{BA} = \mathbf{i} \left[x_1 - b . \frac{\left(bx_1 - ay_1 - \frac{ac}{b} \right)}{(a^2 + b^2)} \right] +$$

$$\mathbf{j} \left[y_1 + \frac{c}{b} + \frac{bx_1 - ay_1 - \frac{ac}{b}}{a^2 + b^2} . a \right]$$

$$= \mathbf{i} \left[\frac{x_1(a^2 + b^2) - b^2x_1 + aby_1 + ac}{a^2 + b^2} \right] +$$

$$\mathbf{j} \left[\frac{(a^2 + b^2)y_1 + \frac{c(a^2 + b^2)}{b} + abx_1 - a^2y_1 - \frac{a^2c}{b}}{a^2 + b^2} \right]$$

$$\left| \overrightarrow{BA} \right| = d = \frac{\sqrt{(a^2x_1 + aby_1 + ac)^2 + \left(b^2y_1 + \frac{c(a^2 + b^2)}{b} + abx_1 - \frac{a^2c}{b} \right)^2}}{a^2 + b^2}$$

$$= d = \frac{\sqrt{(a^2x_1 + aby_1 + ac)^2 + (b^2y_1 + cb + abx_1)^2}}{a^2 + b^2}$$

$$= \frac{\sqrt{a^2(ax_1 + by_1 + c)^2 + b^2(by_1 + c + ax_1)^2}}{a^2 + b^2}$$

$$= \pm \frac{(ax_1 + by_1 + c)}{\sqrt{a^2 + b^2}}$$

35.

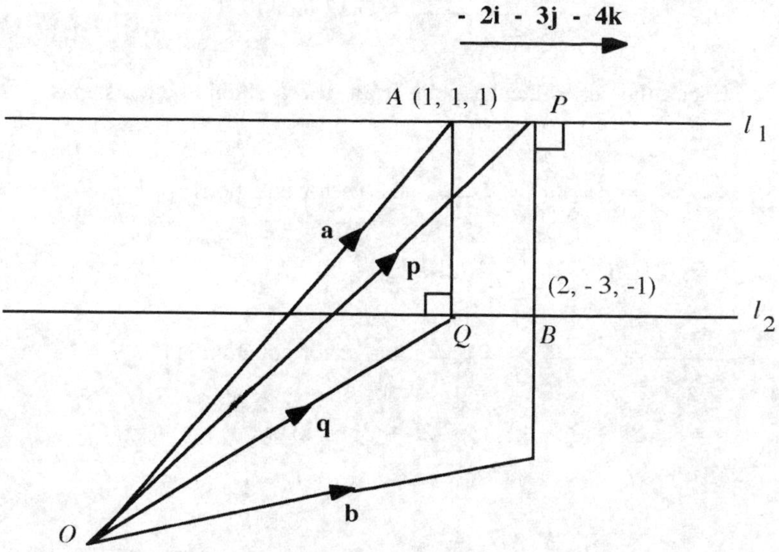

Fig. 8-II/18

$\overrightarrow{OP} = \mathbf{p} = \mathbf{i} + \mathbf{j} + \mathbf{k} + \lambda\,(-2\mathbf{i} - 3\mathbf{j} - 4\mathbf{k})$

$\quad = (1 - 2\lambda)\,\mathbf{i} + (1 - 3\lambda)\,\mathbf{j} + (1 - 4\lambda)\,\mathbf{k}.$

$\overrightarrow{PB} = \mathbf{b} - \mathbf{p} = 2\mathbf{i} - 3\mathbf{j} - \mathbf{k} - [(1 - 2\lambda)\,\mathbf{i} + (1 - 3\lambda)\,\mathbf{j} + (1 - 4\lambda)\,\mathbf{k}]$

$\quad = (2 - 1 + 2\lambda)\,\mathbf{i} + (-3 - 1 + 3\lambda)\,\mathbf{j} + (-1 - 1 + 4\lambda)\,\mathbf{k}$

$\quad = (1 + 2\lambda)\,\mathbf{i} + (-4 + 3\lambda)\,\mathbf{j} + (-2 + 4\lambda)\,\mathbf{k}$

$\overrightarrow{BP}$ is perpendicular to l_1, and l_1 is parallel to $-2\mathbf{i} - 3\mathbf{j} - 4\mathbf{k}$, the direction vector.

$(-2\mathbf{i} - 3\mathbf{j} - 4\mathbf{k}) \,.\, [(1 + 2\lambda)\,\mathbf{i} + (-4 + 3\lambda)\,\mathbf{j} + (-2 + 4\lambda)\,\mathbf{k}] = 0$

$-2\,(1 + 2\lambda) - 3\,(-4 + 3\lambda) - 4\,(-2 + 4\lambda) = 0$

$-2 - 4\lambda + 12 - 9\lambda + 8 - 16\lambda = 0$

$-29\lambda = -18$

$$\lambda = \frac{18}{29}$$

therefore $\overrightarrow{PB} = \left(1 + \frac{36}{29}\right)\mathbf{i} + \left(-4 + \frac{54}{29}\right)\mathbf{j} + \left(-2 + \frac{72}{29}\right)\mathbf{k}$

$$= \frac{65}{29}\mathbf{i} - \frac{62}{29}\mathbf{j} + \frac{14}{29}\mathbf{k}$$

$$\left|\overrightarrow{PB}\right| = \frac{\sqrt{65^2 + 62^2 + 14^2}}{29} = 3.13 \text{ units.}$$

Check the perpendicular point from A to l_2 should be the same.

36. $\frac{x-1}{2} = \frac{y+2}{3} = \frac{z-3}{1}$ the vector equations

$\mathbf{r} = (\mathbf{i} - 2\mathbf{j} + 3\mathbf{k}) + \lambda\,(2\mathbf{i} + 3\mathbf{j} + \mathbf{k}) : l_1$

$\frac{x+3}{2} = \frac{y-3}{3} = \frac{z+1}{1}$ the vector equation is

$\mathbf{r} = (-3\mathbf{i} + 3\mathbf{j} - \mathbf{k}) + \mu\,(2\mathbf{i} + 3\mathbf{j} + \mathbf{k}) : l_2$

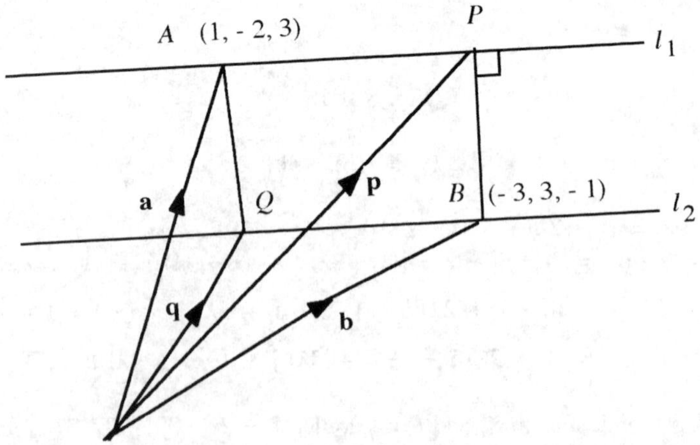

Fig. 8-II/19

$\overrightarrow{OP} = \mathbf{p} = \mathbf{i} - 2\mathbf{j} + 3\mathbf{k} + \lambda\,(2\mathbf{i} + 3\mathbf{j} + \mathbf{k})$

$= (1 + 2\lambda)\,\mathbf{i} + (-2 + 3\lambda)\,\mathbf{j} + (3 + \lambda)\,\mathbf{k}$

$\overrightarrow{PB} = \mathbf{b} - \mathbf{p} = -3\mathbf{i} + 3\mathbf{j} - \mathbf{k} - (1 + 2\lambda)\,\mathbf{i} - (-2 + 3\lambda)\,\mathbf{j} - (3 + \lambda)\,\mathbf{k}$

$= (-3 - 1 - 2\lambda)\,\mathbf{i} + (3 + 2 - 3\lambda)\,\mathbf{j} + (-1 - 3 - \lambda)\,\mathbf{k}$

$= (-4 - 2\lambda)\,\mathbf{i} + (5 - 3\lambda)\,\mathbf{j} + (-4 - \lambda)\,\mathbf{k}$

$\overrightarrow{PB}$ is perpendicular to l_1 and l_1 is parallel to **2i + 3j + k**, the direction vector,

therefore $2(-4 - 2\lambda) + 3(5 - 3\lambda) + (-4 - \lambda) = 0$

$$-8 - 4\lambda + 15 - 9\lambda - 4 - \lambda = 0$$

$$-14\lambda + 3 = 0$$

$$\lambda = \frac{3}{14}$$

therefore $\overrightarrow{PB} = \left(-4 - \frac{3}{7}\right)\mathbf{i} + \left(5 - \frac{9}{14}\right)\mathbf{j} + \left(-4 - \frac{3}{14}\right)\mathbf{k}$

$$= -4.43\mathbf{i} + 4.36\mathbf{j} - 4.21\mathbf{k}$$

$$\left|\overrightarrow{PB}\right| = \sqrt{(4.43)^2 + (4.36)^2 + (4.21)^2} = 7.51 \text{ units.}$$

Repeat the procedure for the perpendicular distance from A to l_2.

SOLUTION 5

1. $\mathbf{r} \cdot \mathbf{n} = d$

$\mathbf{r} = x\mathbf{i} + y\mathbf{j} + z\mathbf{k}$ and $\mathbf{n} = a\mathbf{i} + b\mathbf{j} + c\mathbf{k}$

$a : b : c$ are the direction ratios of a normal to the plane.

$(x\mathbf{i} + y\mathbf{j} + z\mathbf{k}) \cdot (2\mathbf{i} + 3\mathbf{j} + 4\mathbf{k}) = d$ and since $A\ (-1, -2, -3)$ is a point on the plane.

$(-\mathbf{i} - 2\mathbf{j} - 3\mathbf{k}) \cdot (2\mathbf{i} + 3\mathbf{j} + 4\mathbf{k}) = -2 - 6 - 12 = -20.$

The equation of the plane is

$\boxed{\mathbf{r} \cdot \mathbf{n} = -20}$ the vector form of the plane the negative sign indicates that the point and the origin are on the same side of the plane.

$(x\mathbf{i} + y\mathbf{j} + z\mathbf{k}) \cdot (2\mathbf{i} + 3\mathbf{j} + 4\mathbf{k}) = -20$

$\boxed{2x + 3y + 4z + 20 = 0}$ the cartesian form of the plane. The general form for the equation of the plane.

Alternatively

If $P\ (x, y, z)$ is any point on the plane then $\overrightarrow{PA}$ and $2\mathbf{i} + 3\mathbf{j} + 4\mathbf{k}$ are orthogonal.

$$\left[(x + 1)\ (y + 2)\ (z + 3)\right] \cdot \begin{pmatrix} 2 \\ 3 \\ 4 \end{pmatrix} = 0$$

$2x + 2 + 3y + 6 + 4z + 12 = 0$

$$\boxed{2x + 3y + 4z + 20 = 0}$$

2. If $P\ (x, y, z)$ is any point on the plane then $\overrightarrow{PA}$ and $l\mathbf{i} + m\mathbf{j} + n\mathbf{k}$ are orthogonal.

$$\left[(x-2)\ (y+3)\ (z-4)\right] . \begin{pmatrix} l \\ m \\ n \end{pmatrix} = 0$$

$$xl - 2l + ym + 3m + nz - 4n = 0$$

$\boxed{lx + my + nz - 2l + 3m - 4n = 0}$ the cartesian general form

or

$\boxed{\mathbf{r} . \mathbf{n} = 2l - 3m + 4n}$ the vector form where $\mathbf{r} = x\mathbf{i} + y\mathbf{j} + z\mathbf{k}$ and

$\mathbf{n} = l\,\mathbf{i} + m\mathbf{j} + n\mathbf{k}$.

3. The cartesian equation of the plane is $ax + by + cz = d$ where $a : b : c$ are the direction ratios of the line which is perpendicular to the plane.

Since $A\ (-3, 4, 7)$, $B\ (0, -2, 5)$ and $C\ (2, 0, -3)$ lie on the plane, they must satisfy the equations

$$\begin{aligned} -3a + 4b + 7c &= d \quad \ldots (1) \\ -2b + 5c &= d \quad \ldots (2) \\ 2a - 3c &= d \quad \ldots (3) \end{aligned}$$

Solving these equations in terms of d we have

(1)	$-3a + 4b + 7c$	$= d$	
(2) × 2	$-4b + 10c$	$= 2d$	
(1) + (2) × 2	$-3a + 17c$	$= 3d$	... (4)
	$2a - 3c$	$= d$	... (3)
(4) × 2	$-6a + 34c$	$= 6d$	... (5)
(3) × 3	$6a - 9c$	$= 3d$	... (6)
(5) + (6)	$25c$	$= 9d$	

$$\boxed{c = \frac{9d}{25}} \quad \ldots (7)$$

From (3) $2a - \frac{3 \times 9d}{25} = d$

$$2a = d + \frac{27}{25}d = \frac{52d}{25}$$

$$\boxed{a = \frac{26}{25}d} \quad \ldots (8)$$

substituting (7) and (8) in (1)

$$-3a + 4b + 7c = d$$

$$-\frac{78}{25}d + 4b + \frac{63}{25}d = d$$

$$4b = d - \frac{63}{25}d + \frac{78}{25}d$$

$$\boxed{b = \frac{10}{25}d}$$

$$\frac{26}{25}dx + \frac{10}{25}dy + \frac{9d}{25}z = d.$$

$$\boxed{26x + 10y + 9z = 25}$$

Alternatively

Since $\overrightarrow{AB}$ and $\overrightarrow{AC}$ are two vectors in the planes, $\overrightarrow{AB} \times \overrightarrow{AC}$ is normal to the plane. (See next chapter for cross products.)

$$\overrightarrow{AB} = \begin{pmatrix} 3 \\ -6 \\ -2 \end{pmatrix}, \quad \overrightarrow{AC} = \begin{pmatrix} 5 \\ -4 \\ -10 \end{pmatrix},$$

$$\overrightarrow{AB} \times \overrightarrow{AC} = \begin{vmatrix} \mathbf{i} & \mathbf{j} & \mathbf{k} \\ 3 & -6 & -2 \\ 5 & -4 & -10 \end{vmatrix} = \mathbf{i}\begin{vmatrix} -6 & -2 \\ -4 & -10 \end{vmatrix} - \mathbf{j}\begin{vmatrix} 3 & -2 \\ 5 & -10 \end{vmatrix} + \mathbf{k}\begin{vmatrix} 3 & -6 \\ 5 & -4 \end{vmatrix}$$

$$= 52\mathbf{i} + 20\mathbf{j} + 18\mathbf{k} = \begin{pmatrix} 52 \\ 20 \\ 18 \end{pmatrix}$$

If $P\ (x, y, z)$ is any point on the plane, then $\overrightarrow{AP}$ and $\overrightarrow{AB} \times \overrightarrow{AC}$ are

orthogonal, that is $\overrightarrow{AP} \cdot \left(\overrightarrow{AB} \times \overrightarrow{AC}\right) = 0$

$$\left[(x + 3)\ (y - 4)\ (z - 7)\right] \begin{pmatrix} 52 \\ 20 \\ 18 \end{pmatrix} = 0$$

$$52x + 156 + 20y - 80 + 18z - 126 = 0$$

$$52x + 20y + 18z = 50$$

$$\boxed{26x + 10y + 9z = 25}$$

4. $ax + by + cz = d$

$A\ (0, 0, 0)$ $\quad d = 0$

$B\ (1, -2, -3)$ $\quad a - 2b - 3c = 0 \quad \dots (1)$

$C\ (-2, 1, 2)$ $\quad -2a + b + 2c = 0 \quad \dots (2)$

Solving (1) and (2)

$$\begin{array}{ll} (1) & a - 2b - 3c = 0 \\ (2) \times 2 & -4a + 2b + 4c = 0 \\ \hline & -3a + c = 0 \\ & c = 3a \end{array}$$

From (2) $b = 2a - 2c = 2a - 6a = -4a.$

$$ax - 4ay + 3az = 0$$

$$\boxed{x - 4y + 3z = 0}$$

Alternatively

Since $\overrightarrow{AB}$ and $\overrightarrow{AC}$ are two vectors in the plane, $\overrightarrow{AB} \times \overrightarrow{AC}$ is normal to the plane.

$$\overrightarrow{AB} = \begin{pmatrix} 1 \\ -2 \\ -3 \end{pmatrix}, \qquad \overrightarrow{AC} = \begin{pmatrix} -2 \\ 1 \\ 2 \end{pmatrix}$$

$$\overrightarrow{AB} \times \overrightarrow{AC} = \begin{vmatrix} \mathbf{i} & \mathbf{j} & \mathbf{k} \\ 1 & -2 & -3 \\ -2 & 1 & 2 \end{vmatrix}$$

$$= \mathbf{i}\,(-4 + 3) - \mathbf{j}\,(2 - 6) + \mathbf{k}\,(1 - 4)$$

$$= -\mathbf{i} + 4\mathbf{j} - 3\mathbf{k} = \begin{pmatrix} -1 \\ 4 \\ -3 \end{pmatrix}.$$

If $P\,(x, y, z)$ is any point on the plane, then $\overrightarrow{AP}$ and $\overrightarrow{AB} \times \overrightarrow{AC}$ are orthogonal, that is

$$\overrightarrow{AP} \cdot \left(\overrightarrow{AB} \times \overrightarrow{AC}\right) = 0$$

$$(x\mathbf{i} + y\mathbf{j} + z\mathbf{k}) \cdot (-\mathbf{i} + 4\mathbf{j} - 3\mathbf{k}) = 0$$

$$-x + 4y - 3z = 0$$

or $\boxed{x - 4y + 3z = 0}$.

5. (i) If $P\,(x, y, z)$ is any point in the plane then $\overrightarrow{PA}$ and $(\mathbf{i} - 2\mathbf{j} + 3\mathbf{k})$ are orthogonal.

$$\overrightarrow{PA} = x\mathbf{i} + y\,\mathbf{j} + (z - 1)\mathbf{k}$$

$$[x\mathbf{i} + y\mathbf{j} + (z - 1)\mathbf{k}] \cdot (\mathbf{i} - 2\mathbf{j} + 3\mathbf{k}) = 0$$

$x - 2y + 3(z - 1) = 0$

$\boxed{x - 2y + 3z = 3}$

or $\quad \mathbf{r} \cdot (\mathbf{i} - 2\mathbf{j} + 3\mathbf{k}) = 3$ where $\mathbf{n} = (\mathbf{i} - 2\mathbf{j} + 3\mathbf{k})$

the positive sign indicate that the point and the origin are on opposite sides of the plane.

(ii) $\overrightarrow{PB} = (x - 1)\mathbf{i} + y\mathbf{j} + z\mathbf{k}$ and $\overrightarrow{PB} \cdot (4\mathbf{i} - 5\mathbf{j} + 6\mathbf{k}) = 0$

$[(x - 1)\mathbf{i} + y\mathbf{j} + z\mathbf{k}].(4\mathbf{i} - 5\mathbf{j} + 6\mathbf{k})$

$4(x - 1) - 5y + 6z = 0$

$\boxed{4x - 5y + 6z = 4}$

or $\mathbf{r} \cdot \mathbf{n} = 4$

where $\mathbf{n} = 4\mathbf{i} - 5\mathbf{j} + 6\mathbf{k}$.

(iii) $\overrightarrow{PC} = (x - 1)\mathbf{i} + (y - 3)\mathbf{j} + z\mathbf{k}$

$\overrightarrow{PC} \cdot (-\mathbf{i} + 2\mathbf{j} + 4\mathbf{k}) = 0$

$[(x - 1)\mathbf{i} + (y - 3)\mathbf{j} + z\mathbf{k}].(-\mathbf{i} + 2\mathbf{j} + 4\mathbf{k}) = 0$

$-(x - 1) + 2(y - 3) + 4z = 0$

$-x + 2y + 4z + 1 - 6 = 0$

$\boxed{x - 2y - 4z = -5}$

or $\mathbf{r} \cdot \mathbf{n} = -5$

where $\mathbf{n} = -\mathbf{i} + 2\mathbf{j} + 4\mathbf{k}$.

6. (i) $ax + by + cz = d$

$A\ (1, 1, 0) \qquad a + b = d \ \ldots (1)$

$B\ (2, -2, 3) \qquad 2a - 2b + 3c = d \ \ldots (2)$

$C\ (0, 0, 2) \qquad 2c = d \ \ldots (3)$

From (3) $\boxed{c = \frac{d}{2}}$

eliminating b from (1) and (2)

(1) × 2 $\quad 2a + 2b = 2d$

$2a - 2b + 3c = d$

$4a + 3c = 3d$

$4a + 3\left(\frac{d}{2}\right) = 3d$

$4a = \frac{3d}{2}$

$\boxed{a = \frac{3d}{8}}$

From (1) $\quad \frac{3d}{8} + b = d \Rightarrow \boxed{b = \frac{5d}{8}}$

$\frac{3d}{8}x + \frac{5d}{8}y + \frac{d}{2}z = d$

$\frac{3}{8}x + \frac{5}{8}y + \frac{1}{2}z = 1$

$3x + 5y + 4z = 8$

$\mathbf{r} \cdot \mathbf{n} = 8$, $\boxed{\mathbf{r} \cdot (3\mathbf{i} + 5\mathbf{j} + 4\mathbf{k}) = 8}$

where $\mathbf{n} = 3\mathbf{i} - 5\mathbf{j} - 4\mathbf{k}$

(ii) P (0, 1, 0) $\quad \boxed{b = d}$

Q (− 1, 3, − 4) $\quad -a + 3b - 4c = d$ ... (1)

R (1, 0, 2) $\quad a + 2c = d$ ... (2)

eliminating a from (1) and (2)

$3b - 2c = 2d$

$3d - 2c = 2d$

$-2c = -d$

$\boxed{c = \frac{d}{2}}$

$a = d - d = 0 \Rightarrow a = 0$

$dy + \frac{d}{2}z = d$

$y + \frac{1}{2}z = 1$

$\boxed{2y + z = 2}$

(iii) $D\,(-1, -2, -3)$ $\quad -a - 2b - 3c = d$ ... (1)

$E\,(0, 3, 0)$ $\quad 3b = d \Rightarrow \boxed{b = \frac{d}{3}}$

$F\,(1, 2, 4)$ $\quad a + 2b + 4c = d$ ... (2)

adding (1) and (2)

$\boxed{c = 2d}$

$-a = d + 2b + 3c = d + \frac{2d}{3} + 3(2d)$

$-a = \frac{3d + 2d + 18d}{3}$

$\boxed{a = \frac{-23d}{3}}$

$\frac{-23d}{3}x + \frac{d}{3}y + 2dz = d$

$-23x + y + 6z = 3$

$\boxed{23x - y - 6z = -3}$

7. The position vector of the point of intersection will satisfy both the equation of the line and that of the plane.

$\mathbf{r}_1 = (2\mathbf{i} - 3\mathbf{j} + \mathbf{k}) + \lambda\,(-3\mathbf{i} + \mathbf{j} - 3\mathbf{k})$ for the line

$\mathbf{r}_1 \,.\, (\mathbf{i} + \mathbf{j} + \mathbf{k}) = 3$ for the plane

therefore $\left[(2 - 3\lambda)\mathbf{i} + (-3 + \lambda)\mathbf{j} + (1 - 3\lambda)\mathbf{k}\right].\left(\mathbf{i} + \mathbf{j} + \mathbf{k}\right) = 3$

$2 - 3\lambda + (-3 + \lambda) + (1 - 3\lambda) = 3$

$2 - 3\lambda - 3 + \lambda + 1 - 3\lambda = 3$

$-5\lambda = 3$

$$\lambda = -\frac{3}{5}.$$

Thus the position vector is

$$\mathbf{r}_1 = \left[2 - 3\left(-\frac{3}{5}\right)\right]\mathbf{i} + \left(-3 - \frac{3}{5}\right)\mathbf{j} + \left[1 - 3\left(-\frac{3}{5}\right)\right]\mathbf{k}$$

$$\boxed{\mathbf{r}_1 = \frac{19}{5}\mathbf{i} - \frac{18}{5}\mathbf{j} + \frac{14}{5}\mathbf{k}}$$

8. $\mathbf{r}_1 = (-1 + 2t)\mathbf{i} + (4 - t)\mathbf{j} + (-5 - t)\mathbf{k}$

$\left[(-1 + 2t)\mathbf{i} + (4 - t)\mathbf{j} + (-5 - t)\mathbf{k}\right].\left(2\mathbf{i} - 2\mathbf{j} + 4\mathbf{k}\right) = 5$

$2(-1 + 2t) + (4 - t)(-2) + (-5 - t)4 = 5$

$-2 + 4t - 8 + 2t - 20 - 4t = 5$

$2t = 35$

$$t = \frac{35}{2}$$

$\mathbf{r}_1 = (-1 + 35)\,\mathbf{i} + (4 - 17.5)\,\mathbf{j} + (-5 - 17.5)\,\mathbf{k}$

$$\boxed{\mathbf{r}_1 = 34\mathbf{i} - 13.5\mathbf{j} - 22.5\mathbf{k}}$$

9. $\mathbf{r}_1 = (1 + 2\mu)\,\mathbf{i} + (1 - 3\mu)\,\mathbf{j} + (1 + 4\mu)\,\mathbf{k}$

$\mathbf{r}_1 \,.\, (2\mathbf{i} + 5\mathbf{j} - 7\mathbf{k}) = 2$

$2(1 + 2\mu) + 5(1 - 3\mu) - 7(1 + 4\mu) = 2$

$2 + 4\mu + 5 - 15\mu - 7 - 28\mu = 2$

$-39\mu = 2$

$$\mu = -\frac{2}{39}$$

$$\mathbf{r}_1 = \left(1 - \frac{4}{39}\right)\mathbf{i} + \left(1 + \frac{6}{39}\right)\mathbf{j} + \left(1 - \frac{8}{39}\right)\mathbf{k}$$

$$\boxed{\mathbf{r}_1 = \frac{35}{39}\mathbf{i} + \frac{45}{39}\mathbf{j} + \frac{31}{39}\mathbf{k}}$$

10. $\dfrac{x + 1}{2} = \dfrac{y - 3}{3} = \dfrac{z + 2}{4} = \lambda$

$x = 2\lambda - 1$

$y = 3\lambda + 3$

$z = 4\lambda - 2$

$\mathbf{r} = (-\mathbf{i} + 3\mathbf{j} - 2\mathbf{k}) + \lambda(2\mathbf{i} + 3\mathbf{j} + 4\mathbf{k})$

$\mathbf{r}_1 = (-1 + 2\lambda)\,\mathbf{i} + (3\lambda + 3)\,\mathbf{j} + (4\lambda - 2)\,\mathbf{k}$

$\mathbf{r}_1 \,.\, (\mathbf{i} + \mathbf{j} + 2\mathbf{k}) = 4$

$-1 + 2\lambda + 3\lambda + 3 + 8\lambda - 4 = 4$

$13\lambda = 6$

$$\lambda = \frac{6}{13}$$

$$\mathbf{r}_1 = \left(-1 + \frac{12}{13}\right)\mathbf{i} + \left(\frac{18}{13} + 3\right)\mathbf{j} + \left(\frac{24}{13} - 2\right)\mathbf{k}$$

$$\boxed{\mathbf{r}_1 = -\frac{1}{13}\mathbf{i} + \frac{57}{13}\mathbf{j} - \frac{2}{13}\mathbf{k}}$$

11. $x = y = z = \lambda \quad \mathbf{r}_1 = \lambda(\mathbf{i} + \mathbf{j} + \mathbf{k})$

$\mathbf{r}_1 \,.\, (\mathbf{i} + 2\mathbf{j} + 3\mathbf{k}) = 7$

$\lambda + 2\lambda + 3\lambda = 7$

$$\lambda = \frac{7}{6}$$

$$\boxed{\mathbf{r}_1 = \frac{7}{6}(\mathbf{i} + \mathbf{j} + \mathbf{k})}$$

12. $\sin\theta = \dfrac{\mathbf{b}\cdot\hat{\mathbf{n}}}{|\mathbf{b}|} = \dfrac{(-2\mathbf{i}+5\mathbf{j}+\mathbf{k})\cdot(-2\mathbf{i}-\mathbf{j}+\mathbf{k})}{\sqrt{30}\sqrt{6}} = \dfrac{4-5+1}{\sqrt{30}\sqrt{6}} = 0$

where $\mathbf{b} = -2\mathbf{i}+5\mathbf{j}+\mathbf{k}$, $|\mathbf{b}| = \sqrt{4+25+1} = \sqrt{30}$

$$\hat{\mathbf{n}} = \frac{-2\mathbf{i}-\mathbf{j}+\mathbf{k}}{\sqrt{2^2+1+1}}$$

$\theta = 0$, therefore the line and the plane are parallel.

13. $\dfrac{\mathbf{b}\cdot\hat{\mathbf{n}}}{|\mathbf{b}|} = \dfrac{(\mathbf{i}-7\mathbf{j}+4\mathbf{k})\cdot(3\mathbf{i}+\mathbf{j}+\mathbf{k})}{\sqrt{1+7^2+4^2}\sqrt{3^2+1+1}} = 0 = \sin\theta$

the line and the plane are parallel.

Alternatively.
The line is parallel to $\mathbf{i}-7\mathbf{j}+4\mathbf{k}$, the direction vector, and the plane is perpendicular to $3\mathbf{i}+\mathbf{j}+\mathbf{k}$. If we can show that the dot product is zero, then the line is parallel to the plane.

$(\mathbf{i}-7\mathbf{j}+4\mathbf{k})\cdot(3\mathbf{i}+\mathbf{j}+\mathbf{k}) = 3-7+4 = 0.$

Thus the line and plane are both perpendicular to $3\mathbf{i}+\mathbf{j}+\mathbf{k}$ and must therefore be parallel to each other.

14. The line is parallel to direction vector, $-5\mathbf{i}+7\mathbf{j}-8\mathbf{k}$ and the plane is perpendicular to $-2\mathbf{i}+2\mathbf{j}+3\mathbf{k}$.

The dot product, $(-5\mathbf{i}+7\mathbf{j}-8\mathbf{k})\cdot(-2\mathbf{i}+2\mathbf{j}+3\mathbf{k}) = 10+14-24 = 0.$ Therefore the line and the plane are parallel. The distance between the line and the plane is given as follows.
Consider any point on the line, for $t = 1$, $\mathbf{r} = \mathbf{i}-3\mathbf{j}+4\mathbf{k}-5\mathbf{i}+7\mathbf{j}-8\mathbf{k}$
$\mathbf{r} = -4\mathbf{i}+4\mathbf{j}-4\mathbf{k}.$

The perpendicular distance from the point $A\ (-4, 4, -4)$ to the plane is found by applying the formula, the perpendicular distance of the point

$A\ (x_1, y_1, z_1)$ to the plane $ax+by+cz = d$ is $\left|\dfrac{ax_1+by_1+cz_1-d}{\sqrt{a^2+b^2+c^2}}\right|$.

The plane is $\mathbf{r}\cdot(-2\mathbf{i}+2\mathbf{j}+3\mathbf{k}) = 1$ or $-2x+2y+3z = 1$, so the perpendicular distance from $A\ (-4, 4, -4)$ to the plane is

$$\left|\frac{(-2)(-4)+2(4)+(3)(-4)-1}{\sqrt{(-2)^2+2^2+3^2}}\right| = \frac{3}{\sqrt{17}}\cdot\frac{\sqrt{17}}{\sqrt{17}} = \boxed{\frac{3\sqrt{17}}{17}}.$$

15. (i) $(-3\mathbf{i} + 4\mathbf{j} - 5\mathbf{k}) \cdot (2\mathbf{i} - 3\mathbf{j} + \mathbf{k}) = -6 - 12 - 5 = -23$
the line and the plane are not parallel.

(ii) $(2\mathbf{i} - 3\mathbf{j} + \mathbf{k}) \cdot (2\mathbf{i} - 3\mathbf{j} + \mathbf{k}) = 4 + 9 + 1 = 14$
the line and the plane are not parallel.

(iii) $(3\mathbf{i} + 5\mathbf{j} + 9\mathbf{k}) \cdot (2\mathbf{i} - 3\mathbf{j} + \mathbf{k}) = 6 - 15 + 9 = 0$
the line and the plane are parallel.

Therefore (i) and (ii) intersect with the plane.

For (i) $\sin\theta = \dfrac{\mathbf{b} \cdot \hat{\mathbf{n}}}{|\mathbf{b}|}$

$\mathbf{b} = (-3\mathbf{i} + 4\mathbf{j} - 5\mathbf{k}), \quad |\mathbf{b}| = \sqrt{(-3)^2 + 4^2 + (-5)^2} = \sqrt{50}$

$\mathbf{n} = 2\mathbf{i} - 3\mathbf{j} + \mathbf{k}$

$$\hat{\mathbf{n}} = \frac{2}{\sqrt{14}}\mathbf{i} - \frac{3}{\sqrt{14}}\mathbf{j} + \frac{1}{\sqrt{14}}\mathbf{k}$$

$$\sin\theta = \frac{(-3\mathbf{i} + 4\mathbf{j} - 5\mathbf{k}) \cdot \left(\dfrac{2}{\sqrt{14}}\mathbf{i} - \dfrac{3}{\sqrt{14}}\mathbf{j} + \dfrac{1}{\sqrt{14}}\mathbf{k}\right)}{\sqrt{50}}$$

$$= \frac{-\dfrac{3 \times 2}{\sqrt{14}} - \dfrac{12}{\sqrt{14}} - \dfrac{5}{\sqrt{14}}}{\sqrt{50}} = -\frac{23}{\sqrt{14}\sqrt{50}}$$

$\Rightarrow \theta = 60.4^\circ$

(ii) $\sin\theta = \dfrac{\mathbf{b} \cdot \hat{\mathbf{n}}}{|\mathbf{b}|}$

$\mathbf{b} = 2\mathbf{i} - 3\mathbf{j} + \mathbf{k}, \quad |\mathbf{b}| = \sqrt{4 + 9 + 1} = \sqrt{14}$

$\mathbf{n} = 2\mathbf{i} - 3\mathbf{j} + \mathbf{k}, \ \hat{\mathbf{n}} = \dfrac{2}{\sqrt{14}}\mathbf{i} - \dfrac{3}{\sqrt{14}}\mathbf{j} + \dfrac{1}{\sqrt{14}}\mathbf{k}$

$$\sin\theta = \frac{\dfrac{4}{\sqrt{14}} + \dfrac{9}{\sqrt{14}} + \dfrac{1}{\sqrt{14}}}{\sqrt{14}} = 1$$

$\theta = 90^\circ$.

16. (i) $\mathbf{r} = \mathbf{i} + \mathbf{j} + \mathbf{k} + \lambda\,(2\mathbf{i} - \mathbf{j} + 3\mathbf{k}) + s\,(-2\mathbf{i} + 3\mathbf{j} - 7\mathbf{k})$

$\mathbf{r} = \mathbf{i}\,(1 + 2\lambda - 2s) + \mathbf{j}\,(1 - \lambda + 3s) + \mathbf{k}\,(1 + 3\lambda - 7s)$

the parametric vector equation of the plane.

If $P(x, y, z)$ is any point on this plane then

$x = 1 + 2\lambda - 2s$ ... (1)

$y = 1 - \lambda + 3s$ ... (2)

$z = 1 + 3\lambda - 7s$ ... (3).

Eliminating λ and s from (1), (2) and (3) we have:
From (1) and (2)

$x = 1 + 2\lambda - 2s$

$2y = 2 - 2\lambda + 6s$

$x + 2y = 3 + 4s$ ... (4)

From (2) and (3)

$3y = 3 - 3\lambda + 9s$

$z = 1 + 3\lambda - 7s$

$3y + z = 4 + 2s$ ... (5)

Eliminating s from (4) and (5)

$x + 2y = 3 + 4s$ ... (4)

$6y + 2z = 8 + 4s$ ... (5)

(5) − (4)
$-x + 4y + 2z = 5$

$$\boxed{\mathbf{r} \cdot (-\mathbf{i} + 4\mathbf{j} + 2\mathbf{k}) = 5}$$

(ii) $\mathbf{r} = 2\mathbf{j} - 3\mathbf{k} + \mu\,(-3\mathbf{i} + 4\mathbf{j} - \mathbf{k}) + v\,(2\mathbf{i} + 5\mathbf{j} - 5\mathbf{k})$

$\mathbf{r} = \mathbf{i}\,(-3\mu + 2v) + \mathbf{j}\,(2 + 4\mu + 5v) + \mathbf{k}\,(-3 - \mu - 5v)$.

If $P(x, y, z)$ is any point on this plane then

$x = -3\mu + 2v$ ... (1)

$y = 2 + 4\mu + 5v$ ... (2)

$z = -3 - \mu - 5v$ ... (3)

Eliminating v from (1) and (2)

$$5x = -15\mu + 10v$$
$$-2y = -4 - 8\mu - 10v$$
$$\overline{5x - 2y = -4 - 23\mu \ldots (4)}$$

Eliminating v from (2) and (3)

$y + z = -1 + 3\mu \ldots (5)$

Eliminating μ from (4) and (5)

$$15x - 6y = -12 - 69\mu$$
$$23y + 23z = -23 + 69\mu$$
$$\overline{15x + 17y + 23z = -35}$$

$$\boxed{\mathbf{r} \cdot (15\mathbf{i} + 17\mathbf{j} + 23\mathbf{k}) = -35}$$

(iii) $\mathbf{r} = (1 - t - s)(2\mathbf{i} - 3\mathbf{j} - \mathbf{k}) + t(-3\mathbf{i} + 4\mathbf{j} + \mathbf{k}) + s(3\mathbf{j} - 5\mathbf{k})$

$\mathbf{r} = \mathbf{i}(2 - 2t - 2s - 3t) + \mathbf{j}(-3 + 3t + 3s + 4t - 3s) +$

$\quad \mathbf{k}(-1 + t + s + t - 5s).$

If $P(x, y, z)$ is any point on this plane then $x = 2 - 5t - 2s \quad \ldots (1)$

$y = -3 + 7t \quad \ldots (2)$

$z = -1 + 2t - 4s \quad \ldots (3)$

Eliminating t from (1) and (2)

(1) × (7)... $7x = 14 - 35t - 14s$

(2) × (5)... $5y = -15 + 35t$

$$\overline{5y + 7x = -1 - 14s \ldots (4)}$$

Eliminating t from (2) and (3)

(2) × − 2... $-2y = 6 - 14t$

(3) × 7... $7z = -7 + 14t - 28s$

$$\overline{7z - 2y = -1 - 28s \ldots (5)}$$

Eliminating s from (4) and (5)

(4) × − 2... $-10y - 14x = 2 + 28s$

(5) $7z - 2y = -1 - 28s$

$$\overline{-14x - 12y + 7z = 1}$$

or $14x + 12y - 7z = -1$

$$\boxed{\mathbf{r} \cdot (14\mathbf{i} + 12\mathbf{j} - 7\mathbf{k}) = -1}$$

17. The Cartesian forms.

(i) $\mathbf{r} \cdot (2\mathbf{i} + 3\mathbf{j} + 4\mathbf{k}) = 3$

$$(x\mathbf{i} + y\mathbf{j} + z\mathbf{k}) \cdot (2\mathbf{i} + 3\mathbf{j} + 4\mathbf{k}) = 3$$

$$\boxed{2x + 3y + 4z = 3}$$

(ii) $\mathbf{r} \cdot (-3\mathbf{i} + 2\mathbf{j} - \mathbf{k}) = 1$

$$(x\mathbf{i} + y\mathbf{j} + z\mathbf{k}) \cdot (-3\mathbf{i} + 2\mathbf{j} - \mathbf{k}) = 1$$

$$-3x + 2y - z = 1$$

$$\boxed{3x - 2y + z = -1}$$

(iii) $\mathbf{r} \cdot (\mathbf{i} - 2\mathbf{j} + 3\mathbf{k}) = 0$

$$\boxed{x - 2y + 3z = 0}$$

18. (i) The vector equation of the plane in parametric form is given

$$\mathbf{r} = (2\mathbf{i} - 3\mathbf{j} + 5\mathbf{k}) + \lambda (3\mathbf{j} - 4\mathbf{k}) + \mu (\mathbf{i} + 3\mathbf{k})$$

$$x = 2 + \mu \quad \ldots (1)$$
$$y = -3 + 3\lambda \quad \ldots (2)$$
$$z = 5 - 4\lambda + 3\mu \quad \ldots (3)$$

Substitute μ from (1) into (3)

$$z = 5 - 4\lambda + 3(x - 2) = 5 - 4\lambda + 3x - 6$$
$$z - 3x + 1 = -4\lambda \quad \ldots (4)$$

Substitute λ from (2) into (4)

$$z - 3x + 1 = -\frac{4}{3}(y + 3)$$

$$z - 3x + 1 + \frac{4}{3}y + 4 = 0$$

$$-3x + \frac{4}{3}y + z = -5$$

$9x - 4y - 3z = 15$

$$\boxed{\mathbf{r} \cdot (9\mathbf{i} - 4\mathbf{j} - 3\mathbf{k}) = 15}$$

(ii) The vector equation of the plane in parametric form is given

$\mathbf{r} = (2\mathbf{i} - 3\mathbf{k}) + \lambda\,(2\mathbf{i} - 3\mathbf{j}) + \mu\,(3\mathbf{i} - \mathbf{j} - \mathbf{k})$

$x = 2 + 2\lambda + 3\mu$ ... (1)

$y = -3\lambda - \mu$ ... (2)

$z = -3 - \mu$ ... (3)

Substitute μ from (3) into (1) and (2)

$x = 2 + 2\lambda + 3(-3 - z)$ ... (4)

$y = -3\lambda + z + 3$ ... (5)

From (4) $x + 3z + 7 = 2\lambda$ ... (6)

From (5) $y - z - 3 = -3\lambda$ ... (7)

Substitute λ from (7) into (6)

$$x + 3z + 7 = 2\left(\frac{y - z - 3}{-3}\right)$$

$$x + 3z + 7 = -\frac{2}{3}y + \frac{2}{3}z + 2$$

$$x + \frac{2}{3}y + \frac{7}{3}z = -5$$

$3x + 2y + 7z = -15$

$$\boxed{\mathbf{r} \cdot (3\mathbf{i} + 2\mathbf{j} + 7\mathbf{k}) = -15}$$

(iii) The vector equation of the plane in parametric form is given:

$\mathbf{r} = (2\mathbf{i} + 7\mathbf{k}) + \lambda\,(\mathbf{i} + \mathbf{j} - \mathbf{k}) + \mu\,(2\mathbf{i} - 3\mathbf{j} + \mathbf{k})$

$x = 2 + \lambda + 2\mu$ ... (1)

$y = \lambda - 3\mu$ ... (2)

$z = 7 - \lambda + \mu$ ... (3)

Eliminate λ and μ.

$x - 2 - y = 5\mu$ ... (4) from (1) and (2)

$y + z = 7 - 2\mu$ ... (5) from (2) and (3)

Substitute (5) into (4)

$$x - 2 - y = \frac{5(7 - y - z)}{2}$$

$2x - 4 - 2y = 35 - 5y - 5z$

$2x - 2y + 5y + 5z = 35 + 4$

$2x + 3y + 5z = 39$

$\boxed{\mathbf{r} \,.\, (2\mathbf{i} + 3\mathbf{j} + 5\mathbf{k}) = 39}$

19. $\mathbf{a} = 2\mathbf{j} - 3\mathbf{k}$, $\mathbf{b} = -2\mathbf{i} + 7\mathbf{j}$, $\mathbf{c} = \mathbf{i} + \mathbf{j} + \mathbf{k}$

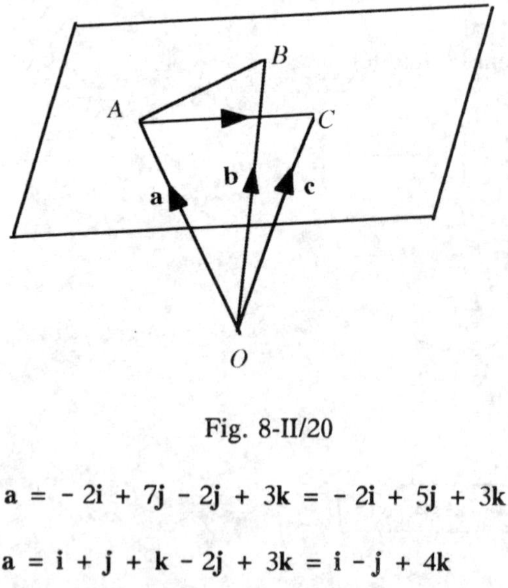

Fig. 8-II/20

$\overrightarrow{AB} = \mathbf{b} - \mathbf{a} = -2\mathbf{i} + 7\mathbf{j} - 2\mathbf{j} + 3\mathbf{k} = -2\mathbf{i} + 5\mathbf{j} + 3\mathbf{k}$

$\overrightarrow{AC} = \mathbf{c} - \mathbf{a} = \mathbf{i} + \mathbf{j} + \mathbf{k} - 2\mathbf{j} + 3\mathbf{k} = \mathbf{i} - \mathbf{j} + 4\mathbf{k}$

$\mathbf{r} = 2\mathbf{j} - 3\mathbf{k} + \lambda\overrightarrow{AB} + \mu\overrightarrow{AC}$

$\boxed{\mathbf{r} = 2\mathbf{j} - 3\mathbf{k} + \lambda(-2\mathbf{i} + 5\mathbf{j} + 3\mathbf{k}) + \mu(\mathbf{i} - \mathbf{j} - 4\mathbf{k})}$

the vector equation of the plane.

20. $A\,(-1, -2, -3)$, $B\,(3, 4, 5)$, $C\,(-6, -7, 8)$

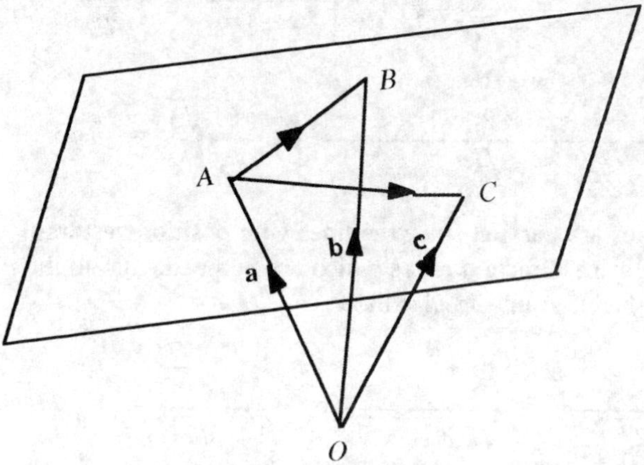

Fig. 8-II/21

$$\overrightarrow{AB} = \mathbf{b} - \mathbf{a} = 4\mathbf{i} + 6\mathbf{j} + 8\mathbf{k}$$

$$\overrightarrow{AC} = \mathbf{c} - \mathbf{a} = -5\mathbf{i} - 5\mathbf{j} + 11\mathbf{k}$$

$$\boxed{\mathbf{r} = -\mathbf{i} - 2\mathbf{j} - 3\mathbf{k} + \lambda\,(4\mathbf{i} + 6\mathbf{j} + 8\mathbf{k}) + \mu\,(-5\mathbf{i} - 5\mathbf{j} + 11\mathbf{k})}$$

the vector equation of the plane.

21. The distance from the origin to the plane π_2 is $\dfrac{2}{\sqrt{1+1+1}}$ and the distance from the origin to the plane π_1 is $\dfrac{1}{\sqrt{1+1+1}}$.

Therefore the distance between the two parallel planes is

$$\frac{2-1}{\sqrt{3}} = \frac{1}{\sqrt{3}}\,\frac{\sqrt{3}}{\sqrt{3}} = \frac{\sqrt{3}}{3}.$$

22. $$\left|\frac{ax_1 + by_1 + cz_1 - d}{\sqrt{a^2 + b^2 + c^2}}\right|$$

(i) $$\left|\frac{1 \times 3 + 2 \times 4 + 3 \times 5 - 12}{\sqrt{3^2 + 4^2 + 5^2}}\right| = \frac{14}{\sqrt{50}} \times \frac{\sqrt{50}}{\sqrt{50}} = \frac{14\sqrt{50}}{50} = \frac{7}{25}\sqrt{50}$$

(ii) $\left|\dfrac{1\times 6 + 2\times 7 + 3\times 8 - 5}{\sqrt{6^2 + 7^2 + 8^2}}\right| = \dfrac{39}{\sqrt{149}} \times \dfrac{\sqrt{149}}{\sqrt{149}} = \dfrac{39}{149}\sqrt{149}$

(iii) $\left|\dfrac{1 \times 1 + 1 \times 2 + 1 \times 3 - 1}{\sqrt{3}}\right| = \dfrac{5}{\sqrt{3}}\,\dfrac{\sqrt{3}}{\sqrt{3}} = \dfrac{5}{3}\sqrt{3}$

23. The planes are parallel since the lines with position vectors (**i** + 2**j** + 3**k**) have the same direction ratios which are perpendicular to the planes. The distance between the circular base is

$$\frac{7 - 4}{\sqrt{1^2 + 2^2 + 3^2}} = \frac{3}{\sqrt{1 + 4 + 9}} = \frac{3}{\sqrt{14}}\,\frac{\sqrt{14}}{\sqrt{14}} = \frac{3}{14}\sqrt{14}\ .$$

24. The point (− 3, 4, − 5) has position vector − 3**i** + 4**j** − 5**k**,

(− 3**i** + 4**j** − 5**k**) . (2**i** − 3**j** − 12**k**) = − 6 − 12 + 60 = 42.

Therefore the point (− 3, 4, − 5) lies in the plane.

25. (i) $\mathbf{b} = 2\mathbf{i} + \mathbf{j} - 3\mathbf{k}, \quad |\mathbf{b}| = \sqrt{4 + 1 + 9} = \sqrt{14}$

$\mathbf{n} = \mathbf{i} + \mathbf{j} + \mathbf{k}, \ \hat{\mathbf{n}} = \dfrac{\mathbf{i}}{\sqrt{3}} + \dfrac{\mathbf{j}}{\sqrt{3}} + \dfrac{\mathbf{k}}{\sqrt{3}}$

$$\sin\theta = \frac{\mathbf{b}\,.\,\hat{\mathbf{n}}}{|\mathbf{b}|} = \frac{(2\mathbf{i} + \mathbf{j} - 3\mathbf{k})\,.\left(\dfrac{\mathbf{i}}{\sqrt{3}} + \dfrac{\mathbf{j}}{\sqrt{3}} + \dfrac{\mathbf{k}}{\sqrt{3}}\right)}{\sqrt{14}}$$

$$= \left(\frac{2}{\sqrt{3}} + \frac{1}{\sqrt{3}} - \frac{3}{\sqrt{3}}\right)\frac{1}{\sqrt{14}}$$

$\therefore \sin\theta = 0$

(ii) $\mathbf{b} = 3\mathbf{i} + 4\mathbf{j} + 5\mathbf{k}, \quad |\mathbf{b}| = \sqrt{3^2 + 4^2 + 5^2} = \sqrt{50}$

$$\mathbf{n} = \mathbf{i} + \mathbf{j} + \mathbf{k}, \quad \hat{\mathbf{n}} = \frac{1}{\sqrt{3}}\mathbf{i} + \frac{1}{\sqrt{3}}\mathbf{j} + \frac{1}{\sqrt{3}}\mathbf{k}$$

$$\sin\theta = \frac{\mathbf{b}\,.\,\hat{\mathbf{n}}}{|\mathbf{b}|} = \frac{(3\mathbf{i} + 4\mathbf{j} + 5\mathbf{k})\,.\left(\frac{1}{\sqrt{3}}\mathbf{i} + \frac{1}{\sqrt{3}}\mathbf{j} + \frac{1}{\sqrt{3}}\mathbf{k}\right)}{\sqrt{50}}$$

$$= \frac{\frac{3}{\sqrt{3}} + \frac{4}{\sqrt{3}} + \frac{5}{\sqrt{3}}}{\sqrt{50}} = \frac{12}{\sqrt{3}\,\sqrt{50}}.$$

26.

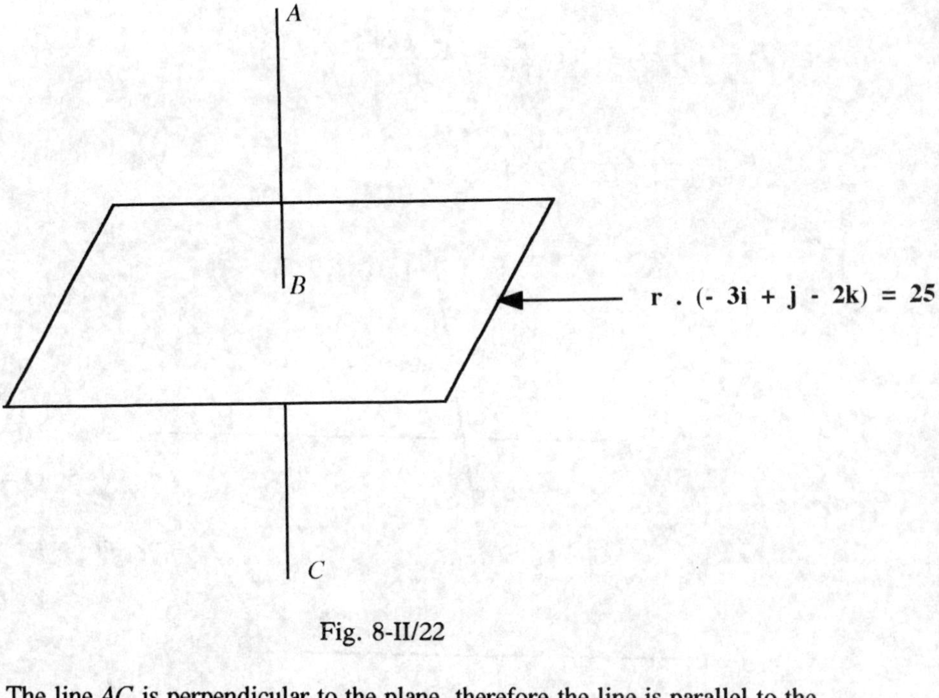

Fig. 8-II/22

The line AC is perpendicular to the plane, therefore the line is parallel to the direction vector $-3\mathbf{i} + \mathbf{j} - 2\mathbf{k}$ hence the vector equation of the line is
$\mathbf{r} = \mathbf{i} + \mathbf{j} + \mathbf{k} + \lambda(-3\mathbf{i} + \mathbf{j} - 2\mathbf{k})$

$x = 1 - 3\lambda, y = 1 + \lambda, z = 1 - 2\lambda.$

The equation of the plane is $-3x + y - 2z = 25$.
Substituting these values, we have

$$-3(1 - 3\lambda) + (1 + \lambda) - 2(1 - 2\lambda) = 25$$

$$-3 + 9\lambda + 1 + \lambda - 2 + 4\lambda = 25$$

$$14\lambda = 29$$

$$\lambda = \frac{29}{14}.$$

The coordinates of B are given

$$x = 1 - 3\left(\frac{29}{14}\right) = \frac{14 - 87}{14} = -\frac{73}{14}$$

$$y = 1 + \frac{29}{14} = \frac{43}{14}$$

$$z = 1 - 2\lambda = 1 - \frac{58}{14} = \frac{14 - 58}{14} = -\frac{44}{14}$$

$$B\left(-\frac{73}{14}, \frac{43}{14}, -\frac{44}{14}\right).$$

27.

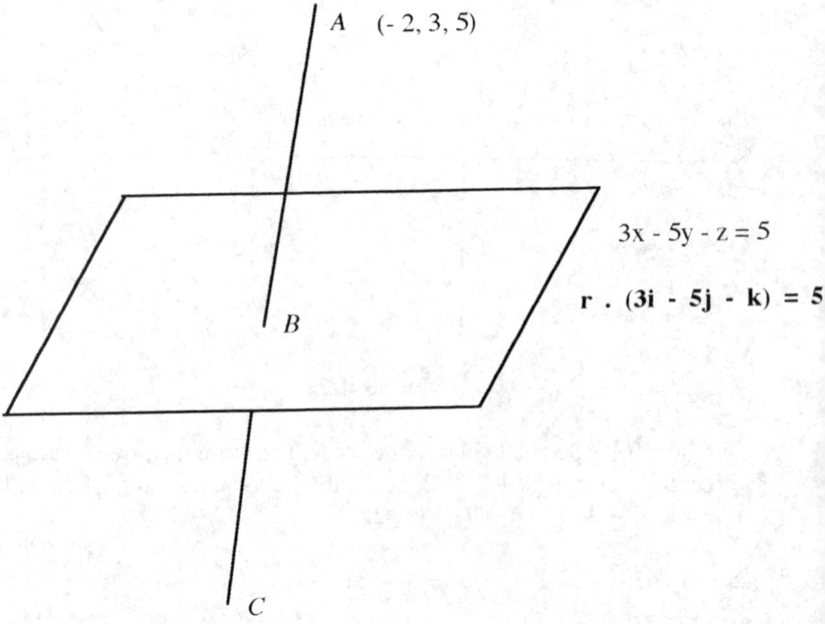

Fig. 8-II/23

AC is perpendicular to the plane with vector equation

$$\mathbf{r} \, . \, (3\mathbf{i} - 5\mathbf{j} - \mathbf{k}) = 5 \ldots (2)$$

The vector equation of the line is

$$\mathbf{r} = (-2\mathbf{i} + 3\mathbf{j} + 5\mathbf{k}) + \lambda\,(3\mathbf{i} - 5\mathbf{j} - \mathbf{k}) \ldots (1)$$

whose direction vector is parallel to $3\mathbf{i} - 5\mathbf{j} - \mathbf{k}$.

To find the point of intersection of the line with the plane.

From (1)

$x = -2 + 3\lambda$

$y = 3 - 5\lambda$

$z = 5 - \lambda.$

Substituting in the equation of the plane

(2) $3\,(-2 + 3\lambda) - 5\,(3 - 5\lambda) - (5 - \lambda) = 5$

$-6 + 9\lambda - 15 + 25\lambda - 5 + \lambda = 5$

$35\lambda = 31$

$\lambda = \dfrac{31}{35}.$

The coordinates of B are $-2 + \dfrac{93}{35},\ 3 - \dfrac{5\,(31)}{35},\ 5 - \dfrac{31}{35}$

or $\left(\dfrac{23}{35},\ -\dfrac{50}{35},\ \dfrac{144}{35}\right).$

The equation of AC is $\mathbf{r} = (-2\mathbf{i} + 3\mathbf{j} + 5\mathbf{k}) + \lambda\,(3\mathbf{i} - 5\mathbf{j} - \mathbf{k})$
B is the mid-point of AC therefore

$-2 + x_2 = \dfrac{46}{35}, \qquad -\dfrac{100}{35} = 3 + y_2, \qquad \dfrac{288}{35} = 5 + z_2$

$x_2 = \dfrac{46}{35} + \dfrac{70}{35} = \dfrac{116}{35}, \qquad y_2 = -3 - \dfrac{100}{35} = -\dfrac{205}{35},$

$z_2 = \dfrac{288}{35} - 5 = \dfrac{288 - 175}{35} = \dfrac{113}{35}$

$C\left(\dfrac{116}{35},\ \dfrac{-205}{35},\ \dfrac{113}{35}\right).$

28. $\mathbf{a} = \mathbf{i} - \mathbf{j} - \mathbf{k}$, $\mathbf{b} = 2\mathbf{i} + 5\mathbf{j} + 7\mathbf{k}$, $\mathbf{c} = -\mathbf{i} - 2\mathbf{j} + 3\mathbf{k}$

$\overrightarrow{AB} = 2\mathbf{i} + 5\mathbf{j} + 7\mathbf{k} - (\mathbf{i} - \mathbf{j} - \mathbf{k}) = \mathbf{i} + 6\mathbf{j} + 8\mathbf{k}$

$\overrightarrow{AC} = (-\mathbf{i} - 2\mathbf{j} + 3\mathbf{k}) - (\mathbf{i} - \mathbf{j} - \mathbf{k}) = -2\mathbf{i} - \mathbf{j} + 4\mathbf{k}$.

The equation of the plane is

$\mathbf{r} = \mathbf{i} - \mathbf{j} - \mathbf{k} + \lambda \overrightarrow{AB} + \mu \overrightarrow{AC}$

$\mathbf{r} = \mathbf{i} - \mathbf{j} - \mathbf{k} + \lambda(\mathbf{i} + 6\mathbf{j} + 8\mathbf{k}) + \mu(-2\mathbf{i} - \mathbf{j} + 4\mathbf{k})$

$\overrightarrow{BC} = (-\mathbf{i} - 2\mathbf{j} + 3\mathbf{k}) - (2\mathbf{i} + 5\mathbf{j} + 7\mathbf{k}) = -3\mathbf{i} - 7\mathbf{j} - 4\mathbf{k}$

$\overrightarrow{BA} = \mathbf{i} - \mathbf{j} - \mathbf{k} - (2\mathbf{i} + 5\mathbf{j} + 7\mathbf{k}) = -\mathbf{i} - 6\mathbf{j} - 8\mathbf{k}$

$\mathbf{r} = 2\mathbf{i} + 5\mathbf{j} + 7\mathbf{k} + \lambda(-3\mathbf{i} - 7\mathbf{j} - 4\mathbf{k}) + \mu(-\mathbf{i} - 6\mathbf{j} - 8\mathbf{k})$

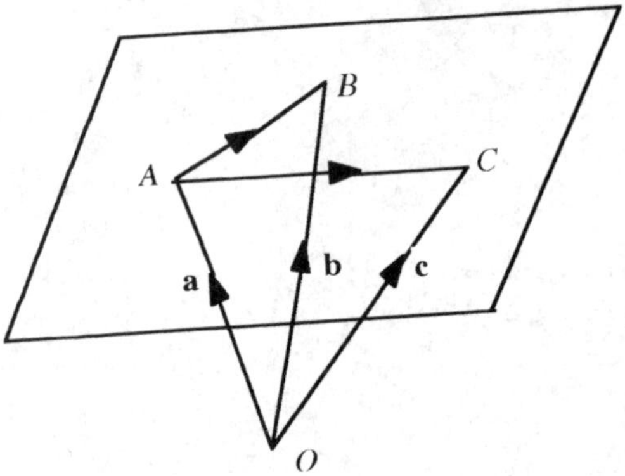

Fig. 8-II/24

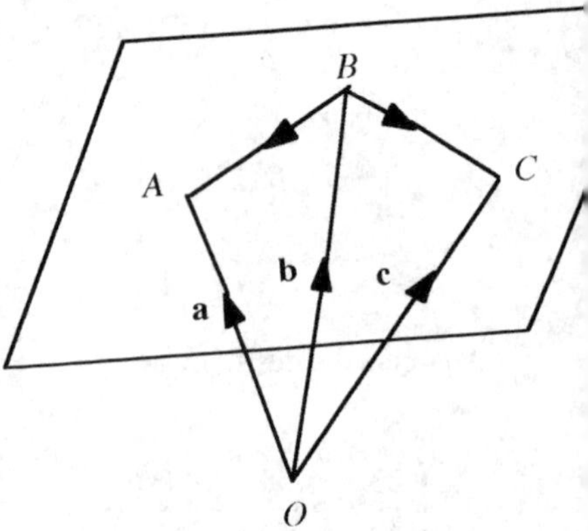

Fig. 8-II/25

$\mathbf{r} = \mathbf{i} - \mathbf{j} - \mathbf{k} + \lambda \overrightarrow{AB} + \mu \overrightarrow{AC}$ $\quad$ $\mathbf{r} = 2\mathbf{i} + 5\mathbf{j} + 7\mathbf{k} + \lambda \overrightarrow{BC} + \mu \overrightarrow{BA}$

The parametric equation of the plane containing, **a**, **b**, **c** is $\mathbf{r} = \lambda\mathbf{a} + \mu\mathbf{b} + t\,\mathbf{c}$ where $\lambda + \mu + t = 1$, $t = 1 - \lambda - \mu$

$\mathbf{r} = \lambda(\mathbf{i} - \mathbf{j} - \mathbf{k}) + \mu(2\mathbf{i} + 5\mathbf{j} + 7\mathbf{k}) + (1 - \lambda - \mu)(-\mathbf{i} - 2\mathbf{j} + 3\mathbf{k})$

$\mathbf{r} = \mathbf{i}(\lambda + 2\mu - 1 + \lambda + \mu) + \mathbf{j}(-\lambda + 5\mu - 2 + 2\lambda + 2\mu) +$
$\quad \mathbf{k}(-\lambda + 7\mu + 3 - 3\lambda - 3\mu)$

$\mathbf{r} = \mathbf{i}(2\lambda + 3\mu - 1) + \mathbf{j}(\lambda + 7\mu - 2) + \mathbf{k}(-4\lambda + 4\mu + 3)$.

If $P(x, y, z)$ is any point on this plane then $x = 2\lambda + 3\mu - 1$, $y = \lambda + 7\mu - 2$, $z = -4\lambda + 4\mu + 3$.

Eliminating λ and μ

$x = 2\lambda + 3\mu - 1 \quad \ldots (1)$

$y = \lambda + 7\mu - 2 \quad \ldots (2)$

$z = -4\lambda + 4\mu + 3 \quad \ldots (3)$

From (1) and (2) we have

$$\begin{aligned} -2y &= -2\lambda - 14\mu + 4 \\ x &= 2\lambda + 3\mu - 1 \end{aligned}$$

$x - 2y = -11\mu + 3 \ldots (4)$

From (2) and (3) we have

$$\begin{aligned} 4y &= 4\lambda + 28\mu - 8 \\ z &= -4\lambda + 4\mu + 3 \end{aligned}$$

$z + 4y = 32\mu - 5 \ldots (5)$

Eliminating μ from (4) and (5)

32(4) and 11(5)

$$\begin{aligned} 32x - 64y &= -352\mu + 96 \\ 11z + 44y &= +352\mu - 55 \end{aligned}$$

$32x - 20y + 11z = 41$

The scalar product from of the equation is

$$\boxed{\mathbf{r} \cdot (32\mathbf{i} - 20\mathbf{j} + 11\mathbf{k}) = 41}$$

29. See text.

30.

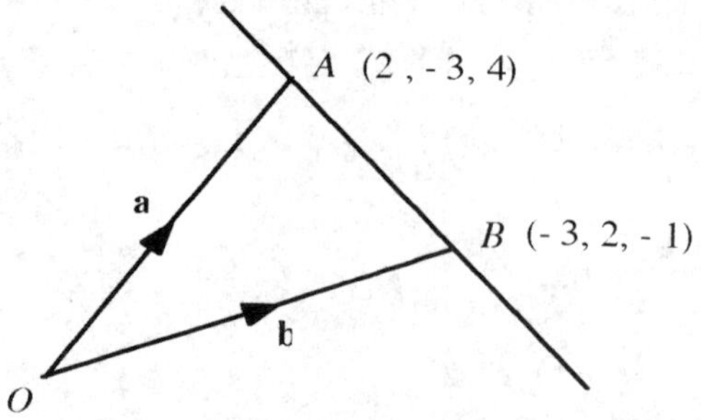

Fig. 8-II/26

The vector equation of a line through two fixed points is given $\mathbf{r} = \mathbf{a} + \lambda(\mathbf{b} - \mathbf{a})$ where **a** is the position vector and **b** − **a** is the direction vector. The vector equation of the line $\mathbf{r} = (2\mathbf{i} - 3\mathbf{j} + 4\mathbf{k}) + \lambda(-5\mathbf{i} + 5\mathbf{j} - 5\mathbf{k})$

$$\sin\theta = \frac{\mathbf{b}\cdot\hat{\mathbf{n}}}{|\mathbf{b}|}$$

$$\mathbf{b} = -5\mathbf{i} + 5\mathbf{j} - 5\mathbf{k},\quad |\mathbf{b}| = \sqrt{(-5)^2 + 5^2 + (-5)^2} = 5\sqrt{3}$$

the vector equation of the plane $= \mathbf{r}\cdot(-4\mathbf{i} + 5\lambda - 7\mathbf{k}) = 27$

$\mathbf{n} = -4\mathbf{i} + 5\mathbf{j} - 7\mathbf{k}$ is the unit vector $\hat{\mathbf{n}} = \dfrac{-4\mathbf{i} + 5\mathbf{j} - 7\mathbf{k}}{\sqrt{4^2 + 5^2 + 7^2}}$

$$\sin\theta = \frac{(-5\mathbf{i} + 5\mathbf{j} - 5\mathbf{k})\cdot(-4\mathbf{i} + 5\mathbf{j} - 7\mathbf{k})}{5\sqrt{3}\sqrt{90}}$$

$$= \frac{20 + 25 + 35}{5\sqrt{3}\sqrt{90}} = 0.974$$

$$\boxed{\sin\theta = 0.974}$$

31. $\sin\theta = \dfrac{\mathbf{b}\cdot\hat{\mathbf{n}}}{|\mathbf{b}|} = \dfrac{(-7\mathbf{i} + 2\mathbf{j} + 3\mathbf{k})}{\sqrt{(-7)^2 + 2^2 + 3^2}}\cdot\dfrac{(\mathbf{i} + 2\mathbf{j} + 3\mathbf{k})}{\sqrt{1^2 + 2^2 + 3^2}}$

$$= \frac{-7 + 4 + 9}{\sqrt{62}\sqrt{14}} = \frac{6}{\sqrt{62}\sqrt{14}} = 0.2037$$

$\theta = 11.8°$

32. The vector equation of the line is

$$\mathbf{r} = (2\mathbf{i} + 2\mathbf{j} + 2\mathbf{k}) + \lambda (3\mathbf{i} - 5\mathbf{j} + 7\mathbf{k})$$

$$\sin\theta = \frac{\mathbf{b}\,.\,\hat{\mathbf{n}}}{|\mathbf{b}|} = \frac{3\mathbf{i} - 5\mathbf{j} + 7\mathbf{k}}{\sqrt{3^2 + 5^2 + 7^2}} \cdot \frac{(-\mathbf{j} + 5\mathbf{k})}{\sqrt{1^2 + 25}}$$

$$= \frac{5 + 35}{\sqrt{83}\,\sqrt{26}} = \frac{40}{\sqrt{83}\,\sqrt{26}}$$

$$= 0.861$$

$$\cos\theta = \sqrt{1 - 0.861^2} = 0.509$$

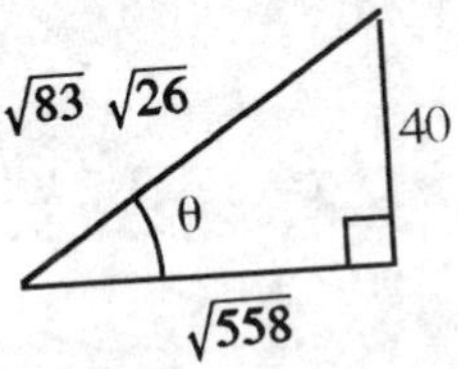

Fig. 8-II/27

33. (a) $\mathbf{r} = 2\mathbf{i} - 3\mathbf{j} + 4\mathbf{k} + \lambda (\mathbf{i} + 5\mathbf{j} - 7\mathbf{k}) + \mu (-3\mathbf{i} + 4\mathbf{j} + 8\mathbf{k})$

or $\mathbf{r} = \mathbf{i} + \mathbf{j} + 9\mathbf{k} + \lambda (\mathbf{i} + 5\mathbf{j} - 7\mathbf{k}) + \mu (-3\mathbf{i} + 4\mathbf{j} + 8\mathbf{k})$

(b) $\mathbf{r} = \mathbf{i} + 5\mathbf{j} + 9\mathbf{k} + \lambda (\mathbf{i} + 3\mathbf{j} - 2\mathbf{k}) + \mu (3\mathbf{j} + 5\mathbf{k})$

or $\mathbf{r} = 2\mathbf{i} + 5\mathbf{j} - \mathbf{k} + \lambda (\mathbf{i} + 3\mathbf{j} - 2\mathbf{k}) + \mu (3\mathbf{j} + 5\mathbf{k})$.

SOLUTIONS 6

1. (i) $$\mathbf{u} \times \mathbf{v} = \begin{vmatrix} \mathbf{i} & \mathbf{j} & \mathbf{k} \\ 3 & 3 & 5 \\ -2 & 4 & 1 \end{vmatrix}$$

$$= \mathbf{i}\,(3 - 20) - \mathbf{j}\,(3 + 10) + \mathbf{k}\,(12 + 6)$$

$$= -17\mathbf{i} - 13\mathbf{j} + 18\mathbf{k} = \begin{pmatrix} -17 \\ -13 \\ 18 \end{pmatrix}$$

$$\mathbf{v} \times \mathbf{u} = \begin{vmatrix} \mathbf{i} & \mathbf{j} & \mathbf{k} \\ -2 & 4 & 1 \\ 3 & 3 & 5 \end{vmatrix}$$

$$= \mathbf{i}\,(20 - 3) - \mathbf{j}\,(-10 - 3) + \mathbf{k}\,(-6 - 12)$$

$$= 17\mathbf{i} + 13\mathbf{j} - 18\mathbf{k} = \begin{pmatrix} 17 \\ 13 \\ -18 \end{pmatrix}$$

2. (a) $$\mathbf{u} \times \mathbf{v} = \begin{vmatrix} \mathbf{i} & \mathbf{j} & \mathbf{k} \\ 1 & 1 & 1 \\ -2 & -1 & 1 \end{vmatrix} = \mathbf{i}\,(1 + 1) - \mathbf{j}\,(1 + 2) + \mathbf{k}\,(-1 + 2)$$

$$= 2\mathbf{i} - 3\mathbf{j} + \mathbf{k} = \begin{pmatrix} 2 \\ -3 \\ 1 \end{pmatrix}$$

$$\mathbf{v} \times \mathbf{u} = \begin{vmatrix} \mathbf{i} & \mathbf{j} & \mathbf{k} \\ -2 & -1 & 1 \\ 1 & 1 & 1 \end{vmatrix}$$

$$= \mathbf{i}\,(-1 - 1) - \mathbf{j}\,(-2 - 1) + \mathbf{k}\,(-2 + 1)$$

$$= -2\mathbf{i} + 3\mathbf{j} - \mathbf{k} = \begin{pmatrix} -2 \\ 3 \\ -1 \end{pmatrix}$$

(b) $\mathbf{u} \times \mathbf{v} = \begin{vmatrix} \mathbf{i} & \mathbf{j} & \mathbf{k} \\ 3 & -5 & 3 \\ -5 & 3 & 1 \end{vmatrix} = \mathbf{i}\,(-5-9) - \mathbf{j}\,(3+15) + \mathbf{k}\,(9-25)$

$$= -14\mathbf{i} - 18\mathbf{j} - 16\mathbf{k} = \begin{pmatrix} -14 \\ -18 \\ -16 \end{pmatrix}$$

$$\mathbf{v} \times \mathbf{u} = \begin{vmatrix} \mathbf{i} & \mathbf{j} & \mathbf{k} \\ -5 & 3 & 1 \\ 3 & -5 & 3 \end{vmatrix} = \mathbf{i}\,(9+5) - \mathbf{j}\,(-15-3) + \mathbf{k}\,(25-9)$$

$$= 14\mathbf{i} + 18\mathbf{j} + 16\mathbf{k} = \begin{pmatrix} 14 \\ 18 \\ 16 \end{pmatrix}.$$

(c) $\mathbf{v} \times \mathbf{w} = \begin{vmatrix} \mathbf{i} & \mathbf{j} & \mathbf{k} \\ -3 & -4 & 5 \\ 1 & 1 & 1 \end{vmatrix} = \mathbf{i}\,(-4-5) - \mathbf{j}\,(-3-5) + \mathbf{k}\,(-3+4)$

$$= -9\mathbf{i} + 8\mathbf{j} + \mathbf{k} = \begin{pmatrix} -9 \\ 8 \\ 1 \end{pmatrix}$$

$$\mathbf{w} \times \mathbf{v} = \begin{vmatrix} \mathbf{i} & \mathbf{j} & \mathbf{k} \\ 1 & 1 & 1 \\ -3 & -4 & 5 \end{vmatrix} = \mathbf{i}\,(5+4) - \mathbf{j}\,(5+3) + \mathbf{k}\,(-4+3)$$

$$= 9\mathbf{i} - 8\mathbf{j} - \mathbf{k} = \begin{pmatrix} +9 \\ -8 \\ -1 \end{pmatrix}$$

3. (i) $(\mathbf{a} \times \mathbf{b}) \,.\, \mathbf{a}$

let $\mathbf{a} = a_1\mathbf{i} + a_2\mathbf{j} + a_3\mathbf{k}$

$\mathbf{b} = b_1\mathbf{i} + b_2\mathbf{j} + b_3\mathbf{k}$

$$\mathbf{a} \times \mathbf{b} = \begin{vmatrix} \mathbf{i} & \mathbf{j} & \mathbf{k} \\ a_1 & a_2 & a_3 \\ b_1 & b_2 & b_3 \end{vmatrix}$$

$$= \mathbf{i}\left(a_2 b_3 - a_3 b_2\right) - \mathbf{j}\left(a_1 b_3 - b_1 a_3\right) + \mathbf{k}\left(a_1 b_2 - a_2 b_1\right)$$

$$(\mathbf{a} \times \mathbf{b}) \,.\, \mathbf{a} = \left[\mathbf{i}\left(a_2 b_3 - a_3 b_2\right) - \mathbf{j}\left(a_1 b_3 - b_1 a_3\right) + \mathbf{k}\left(a_1 b_2 - a_2 b_1\right)\right] .$$
$$\left(a_1 \mathbf{i} + a_2 \mathbf{j} + a_3 \mathbf{k}\right)$$

$$= a_1\left(a_2 b_3 - a_3 b_2\right) - a_2\left(a_1 b_3 - b_1 a_3\right) + a_3\left(a_1 b_2 - a_2 b_1\right)$$

$$= a_1 a_2 b_3 - a_1 a_3 b_2 - a_1 a_2 b_3 + a_2 b_1 a_3 + a_3 a_1 b_2 - a_3 a_2 b_1$$

$$= 0$$

therefore the vectors are orthogonal.

$$\text{(ii)} \quad (\mathbf{a} \times \mathbf{b}) \,.\, \mathbf{b} = \begin{vmatrix} \mathbf{i} & \mathbf{j} & \mathbf{k} \\ a_1 & a_2 & a_3 \\ b_1 & b_2 & b_3 \end{vmatrix} . \left(b_1 \mathbf{i} + b_2 \mathbf{j} + b_3 \mathbf{k}\right)$$

$$= \left[\mathbf{i}\left(a_2 b_3 - a_3 b_2\right) - \mathbf{j}\left(a_1 b_3 - b_1 a_3\right) + \mathbf{k}\left(a_1 b_2 - a_2 b_1\right)\right] .$$
$$\left(b_1 \mathbf{i} + b_2 \mathbf{j} + b_3 \mathbf{k}\right)$$

$$= b_1\left(a_2 b_3 - a_3 b_2\right) - b_2\left(a_1 b_3 - b_1 a_3\right) + b_3\left(a_1 b_2 - a_2 b_1\right)$$

$$= a_2 b_1 b_3 - a_3 b_1 b_2 - a_1 b_2 b_3 + a_3 b_1 b_2 + a_1 b_2 b_3 - a_2 b_1 b_3$$

$$= 0$$

therefore the vectors are orthogonal.

4. $\mathbf{a} = a_1 \mathbf{i} + a_2 \mathbf{j} + a_3 \mathbf{k}$

$\mathbf{b}_1 = b_1 \mathbf{i} + b_2 \mathbf{j} + b_3 \mathbf{k}$

if **a** is parallel to **b** then

$a_1 : a_2 : a_3 \equiv b_1 : b_2 : b_3 .$

$$\mathbf{a} \times \mathbf{b} = \begin{vmatrix} \mathbf{i} & \mathbf{j} & \mathbf{k} \\ a_1 & a_2 & a_3 \\ b_1 & b_2 & b_3 \end{vmatrix} = \mathbf{i}\left(a_2 b_3 - a_3 b_2\right) - \mathbf{j}\left(a_1 b_3 - a_3 b_1\right) + \mathbf{k}\left(a_1 b_2 - a_2 b_1\right)$$

$\mathbf{a} \times \mathbf{b} = \mathbf{O}$

if $a_2 b_3 - a_3 b_2 = 0 \qquad \dfrac{a_2}{a_3} = \dfrac{b_2}{b_3}$

$a_1 b_3 - a_3 b_1 = 0 \qquad \dfrac{a_1}{a_3} = \dfrac{b_1}{b_3}$

$a_1 b_2 - a_2 b_1 = 0 \qquad \dfrac{a_1}{a_2} = \dfrac{b_1}{b_2}$ where

$\mathbf{O} = \begin{pmatrix} 0 \\ 0 \\ 0 \end{pmatrix}$, since $a_1 : a_2 : a_3 \equiv b_1 : b_2 : b_3$.

5. (i) $\mathbf{u} \times \mathbf{v} = \begin{vmatrix} \mathbf{i} & \mathbf{j} & \mathbf{k} \\ 1 & 2 & 3 \\ -1 & 2 & 1 \end{vmatrix} = \mathbf{i}\ (2 - 6) - \mathbf{j}\ (1 + 3) + \mathbf{k}\ (2 + 2)$

$= -4\mathbf{i} - 4\mathbf{j} + 4\mathbf{k} = \begin{pmatrix} -4 \\ -4 \\ 4 \end{pmatrix}$

(ii) $\mathbf{u} \times \mathbf{v} = \begin{vmatrix} \mathbf{i} & \mathbf{j} & \mathbf{k} \\ 4 & 0 & 3 \\ 0 & 3 & -1 \end{vmatrix} = \mathbf{i}\ (-9) - \mathbf{j}\ (-4) + 12\mathbf{k} = -9\mathbf{i} + 4\mathbf{j} + 12\mathbf{k}$

$= \begin{pmatrix} -9 \\ 4 \\ 12 \end{pmatrix}$

(iii) $\mathbf{u} \times \mathbf{v} = \begin{vmatrix} \mathbf{i} & \mathbf{j} & \mathbf{k} \\ 2 & 1 & 2 \\ 1 & -1 & 2 \end{vmatrix} = \mathbf{i}\ (2 + 2) - \mathbf{j}\ (4 - 2) + \mathbf{k}\ (-2 - 1)$

$= 4\mathbf{i} - 2\mathbf{j} - 3\mathbf{k} = \begin{pmatrix} 4 \\ -2 \\ -3 \end{pmatrix}$.

6. (i) $\mathbf{i} \times \mathbf{j} = \begin{pmatrix} \mathbf{i} & \mathbf{j} & \mathbf{k} \\ 1 & 0 & 0 \\ 0 & 1 & 0 \end{pmatrix} = 0\mathbf{i} - 0\mathbf{j} + \mathbf{k} = \mathbf{k}$

(ii) $\mathbf{i} \times \mathbf{k} = \begin{pmatrix} \mathbf{i} & \mathbf{j} & \mathbf{k} \\ 1 & 0 & 0 \\ 0 & 0 & 1 \end{pmatrix} = 0\mathbf{i} - (1)\,\mathbf{j} + 0\mathbf{k} = -\mathbf{j}$

(iii) $\mathbf{j} \times \mathbf{k} = \begin{vmatrix} \mathbf{i} & \mathbf{j} & \mathbf{k} \\ 0 & 1 & 0 \\ 0 & 0 & 1 \end{vmatrix} = (1)\,\mathbf{i} - 0\mathbf{j} + (0)\,\mathbf{k} = \mathbf{i}$

(iv) $\mathbf{k} \times \mathbf{i} = \begin{vmatrix} \mathbf{i} & \mathbf{j} & \mathbf{k} \\ 0 & 0 & 1 \\ 1 & 0 & 0 \end{vmatrix} = 0\mathbf{i} + \mathbf{j} + (0)\,\mathbf{k} = \mathbf{j}$

(v) $\mathbf{i} \times \mathbf{j} \times \mathbf{k} = \begin{vmatrix} \mathbf{i} & \mathbf{j} & \mathbf{k} \\ 1 & 0 & 0 \\ 0 & 1 & 0 \end{vmatrix} \times \mathbf{k} = [(0)\,\mathbf{i} - (0)\,\mathbf{j} + \mathbf{k}] \times \mathbf{k} = \mathbf{k} \times \mathbf{k}$

$\mathbf{k} \times \mathbf{k} = \begin{vmatrix} \mathbf{i} & \mathbf{j} & \mathbf{k} \\ 0 & 0 & 1 \\ 0 & 0 & 1 \end{vmatrix} = (0)\,\mathbf{i} - (0)\,\mathbf{j} + (0)\,\mathbf{k}.$

Similarly $\mathbf{j} \times \mathbf{k} \times \mathbf{i} = 0$, $\mathbf{k} \times \mathbf{i} \times \mathbf{j} = 0$.

7.

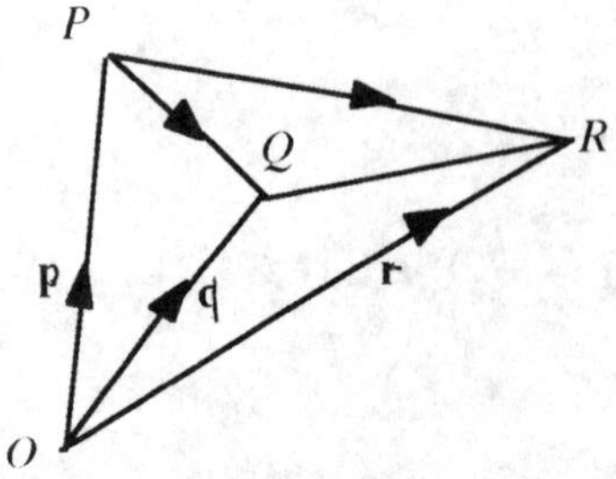

Fig. 8-II/28

$\overrightarrow{PQ} = (-3\mathbf{i} + 4\mathbf{j} - \mathbf{k}) - (\mathbf{i} + 2\mathbf{j} - 5\mathbf{k})$

$\overrightarrow{PQ} = -4\mathbf{i} + 2\mathbf{j} + 4\mathbf{k}$

$\overrightarrow{PR} = \mathbf{r} - \mathbf{p} = (3\mathbf{j} + 5\mathbf{k}) - (\mathbf{i} + 2\mathbf{j} - 5\mathbf{k})$

$\overrightarrow{PR} = -\mathbf{i} + \mathbf{j} + 10\mathbf{k}$

$$\overrightarrow{PQ} \times \overrightarrow{PR} = (-4\mathbf{i} + 2\mathbf{j} + 4\mathbf{k}) \times (-\mathbf{i} + \mathbf{j} + 10\mathbf{k})$$

$$= \begin{vmatrix} \mathbf{i} & \mathbf{j} & \mathbf{k} \\ -4 & 2 & 4 \\ -1 & 1 & 10 \end{vmatrix} = 16\mathbf{i} + 36\mathbf{j} - 2\mathbf{k}.$$

Let $A\ (x, y, z)$ be any point in the plane, $\overrightarrow{PA}$ and $\overrightarrow{PQ} \times \overrightarrow{PR}$ are orthogonal.

$$\overrightarrow{PA} . \left(\overrightarrow{PQ} \times \overrightarrow{PR}\right) = [(x-1)\mathbf{i} + (y-2)\mathbf{j} + (z+5)\mathbf{k}] . (16\mathbf{i} + 36\mathbf{j} - 2\mathbf{k})$$
$$= 0$$

$$16(x-1) + 36(y-2) - 2(z+5) = 0$$

$$16x + 36y - 2z = 16 + 72 + 10 = 98$$

$$8x + 18y - z = 49$$

$$\boxed{\mathbf{r} . (8\mathbf{i} + 18\mathbf{j} - \mathbf{k}) = 49}$$

3. $\overrightarrow{PQ} = (-3\mathbf{i} + 4\mathbf{j} - \mathbf{k}) - (\mathbf{i} + 2\mathbf{j} - 5\mathbf{k}) = -4\mathbf{i} + 2\mathbf{j} + 4\mathbf{k}$

$\overrightarrow{PR} = (3\mathbf{i} + 5\mathbf{k}) - (\mathbf{i} + 2\mathbf{j} - 5\mathbf{k}) = 2\mathbf{i} - 2\mathbf{j} + 10\mathbf{k}$

$$\overrightarrow{PQ} \times \overrightarrow{PR} = \begin{vmatrix} \mathbf{i} & \mathbf{j} & \mathbf{k} \\ -4 & 2 & 4 \\ 2 & -2 & 10 \end{vmatrix} = 28\mathbf{i} + 48\mathbf{j} + 4\mathbf{k}$$

$A\ (x, y, z)$

$$\overrightarrow{PA} . \left(\overrightarrow{PQ} \times \overrightarrow{PR}\right) = 0$$

$$[(x-1)\,\mathbf{i} + (y-2)\,\mathbf{j} + (z+5)\,\mathbf{k}] . (28\mathbf{i} + 48\mathbf{j} + 4\mathbf{k}) = 0$$

$$28(x-1) + 48(y-2) + 4(z+5) = 0$$

$$28x - 28 + 48y - 96 + 4z + 20 = 0$$

$$28x + 48y + 4z = 96 + 28 - 20 = 104$$

$$7x + 12y + z = 26$$

$$\boxed{\mathbf{r} . (7\mathbf{i} + 12\mathbf{j} + \mathbf{k}) = 26}\ .$$

9. $d = \dfrac{|\mathbf{b} \times (\mathbf{c} - \mathbf{a})|}{|\mathbf{b}|}$

$\mathbf{b} = -2\mathbf{i} + 3\mathbf{j} - \mathbf{k} \qquad |\mathbf{b}| = \sqrt{(-2)^2 + 3^2 + (-1)^2} = \sqrt{14}$

$\mathbf{a} = \mathbf{i} + \mathbf{j} + \mathbf{k}$

$\mathbf{c} = 4\mathbf{i} + 5\mathbf{j} + 6\mathbf{k}$

$$d = \frac{|(-2\mathbf{i} + 3\mathbf{j} - \mathbf{k}) \times (4\mathbf{i} + 5\mathbf{j} + 6\mathbf{k} - \mathbf{i} - \mathbf{j} - \mathbf{k})|}{\sqrt{14}}$$

$$= \frac{|(-2\mathbf{i} + 3\mathbf{j} - \mathbf{k}) \times (3\mathbf{i} + 4\mathbf{j} + 5\mathbf{k})|}{\sqrt{14}}$$

$$(-2\mathbf{i} + 3\mathbf{j} - \mathbf{k}) \times (3\mathbf{i} + 4\mathbf{j} + 5\mathbf{k}) = \begin{vmatrix} \mathbf{i} & \mathbf{j} & \mathbf{k} \\ -2 & 3 & -1 \\ 3 & 4 & 5 \end{vmatrix} = 19\mathbf{i} + 7\mathbf{j} - 17\mathbf{k}$$

$$d = \frac{|19\mathbf{i} + 7\mathbf{j} - 17\mathbf{k}|}{\sqrt{14}} = \frac{\sqrt{19^2 + 7^2 + (-17)^2}}{\sqrt{14}} = \frac{\sqrt{699}}{\sqrt{14}}$$

$$\boxed{d = 7.07}$$

10. $d = \dfrac{|\mathbf{b} \times (\mathbf{c} - \mathbf{a})|}{|\mathbf{b}|}$

$|\mathbf{b}| = |5\mathbf{i} - \mathbf{j} - \mathbf{k}| = \sqrt{25 + 1 + 1} = \sqrt{27} = 3\sqrt{3}$

$\mathbf{a} = -2\mathbf{i} + \mathbf{j} - \mathbf{k}$

$\mathbf{c} = 2\mathbf{i} - \mathbf{j} + 3\mathbf{k} \qquad \mathbf{c} - \mathbf{a} = 4\mathbf{i} - 2\mathbf{j} + 4\mathbf{k}$

$$d = \frac{|(5\mathbf{i} - \mathbf{j} - \mathbf{k}) \times (4\mathbf{i} - 2\mathbf{j} + 4\mathbf{k})|}{3\sqrt{3}}$$

$$(5\mathbf{i} - \mathbf{j} - \mathbf{k}) \times (4\mathbf{i} - 2\mathbf{j} + 4\mathbf{k}) = \begin{vmatrix} \mathbf{i} & \mathbf{j} & \mathbf{k} \\ 5 & -1 & -1 \\ 4 & -2 & 4 \end{vmatrix} = -6\mathbf{i} - 24\mathbf{j} - 6\mathbf{k}$$

$$d = \frac{|-6\mathbf{i} - 24\mathbf{j} - 6\mathbf{k}|}{3\sqrt{3}} = \frac{\sqrt{36 + 576 + 36}}{3\sqrt{3}} = \frac{\sqrt{648}}{3\sqrt{3}}$$

$$d = \frac{18\sqrt{2}}{3\sqrt{3}}$$

$$\boxed{d = 6\sqrt{\frac{2}{3}}}$$

1. See text.

2. See text.

3. See text.

4. See text.

5.

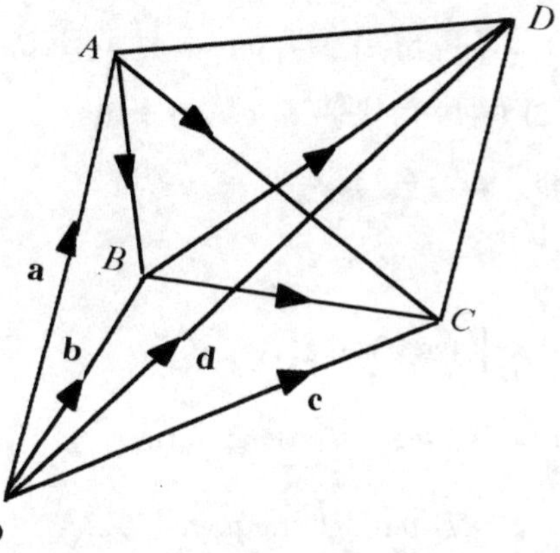

Fig. 8-II/29

(i) Plane ABC has position vector A (1, − 2, 6), B (2, 3, − 1) and C (5, − 4, − 3). The equation of the plane ABC through the three points in given as follows

$$\overrightarrow{AB} = (2 - 1)\,\mathbf{i} + (3 + 2)\,\mathbf{j} + (-1 - 6)\,\mathbf{k}$$

$\overrightarrow{AB} = \mathbf{i} + 5\mathbf{j} - 7\mathbf{k} \quad \ldots (1)$

$\overrightarrow{AC} = (5 - 1)\,\mathbf{i} + (-4 + 2)\,\mathbf{j} + (-3 - 6)\,\mathbf{k}$

$\overrightarrow{AC} = 4\mathbf{i} - 2\mathbf{j} - 9\mathbf{k} \quad \ldots (2)$

(1) and (2) are two vectors in the plane ABC.

$$\overrightarrow{AB} \times \overrightarrow{AC} = \begin{vmatrix} \mathbf{i} & \mathbf{j} & \mathbf{k} \\ 1 & 5 & -7 \\ 4 & -2 & -9 \end{vmatrix} = \mathbf{i}\,(-45 - 14) - \mathbf{j}\,(-9 + 28) + \mathbf{k}\,(-2 - 20)$$

$$= -59\mathbf{i} - 19\mathbf{j} - 22\mathbf{k}.$$

If $P\,(x, y, z)$ is any point in the plane $\overrightarrow{AP}$ and $\overrightarrow{AB} \times \overrightarrow{AC}$ are orthogonal

$\overrightarrow{AP} \cdot \left(\overrightarrow{AB} \times \overrightarrow{AC}\right) = 0$

$[(x - 1)\,\mathbf{i} + (y + 2)\,\mathbf{j} + (z - 6)\,\mathbf{k}] \cdot (-59\mathbf{i} - 19\mathbf{j} - 22\mathbf{k}) = 0$

$-(x - 1)\,59 + (y + 2)(-19) + (z - 6)(-22) = 0$

$-59x + 59 - 19y - 38 - 22z + 132 = 0$

$-59x - 19y - 22z = -153$

$\boxed{59x + 19y + 22z = 153}$ the plane of ABC

$\mathbf{r} \cdot (59\mathbf{i} + 19\mathbf{j} + 22\mathbf{k}) = 153$ the dot product form.

The equation of the plane BCD through the points $B\,(2, 3, -1)$, $C\,(5, -4, -3)$, $D\,(-3, 2, 2)$ is as follows:

$\overrightarrow{BC} = (5 - 2)\mathbf{i} + (-4 - 3)\,\mathbf{j} + (-3 + 1)\,\mathbf{k}$

$\overrightarrow{BC} = 3\mathbf{i} - 7\mathbf{j} - 2\mathbf{k} \ldots (1)$

$\overrightarrow{BD} = (-3 - 2)\,\mathbf{i} + (2 - 3)\,\mathbf{j} + (2 + 1)\,\mathbf{k}$

$\overrightarrow{BD} = -5\mathbf{i} - \mathbf{j} + 3\mathbf{k} \ldots (2)$

(1) and (2) are two vectors in the plane BCD

$$\overrightarrow{BC} \times \overrightarrow{BD} = \begin{vmatrix} \mathbf{i} & \mathbf{j} & \mathbf{k} \\ 3 & -7 & -2 \\ -5 & -1 & 3 \end{vmatrix} = \mathbf{i}\,(-21 - 2) - \mathbf{j}\,(9 - 10) + \mathbf{k}\,(-3 - 35)$$

$$= -23\mathbf{i} + \mathbf{j} - 38\mathbf{k}$$

If $P(x, y, z)$ is any point in the plane $\overrightarrow{BP}$ and $\overrightarrow{BC} \times \overrightarrow{BD}$ are orthogonal

$\overrightarrow{BP} \cdot \left(\overrightarrow{BC} \times \overrightarrow{BD}\right) = 0$

$[(x - 2)\,\mathbf{i} + (y - 3)\,\mathbf{j} + (z + 1)\,\mathbf{k}] \cdot (-23\mathbf{i} + \mathbf{j} - 38\mathbf{k}) = 0$

$-23(x - 2) + (y - 3) - 38(z + 1) = 0$

$-23x + 46 + y - 3 - 38z - 38 = 0$

$-23x + y - 38z = 38 + 3 - 46$

$\boxed{23x - y + 38z = 5}$ the plane of BCD

$\mathbf{r} \cdot (23\mathbf{i} - \mathbf{j} + 38\mathbf{k}) = 5.$

The angle between the faces if given by

$$\cos\theta = \hat{\mathbf{n}}_1 \cdot \hat{\mathbf{n}}_2$$

$$= \frac{59\mathbf{i} + 19\mathbf{j} + 22\mathbf{k}}{\sqrt{59^2 + 19^2 + 22^2}} \cdot \frac{(23\mathbf{i} - \mathbf{j} + 38\mathbf{k})}{\sqrt{23^2 + 1^2 + 38^2}}$$

$$= \frac{59\mathbf{i} + 19\mathbf{j} + 22\mathbf{k}}{65.8} \cdot \frac{23\mathbf{i} - \mathbf{j} + 38\mathbf{k}}{44.4}$$

$$= \frac{59 \times 23 - 19 \times 1 + 22 \times 38}{2921.52}$$

$$= 0.744$$

$$\boxed{\theta = 41.9^{\mathbf{o}}}$$

ii) Plane ACD

$\overrightarrow{AC} = \mathbf{c} - \mathbf{a} = 4\mathbf{i} - 2\mathbf{j} - 9\mathbf{k}$

$\overrightarrow{AD} = \mathbf{d} - \mathbf{a} = -4\mathbf{i} + 4\mathbf{j} - 4\mathbf{k}$

$$\overrightarrow{AC} \times \overrightarrow{AD} = \begin{vmatrix} \mathbf{i} & \mathbf{j} & \mathbf{k} \\ 4 & -2 & -9 \\ -4 & 4 & -4 \end{vmatrix} = \mathbf{i}\,(8 + 36) - \mathbf{j}\,(-16 - 36) + \mathbf{k}\,(16 - 8)$$

$$= 44\mathbf{i} + 52\mathbf{j} + 8\mathbf{k}$$

$$\overrightarrow{AP} = (x - 1)\,\mathbf{i} + (y + 2)\,\mathbf{j} + (z - 6)\,\mathbf{k}$$

$$\overrightarrow{AP} \cdot \left(\overrightarrow{AC} \times \overrightarrow{AD}\right) = 0$$

$$[(x - 1)\,\mathbf{i} + (y + 2)\,\mathbf{j} + (z - 6)\,\mathbf{k}] \cdot (44\mathbf{i} + 52\mathbf{j} + 8\mathbf{k}) = 0$$

$$44\,(x - 1) + 52\,(y + 2) + 8\,(z - 6) = 0$$

$$44x + 52y + 8z - 44 + 104 - 48 = 0$$

$$\boxed{44x + 52y + 8z = -12}$$

$$\mathbf{r} \cdot (44\mathbf{i} + 52\mathbf{j} + 8\mathbf{k}) = -12$$

$$\mathbf{r} \cdot (11\mathbf{i} + 13\mathbf{j} + 2\mathbf{k}) = -3 \; \ldots \; (3)$$

Plane *ABD*

$$\overrightarrow{AB} = \mathbf{i} + 5\mathbf{j} - 7\mathbf{k}$$

$$\overrightarrow{AD} = -4\mathbf{i} + 4\mathbf{j} - 4\mathbf{k}$$

$$\overrightarrow{AB} \times \overrightarrow{AD} = \begin{vmatrix} \mathbf{i} & \mathbf{j} & \mathbf{k} \\ 1 & 5 & -7 \\ -4 & 4 & -4 \end{vmatrix} = \mathbf{i}\,(-20 + 28) - \mathbf{j}\,(-4 - 28) + \mathbf{k}\,(4 + 20)$$

$$= 8\mathbf{i} + 32\mathbf{j} + 24\mathbf{k}$$

$$\overrightarrow{AP} \cdot \left(\overrightarrow{AB} \times \overrightarrow{AD}\right) = 0$$

$$[(x - 1)\,\mathbf{i} + (y + 2)\,\mathbf{j} + (z - 6)\,\mathbf{k}] \cdot (8\mathbf{i} + 32\mathbf{j} + 24\mathbf{k}) = 0$$

$$8\,(x - 1) + 32\,(y + 2) + 24\,(z - 6) = 0$$

$$8x + 32y + 24z = 8 - 64 + 144$$

$$8x + 32y + 24z = 88$$

$$\boxed{x + 4y + 3z = 11} \qquad \boxed{\mathbf{r} \cdot (\mathbf{i} + 4\mathbf{j} + 3\mathbf{k}) = 11} \; \ldots \; (4)$$

The angle between the planes (3) and (4) is given by $\cos\theta = \hat{\mathbf{n}}_1 \cdot \hat{\mathbf{n}}_2$

$$\cos\theta = \frac{11\mathbf{i} + 13\mathbf{j} + 2\mathbf{k}}{\sqrt{11^2 + 13^2 + 2^2}} \cdot \frac{\mathbf{i} + 4\mathbf{j} + 3\mathbf{k}}{\sqrt{1 + 4^2 + 9}}$$

$$= \frac{11 + 52 + 6}{\sqrt{121 + 169 + 4}\,.\sqrt{26}} = \frac{69}{17.15 \times 5.1} = 0.7890396$$

$$\boxed{\theta = 37.9^{\circ}}\,.$$

16. (a) $\overrightarrow{PQ} = (-3\mathbf{i} + \mathbf{j} + 4\mathbf{k}) - (2\mathbf{i} - 3\mathbf{j} + 2\mathbf{k}) = -5\mathbf{i} + 4\mathbf{j} + 2\mathbf{k}$

$\overrightarrow{PR} = (3\mathbf{i} + 2\mathbf{j} - 3\mathbf{k}) - (2\mathbf{i} - 3\mathbf{j} + 2\mathbf{k}) = \mathbf{i} + 5\mathbf{j} - 5\mathbf{k}$

$$\overrightarrow{PQ} \times \overrightarrow{PR} = \begin{vmatrix} \mathbf{i} & \mathbf{j} & \mathbf{k} \\ -5 & 4 & 2 \\ 1 & 5 & -5 \end{vmatrix}$$

$$= \mathbf{i}(-20 - 10) - \mathbf{j}(25 - 2) + \mathbf{k}(-25 - 4)$$

$$= -30\mathbf{i} - 23\mathbf{j} - 29\mathbf{k}.$$

(b) Area of $\Delta\, PQR = \frac{1}{2}\left|\overrightarrow{PQ} \times \overrightarrow{PR}\right|$

$$= \frac{1}{2}\left|-30\mathbf{i} - 23\mathbf{j} - 29\mathbf{k}\right|$$

$$= \frac{1}{2}\sqrt{30^2 + 23^2 + 29^2} = 23.8 \text{ square units.}$$

(c) Consider a point $A\,(x, y, z)$ on the plane

$\overrightarrow{PA} \cdot \left(\overrightarrow{PQ} \times \overrightarrow{PR}\right) = 0$

$[(x-2)\,\mathbf{i} + (y+3)\,\mathbf{j} + (z-2)\,\mathbf{k}] \cdot (-30\mathbf{i} - 23\mathbf{j} - 29\mathbf{k}) = 0$

$-30\,(x-2) + (y+3)\,(-23) - 29\,(z-2) = 0$

$-30x + 60 - 23y - 69 - 29z + 58 = 0$

$30x + 23y + 29z = 58 + 60 - 69 = 49$

$30x + 23y + 29z = 49$

$\boxed{\mathbf{r} \cdot (30\mathbf{i} + 23\mathbf{j} + 29\mathbf{k}) = 49}$.

17. (a) $\overrightarrow{AB} = (2\mathbf{i} - \mathbf{j} + \mathbf{k}) - (4\mathbf{j} - 5\mathbf{k})$

$\overrightarrow{AB} = 2\mathbf{i} - 5\mathbf{j} + 6\mathbf{k}$

$\overrightarrow{AC} = (-3\mathbf{i} + \mathbf{j} + 7\mathbf{k}) - (4\mathbf{j} - 5\mathbf{k}) = -3\mathbf{i} - 3\mathbf{j} + 12\mathbf{k}$

$$\overrightarrow{AB} \times \overrightarrow{AC} = \begin{vmatrix} \mathbf{i} & \mathbf{j} & \mathbf{k} \\ 2 & -5 & 6 \\ -3 & -3 & 12 \end{vmatrix}$$

$$= \mathbf{i}\,(-60 + 18) - \mathbf{j}\,(24 + 18) + \mathbf{k}\,(-6 - 15)$$

$$= -42\mathbf{i} - 42\mathbf{j} - 21\mathbf{k}$$

(b) Area of $\Delta\, ABC$ $= \frac{1}{2} \left| \overrightarrow{AB} \times \overrightarrow{AC} \right|$

$$= \frac{1}{2} \left| -42\mathbf{i} - 42\mathbf{j} - 21\mathbf{k} \right|$$

$$= \frac{1}{2} \sqrt{42^2 + 42^2 + 21^2}$$

$$= 31.5 \text{ square units.}$$

(c) Consider the point $P\,(x, y, z)$ on the plane

$$[\,x\,\mathbf{i} + (y - 4)\,\mathbf{j} + (z + 5)\,\mathbf{k}] \,.\, (-42\mathbf{i} - 42\mathbf{j} - 21\mathbf{k}) = 0$$

$$-42x - 42\,(y - 4) - 21\,(z + 5) = 0$$

$$-42x - 42y + 168 - 21z - 105 = 0$$

$$-42x - 42y - 21z = 105 - 168$$

$$42x + 42y + 21z = 63$$

$$2x + 2y + z = 3$$

$$\boxed{\mathbf{r} \,.\, (2\mathbf{i} + 2\mathbf{j} + \mathbf{k}) = 3}$$

18. See text.

19. $d = \dfrac{|\mathbf{b} \times (\mathbf{c} - \mathbf{a})|}{|\mathbf{b}|}$

(i) $\mathbf{r} = (2 + 3\lambda)\,\mathbf{i} + (1 - 2\lambda)\,\mathbf{j} + (3 + \lambda)\,\mathbf{k}$

$\mathbf{r} = (2\mathbf{i} + \mathbf{j} + 3\mathbf{k}) + \lambda\,(3\mathbf{i} - 2\mathbf{j} + \mathbf{k})$

$\mathbf{a} = 2\mathbf{i} + \mathbf{j} + 3\mathbf{k}, \;\; \mathbf{b} = 3\mathbf{i} - 2\mathbf{j} + \mathbf{k}$

$\mathbf{c} = \mathbf{i} + \mathbf{j} + \mathbf{k}$

$$|\mathbf{b}| = \sqrt{3^2 + 2^2 + 1} = \sqrt{14}$$

$$\mathbf{c} - \mathbf{a} = -\mathbf{i} - 2\mathbf{k}$$

$$\mathbf{b} \times (\mathbf{c} - \mathbf{a}) = (3\mathbf{i} - 2\mathbf{j} + \mathbf{k}) \times (-\mathbf{i} - 2\mathbf{k})$$

$$= \begin{vmatrix} \mathbf{i} & \mathbf{j} & \mathbf{k} \\ 3 & -2 & 1 \\ -1 & 0 & -2 \end{vmatrix} = 4\mathbf{i} + 5\mathbf{j} - 2\mathbf{k}$$

$$d = \frac{|\mathbf{b} \times (\mathbf{c} - \mathbf{a})|}{|\mathbf{b}|} = \frac{|4\mathbf{i} + 5\mathbf{j} - 2\mathbf{k}|}{\sqrt{14}} = \frac{\sqrt{4^2 + 5^2 + 2^2}}{\sqrt{14}} = \frac{\sqrt{45}}{\sqrt{14}}$$

$$\boxed{d = 1.79}$$

(ii) $\mathbf{r} = (1 - t)\,\mathbf{i} + (1 + t)\,\mathbf{j} + (1 - 2t)\,\mathbf{k}$

$= (\mathbf{i} + \mathbf{j} + \mathbf{k}) + t\,(-\mathbf{i} + \mathbf{j} - 2\mathbf{k})$

$\mathbf{b} = -\mathbf{i} + \mathbf{j} - 2\mathbf{k}$, $|\mathbf{b}| = \sqrt{1 + 1 + 4} = \sqrt{6}$, $\mathbf{a} = \mathbf{i} + \mathbf{j} + \mathbf{k}$

$\mathbf{c} - \mathbf{a} = \mathbf{i} + \mathbf{j} + \mathbf{k} - (\mathbf{i} + \mathbf{j} + \mathbf{k}) = 0$, $\quad d = 0$

(iii) $\mathbf{r} = \mathbf{i} + \mathbf{j} - 3\mathbf{k} + t\,(-2\mathbf{i} + 3\mathbf{j} + 4\mathbf{k})$

$\mathbf{a} = \mathbf{i} + \mathbf{j} - 3\mathbf{k}$ $\qquad$ $\mathbf{b} = -2\mathbf{i} + 3\mathbf{j} + 4\mathbf{k}$

$\mathbf{c} - \mathbf{a} = \mathbf{i} + \mathbf{j} + \mathbf{k} - \mathbf{i} - \mathbf{j} + 3\mathbf{k}$ $\qquad$ $|\mathbf{b}| = \sqrt{4 + 9 + 16} = \sqrt{29}$

$= 4\mathbf{k}$ $\qquad$ $d = \dfrac{|(-2\mathbf{i} + 3\mathbf{j} + 4\mathbf{k}) \times 4\mathbf{k}|}{\sqrt{29}}$

$$(-2\mathbf{i} + 3\mathbf{j} + 4\mathbf{k}) \times 4\mathbf{k} = \begin{vmatrix} \mathbf{i} & \mathbf{j} & \mathbf{k} \\ -2 & 3 & 4 \\ 0 & 0 & 4 \end{vmatrix} = 12\mathbf{i} + 8\mathbf{j}$$

$$d = \frac{|12\mathbf{i} + 8\mathbf{j}|}{\sqrt{29}} = \frac{\sqrt{144 + 64}}{\sqrt{29}} = 2.68$$

$$\boxed{d = 2.68}$$

20. $\mathbf{a} = -\mathbf{i} + 7\mathbf{k} \quad \mathbf{b} = \mathbf{i} - 2\mathbf{j} - 3\mathbf{k}$

$\mathbf{c} - \mathbf{a} = -\mathbf{i} - 2\mathbf{j} - 4\mathbf{k} - (-\mathbf{i} + 7\mathbf{k}) = -2\mathbf{j} - 11\mathbf{k}$

$\mathbf{b} \times (\mathbf{c} - \mathbf{a})$

$(\mathbf{i} - 2\mathbf{j} - 3\mathbf{k}) \times (-2\mathbf{j} - 11\mathbf{k})$

$$= \begin{vmatrix} \mathbf{i} & \mathbf{j} & \mathbf{k} \\ 1 & -2 & -3 \\ 0 & -2 & -11 \end{vmatrix} = 16\mathbf{i} + 11\mathbf{j} - 2\mathbf{k}$$

$$d = \frac{|16\mathbf{i} + 11\mathbf{j} - 2\mathbf{k}|}{|\mathbf{i} - 2\mathbf{j} - 3\mathbf{k}|} = \sqrt{\frac{256 + 121 + 4}{1 + 4 + 9}}$$

$$\boxed{d = 5.22}$$

21. $\mathbf{a} = 2\mathbf{i} + 5\mathbf{k} \qquad \mathbf{b} = 3\mathbf{i} + 4\mathbf{j} + 8\mathbf{k}$

$\mathbf{c} - \mathbf{a} = 5\mathbf{i} + 8\mathbf{j} + 9\mathbf{k} - 2\mathbf{i} - 5\mathbf{k} = 3\mathbf{i} + 8\mathbf{j} + 4\mathbf{k}$

$\mathbf{b} \times (\mathbf{c} - \mathbf{a})$

$= (3\mathbf{i} + 4\mathbf{j} + 8\mathbf{k}) \times (3\mathbf{i} + 8\mathbf{j} + 4\mathbf{k})$

$$= \begin{vmatrix} \mathbf{i} & \mathbf{j} & \mathbf{k} \\ 3 & 4 & 8 \\ 3 & 8 & 4 \end{vmatrix}$$

$= -48\mathbf{i} + 12\mathbf{j} + 12\mathbf{k}$

$$d = \frac{|\mathbf{b} \times (\mathbf{c} - \mathbf{a})|}{|\mathbf{b}|} = \frac{|-48\mathbf{i} + 12\mathbf{j} + 12\mathbf{k}|}{|3\mathbf{i} + 4\mathbf{j} + 8\mathbf{k}|} = \sqrt{\frac{2304 + 144 + 144}{9 + 16 + 64}}$$

$$= \sqrt{\frac{2592}{89}} = 5.4.$$

$$\boxed{d = 5.4}$$

22.

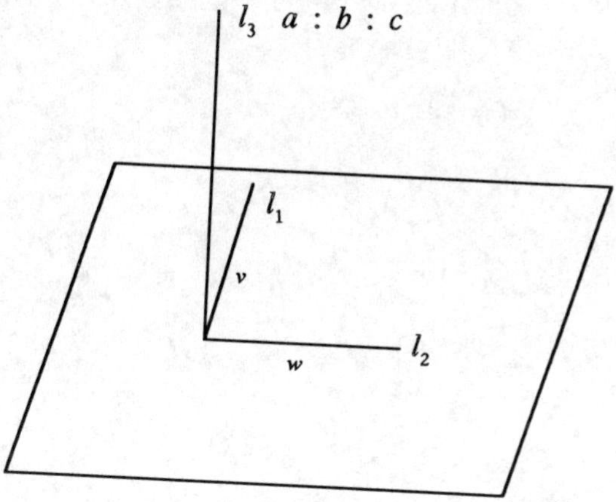

Fig. 8-II/30

The direction ratio of **v** is $1 : -1 : 1$.

The direction ratio of **w** is $2 : 1 : 3$.

l_3 is perpendicular to l_1 and l_2

$(a\mathbf{i} + b\mathbf{j} + c\mathbf{k}) \cdot (\mathbf{i} - \mathbf{j} + \mathbf{k}) = 0$ $\boxed{a - b + c = 0}$ ... (1)

$(a\mathbf{i} + b\mathbf{j} + c\mathbf{k}) \cdot (2\mathbf{i} + \mathbf{j} + 3\mathbf{k}) = 0$ $\boxed{2a + b + 3c = 0}$ ... (2)

(1) + (2)

$3a + 4c = 0$

$$\frac{a}{c} = -\frac{4}{3} \Rightarrow a = -\frac{4}{3}c$$

$$2\left(-\frac{4}{3}c\right) + b + 3c = 0$$

$$b = \frac{8}{3}c - \frac{9}{3} = -\frac{c}{3}$$

$$\frac{b}{c} = -\frac{1}{3}$$

$a : b : c = 4 : 1 : -3$

$$\boxed{\mathbf{r} = (\mathbf{i} + 2\mathbf{j} - \mathbf{k}) + t\,(4\mathbf{i} + \mathbf{j} - 3\mathbf{k})}$$

8. VECTORS IN TWO AND THREE DIMENSIONS

Miscellaneous

. Referred to an origin O, the planes π_1 and π_2 have equation $\mathbf{r} \cdot (\mathbf{i} - 2\mathbf{j} + 2\mathbf{k}) = 1$ and $\mathbf{r} \cdot (2\mathbf{i} + 2\mathbf{j} - \mathbf{k}) = 3$ respectively. Calculate, to the nearest tenth of a degree, the acute angle between π_1 and π_2.
(4 marks)

By using a vector product, or otherwise, show that the vector $2\mathbf{i} - 5\mathbf{j} - 6\mathbf{k}$ is parallel to the line of intersection L of π_1 and π_2. (4 marks)

The plane π_3 is perpendicular to L and passes through the point with position vector $-3\mathbf{i} - 3\mathbf{j} + 3\mathbf{k}$. Find the equation of the plane π_3 in the form $\mathbf{r} \cdot \mathbf{n} = p$. (3 marks)

Prove that the point of intersection of π_1, π_2 and π_3 is at a distance $\sqrt{3}$ from O. (4 marks)

(Ans. 63.6°; $\mathbf{r} \cdot (2\mathbf{i} - 5\mathbf{j} - 6\mathbf{k}) = -9$) **AEB P2 (10) J. 1986**

2. The line l with vector equation $\mathbf{r} = \mathbf{a} + \lambda\mathbf{b}$ passes through the point A with position vector $\mathbf{a} = 2\mathbf{i} + 5\mathbf{j} - 3\mathbf{k}$ and has the direction of the vector $\mathbf{b} = 5\mathbf{i} - 2\mathbf{j} - 4\mathbf{k}$. The point C, with position vector $\mathbf{c}$, has coordinates $(2, 7, -4)$.

(a) Find the vector product

$$\mathbf{b} \times (\mathbf{c} - \mathbf{a})$$

and hence, or otherwise, find the equation of the plane p_1 which contains the line l and the point C, giving your answer in the form $\mathbf{r} \cdot \mathbf{n} = k$. (5 marks)

(b) The plane p_2 has equation $\mathbf{r} \cdot (5\mathbf{i} + \mathbf{j} + 2\mathbf{k}) = -6$. Prove that the angle between the line l and the plane p_2 is $\sin^{-1}\left(\frac{1}{\sqrt{6}}\right)$ and find the coordinates of P, the point of intersection of l and p_2. (7 marks)

Find the lengths of PA in surd form and hence, or otherwise, determine the shortest distance of A from the plane p_2. (3 marks)

Ans. (a) $10\mathbf{i} + 5\mathbf{j} + 10\mathbf{k}$; $\mathbf{r} \cdot (2\mathbf{i} + \mathbf{j} + 2\mathbf{k}) = 3$

(b) $(-3, 7, 1)$ $PA = 3\sqrt{5}$, $\frac{\sqrt{30}}{2}$. **AEB P2 (7) Nov. 1986**

3. The lines l_1, l_2 and l_3 are given by

$$l_1 : \mathbf{r} = 5\mathbf{i} + \mathbf{j} + 5\mathbf{k} + \lambda\,(\mathbf{i} - \mathbf{j} - 2\mathbf{k})$$

$$l_2 : \mathbf{r} = \mathbf{i} - 4\mathbf{j} + 10\mathbf{k} + \mu\,(2\mathbf{i} + 7\mathbf{j} - \mathbf{k})$$

$$l_3 : \mathbf{r} = \mathbf{i} + 11\mathbf{j} + 2\mathbf{k} + \nu\,(-4\mathbf{i} - 14\mathbf{j} + 2\mathbf{k}).$$

(a) Show that the lines l_2 and l_3 are parallel. (1 mark)

(b) Show that the line l_1 and l_2 intersect and determine the coordinates of the point of intersection. Find also the acute angle between the lines l_1 and l_2. (5 marks)

(c) Find the cartesian equation of the plane p_1 containing the lines l_1 and l_2. (4 marks)

(d) Write down the cartesian equation of the plane p_2 which is parallel to the plane p_1 and which contains the origin. Show that the plane p_2 contains the line l_3. (3 marks)

(e) Determine the shortest distance between the lines l_1 and l_3. (2 marks)

Ans. (b) $\cos^{-1}\left(\frac{1}{6}\right)$; (c) $5x - y + 32 = 39$

(d) $5x - y + 32 = 0$ (e) $\frac{39}{\sqrt{35}}$. **AEB P2 (8) J. 1987**

4. Referred to a fixed origin O and the coordinate axes Ox, Oy and Oz, the lines l_1, l_2 and l_3 have equations

$$l_1 : \mathbf{r} = 4\mathbf{i} + 7\mathbf{j} - 3\mathbf{k} + t_1\,(\mathbf{i} + 3\mathbf{j} - 4\mathbf{k}),$$

$$l_2 : \mathbf{r} = 3\mathbf{i} + 10\mathbf{j} - \mathbf{k} + t_2\,(-3\mathbf{j} + \mathbf{k}),$$

$$l_3 : \mathbf{r} = 3\mathbf{i} + 4\mathbf{j} + \mathbf{k} + t_3\,(4\mathbf{i} - 5\mathbf{j} - \mathbf{k}),$$

where t_1, t_2 and t_3 are scalar parameters and the unit vectors $\mathbf{i}$, $\mathbf{j}$ and $\mathbf{k}$ are parallel to Ox, Oy and Oz respectively.

Show that l_1, l_2 and l_3 intersect at the point A whose position vector is $3\mathbf{i} + 4\mathbf{j} + \mathbf{k}$. (3 marks)

Calculate the shortest distance from A to the plane π whose equation is $\mathbf{r} \cdot (6\mathbf{i} + 3\mathbf{j} + 2\mathbf{k}) = 25$. (4 marks)

The lines l_1, l_2 and l_3 meet the plane π in the points B, C, and D respectively.

Show that B has position vector $(2\mathbf{i} + \mathbf{j} + 5\mathbf{k})$ and determine the position vectors of C and D. (4 marks)

Calculate the area of the triangle BCD and hence find the volume of the tetrahedron $ABCD$.

Ans. distance = 1 $\mathbf{c} = 3\mathbf{i} + \mathbf{j} + 2\mathbf{k}$ $\mathbf{d} = -\mathbf{i} + 9\mathbf{j} + 2\mathbf{k}$

area = 14 volume = $\frac{14}{3}$. **AEB P2 (5) Nov. 1987**

5. With respect to a fixed origin O, the lines l_1 and l_2 are given by the vector equations

$l_1 : \mathbf{r} = 9\mathbf{i} - 4\mathbf{j} + 5\mathbf{k} + t\,(2\mathbf{i} - \mathbf{j} + \mathbf{k})$,

$l_2 : \mathbf{r} = 2\mathbf{i} - 8\mathbf{j} + 12\mathbf{k} + s\,(\mathbf{i} + 2\mathbf{j} - 3\mathbf{k})$,

where t and s are scalar parameters.

The point A lies on l_1 and OA is perpendicular to l_1. Determine the position vector of A and hence find in the form $\mathbf{r} \cdot \mathbf{n} = p$ an equation of the plane π_1 which passes through A and is perpendicular to OA. (5 marks)

Show that l_1 and l_2 intersect and find the position vector of B, their point of intersection. (4 marks)

Find a vector which is perpendicular to both l_1 and l_2 and hence find an equation for the plane π_2 which contains l_1 and l_2. (4 marks)

Find, to the nearest one tenth of a degree, the acute angle between the planes π_1 and π_2. (2 marks)

Ans. $\mathbf{a} = \frac{1}{2}\mathbf{j} + \frac{1}{2}\mathbf{k}$ $\mathbf{r} \cdot (\mathbf{j} + \mathbf{k}) = 1$ $\mathbf{b} = 5\mathbf{i} - 2\mathbf{j} + 3\mathbf{k}$

$\mathbf{i} + 7\mathbf{j} + 5\mathbf{k}$ $\mathbf{r} \cdot (\mathbf{i} + 7\mathbf{j} + 5\mathbf{k}) = 6$ 11.5° **AEB P2 (9) J. 1988**

6. Referred to a fixed origin O, the point A (4, 1, 3), B (− 2, 7, 6) and C (1, 1, 4) have position vectors **a**, **b** and **c** respectively.

Find $(\mathbf{b} - \mathbf{a}) \times (\mathbf{c} - \mathbf{a})$ and hence, or otherwise, determine in the form $\mathbf{r} \cdot \mathbf{n} = p$ an equation of the plane ABC. (6 marks)

The point D with position vector $\mathbf{d} = 5\mathbf{i} - 3\mathbf{j} + \lambda\mathbf{k}$ lies in the plane ABC. Find the value of λ. (2 marks)

Prove that $ABCD$ is a trapezium and find its area. (7 marks)

AEB P2 (5) Nov. 1988

7. The line l has vector equation $\mathbf{r} = \mathbf{a} + \lambda\mathbf{d}$ where $\mathbf{a} = 3\mathbf{i} + 4\mathbf{j} - 3\mathbf{k}$ and $\mathbf{d} = 2\mathbf{i} - \mathbf{j} - 2\mathbf{k}$. The points P and Q have position vectors $\mathbf{p} = 4\mathbf{j} + 3\mathbf{k}$ and $\mathbf{q} = 2\mathbf{i} + 6\mathbf{j} + 2\mathbf{k}$ respectively. The plane π contains the line l and the point P.

(a) Find the vector product $\mathbf{d} \times (\mathbf{a} - \mathbf{p})$. Hence, or otherwise, find the equation of the plane π in the form $\mathbf{r} \cdot \mathbf{n} = k$. (6 marks)

(b) Determine the angle between the line passing through the points P and Q and the plane π. (3 marks)

(c) Prove that the point P is equidistant from the line l and the point Q. (6 marks)

Ans. (a) $6\mathbf{i} + 6\mathbf{j} + 3\mathbf{k}$; $\mathbf{r} \cdot (2\mathbf{i} + 2\mathbf{j} + \mathbf{k}) = 11$;

(b) $\sin^{-1} \frac{7}{9}$. **AEB P2 (7) J. 1989**

8. Referred to a fixed origin O, the position vectors of the points A, B, C and D are respectively

$(-\mathbf{j} + \mathbf{k})$, $(2\mathbf{i} - \mathbf{j} + 3\mathbf{k})$, $(-\mathbf{i} - 2\mathbf{j} + 2\mathbf{k})$ and $(7\mathbf{i} - 4\mathbf{j} + 2\mathbf{k})$.

(a) Find a vector which is perpendicular to the plane ABC. (4 marks)

(b) Show that the length of the perpendicular from D to the plane ABC is of length $2\sqrt{6}$. (4 marks)

(c) Show that the planes ABC and BCD are perpendicular. (4 marks)

(d) Find the acute angle between the line BD and the plane ABC, giving your answer to the nearest degree. (3 marks)

Ans. (a) Any multiple of $\mathbf{i} - 2\mathbf{j} - \mathbf{k}$ (d) 56°.

AEB P2 (2) J. 1990

9. The points A, B and C have position vectors $\mathbf{a} = \mathbf{i} + 2\mathbf{j} + 4\mathbf{k}$, $\mathbf{b} = -2\mathbf{i} + 3\mathbf{j} + 5\mathbf{k}$, $\mathbf{c} = 3\mathbf{i} - \mathbf{j} + 2\mathbf{k}$ respectively with respect to a fixed origin.

(a) Show that the point $P\ (1 - 3\lambda, 2 + \lambda, 4 + \lambda)$ lies on the straight line through A and B. Express PC^2 in terms of λ and show that, as λ varies, the least value of PC^2 is 6. Verify that in this case the line PC is perpendicular to the line AB. (4 marks)

(b) Find a vector perpendicular to AB and AC and hence, or otherwise, find an equation for the plane ABC in the form $\mathbf{r} \cdot \mathbf{n} = p$. (4 marks)

(c) Find a cartesian equation of the plane π which contains the line AB and which is perpendicular to the plane ABC. (4 marks)

(d) Verify that the point D with position vector $2\mathbf{i} - 2\mathbf{j} + 11\mathbf{k}$ lies in the plane π and is such that DA is perpendicular to AB. Hence or otherwise, calculate the volume of the tetrahedron $ABCD$. (3 marks)

Ans. (a) $11(\lambda + 1)^2 + 6\mathbf{i}$ (b) $\mathbf{i} - 4\mathbf{j} + 7\mathbf{k} = n$; $\mathbf{r} \cdot \mathbf{n} = 21$;

(c) $x + 2y + z = 9$; (d) 11. **AEB P2 (9) Nov. 1990**

10. The lines l_1 and l_2 have equations $\mathbf{r} = (3\mathbf{i} + \mathbf{j} - \mathbf{k}) + \alpha(\mathbf{i} + 2\mathbf{j} + 3\mathbf{k})$ and $\mathbf{r} = (2\mathbf{i} + 5\mathbf{j}) + \beta(\mathbf{i} - \mathbf{j} + \mathbf{k})$ respectively.

(a) Prove that l_1 and l_2 intersect and find the position vector of P, the point of intersection (3 marks)

(b) Determine the equation of the plane π containing l_1 and l_2, giving your answer in the form $\mathbf{r} \cdot \mathbf{n} = d$. (4 marks)

(c) The point Q has position vector $\mathbf{i} + \mathbf{j} - 3\mathbf{k}$. The point R is such that QR is perpendicular to π and $QR = 2\,PQ$. Determine

(i) the position vectors of both possible positions of R. (4 marks)

(ii) the area of the triangle PQR, giving your answer to three significant figures. (4 marks)

Ans. (a) $4\mathbf{i} + 3\mathbf{j} + 2\mathbf{k}$ (b) $\mathbf{r} \cdot \mathbf{n} = 20$

(c) $11\mathbf{i} + 5\mathbf{j} - 9\mathbf{k}$ or $-9\mathbf{i} - 3\mathbf{j} + 3\mathbf{k}$ (d) 37.8

AEB P2 (3) J. 1991

11. The plane π_1 contains the points (1, 4, 2), (1, 0, 5) and (0, 8, − 1). Find its equation in cartesian form. (3 marks)

The plane π_2 contains the point (2, 2, 3) and has normal vector $(\mathbf{i} + 2\mathbf{j} + 2\mathbf{k})$. Find its equation in cartesian form. (2 marks)

The point $(p, 0, q)$ lies on both the planes π_1 and π_2. Find p and q and express the equation of the line of intersection of the two planes in the form $\mathbf{r} = \mathbf{a} + \lambda\mathbf{b}$ (5 marks)

The point $(1, 1, \mu)$ is equidistant from the planes π_1 and π_2. Find the two possible values of μ. (5 marks)

(Ans. $3y + 4z = 20$, $x + 2y + 2z = 12$; $p = 2, q = 5$;

$\mathbf{r} = (2, 0, 5) + \lambda(-2, 4, -2)$; $\mu = 3, \frac{48}{11}$.)

AEB P2 (5) Nov. 1991

12. The plane π_1 and π_2, with equation $\mathbf{r} \cdot (2\mathbf{i} - 3\mathbf{j} + \mathbf{k}) = 1$ and $\mathbf{r} \cdot (4\mathbf{i} + 3\mathbf{j} + 2\mathbf{k}) = 11$ respectively, intersect in the line l.

(a) Calculate to the nearest degree, the acute angle between the planes. (4 marks)

(b) Evaluate the vector product $(2\mathbf{i} - 3\mathbf{j} + \mathbf{k}) \times (4\mathbf{i} + 3\mathbf{j} + 2\mathbf{k})$. Show that the point $(3, 1, -2)$ lies in each of the planes π_1 and π_2, and hence write down a vector equation for the line l. (5 marks)

(c) Find a vector equation for the plane π_3, which contains the point $(0, 1, -1)$ and which is perpendicular to each of the plane π_1 and π_2. (3 marks)

(d) Find the coordinates of the point which is common to all three planes π_1, π_2 and π_3. (3 marks)

Ans. (a) $87°$ **AEB P2 (7) J. 1992**

13. Planes π_1 and π_2 have equations given by

$$\pi_1 : \mathbf{r}\ (2\mathbf{i} - \mathbf{j} + \mathbf{k}) = 0,$$
$$\pi_2 : \mathbf{r}\ (\mathbf{i} + 5\mathbf{j} + 3\mathbf{k}) = 1.$$

(a) Show that the point $A\ (2, -2, 3)$ lies in π_2.
(b) Show that π_1 is perpendicular to π_2.

(c) Find, in vector form, an equation of the straight line through A which is perpendicular to π_1.

(d) Determine the coordinates of the point where this line meets π_1.

(e) Find the perpendicular distance of A from π_1.

(f) Find a vector equation of the plane through A parallel to π_1. (13 marks)

U.L. P1 (14) June 1989

14. Referred to a fixed origin O, the point A has position vector $a\ (4\mathbf{i} + \mathbf{j} + 2\mathbf{k})$ and the plane π has equation $\mathbf{r} \cdot (\mathbf{i} - 5\mathbf{j} + 3\mathbf{k}) = 5a$, where a is a scalar constant.

(a) Show that A lies in the plane π.
The point B has position vector $a\ (2\mathbf{i} + 11\mathbf{j} - 4\mathbf{k})$.

(b) Show that $\overrightarrow{BA}$ is perpendicular to the plane π.

(c) Calculate, to the nearest one tenth of a degree, $\angle OBA$.

(9 marks)

U.L. P2 (12) Jan. 1989

15. With respect to a fixed origin O, the straight line l_1 and l_2 are given by

$l_1 : \mathbf{r} = \mathbf{i} - \mathbf{j} + \lambda(2\mathbf{i} + \mathbf{j} - 2\mathbf{k})$,

$l_2 : \mathbf{r} = \mathbf{i} + 2\mathbf{j} + 2\mathbf{k} + \mu(-3\mathbf{i} + 4\mathbf{k})$,

where λ and μ are scalar parameters.

(a) Show that the lines intersect.

(b) Find the position vector of their point of intersection.

(c) Find the cosine of the acute angle contained between the lines.

(d) Find a vector equation of the plane containing the lines.

(10 marks)

U.L. P2 (13) June 88

16. Referred to a fixed origin O, the points A, B and C have position vectors $3\mathbf{i} - \mathbf{j} + 2\mathbf{k}$, $7\mathbf{i} + 2\mathbf{j} + 7\mathbf{k}$ and $\mathbf{i} + \mathbf{j} + 3\mathbf{k}$

respectively. The vector $\mathbf{n}$ is the vector product $\overrightarrow{AB} \times \overrightarrow{AC}$.

Express $\mathbf{n}$ in terms of $\mathbf{i}$, $\mathbf{j}$ and $\mathbf{k}$ and describe the direction of $\mathbf{n}$ in relation to the plane ABC. (5 marks)

Find an equation for the plane ABC in form $\mathbf{r} \cdot \mathbf{n} = p$ and hence find the shortest distance from O to the plane ABC. (4 marks)

Show that the plane OCA has equation $\mathbf{r} \cdot (5\mathbf{i} + 7\mathbf{j} - 4\mathbf{k}) = 0$ (2 marks)

Hence find, to $0.1°$, the acute angle between the plane OCA and the plane ABC. (4 marks)

Ans. $\mathbf{n} = -7\mathbf{i} - 14\mathbf{j} + 14\mathbf{k}$ $\mathbf{n}$ is perpendicular to plane ABC

$\mathbf{r} \cdot (-\mathbf{i} - 2\mathbf{j} + 2\mathbf{k}) = 3$; Shortest distance = 1. Angle = $18.4°$.

AEB P2 (8) Nov. 1989

17. Referred to a fixed origin O, the point A, B and C have position vector $\mathbf{i} - 2\mathbf{j} + 2\mathbf{k}$, $3\mathbf{i} - \mathbf{k}$ and $-\mathbf{i} + \mathbf{j} + 4\mathbf{k}$ respectively.

Calculate the cosine of the angle BAC. (4 marks)

Hence, or otherwise, find the area of the triangle ABC, giving your answer to three significant figures. (3 marks)

Ans. $-\frac{4}{17}$; 8.26. **AEB P1 (5) Nov. 1989**

18. With respect to a fixed origin O, the points A, B and C have position vectors $\mathbf{r}_1$, $\mathbf{r}_2$ and $\mathbf{r}_3$ where

$\mathbf{r}_1 = \mathbf{i} + \mathbf{j} + 2\mathbf{k}$, $\mathbf{r}_2 = \mathbf{i} + 2\mathbf{j} + \mathbf{k}$, $\mathbf{r}_3 = s\,\mathbf{i} + t\,\mathbf{j} + u\,\mathbf{k}$,

and s, t and u are constants $s > 0$. The point C lies on the line with vector equation

$\mathbf{r} = \mathbf{i} + \mathbf{j} - \mathbf{k} + \lambda(\mathbf{i} + 2\mathbf{k})$, where $\lambda \in \mathbb{R}$.

(a) Show that $u = 2s - 3$.

(b) Find $\overrightarrow{BA} \times \overrightarrow{BC}$ in terms of s.

Given also that the area of triangle ABC is $\frac{1}{2}\sqrt{57}$, find

(c) the value of s,

(d) an equation of the plane ABC, in the form $\mathbf{r} \cdot \mathbf{n} = p$,

(e) the volume of the tetrahedron $OABC$.

U.L. P3 (6) Jan. 1992

19. Relative to an origin O, points A, B, and C have position vector $\mathbf{a}$, $\mathbf{b}$, and $\mathbf{c}$ respectively, where

$\mathbf{a} = 4\mathbf{i} - 3\mathbf{j} + 3\mathbf{k}$, $\mathbf{b} = -\mathbf{i} - 2\mathbf{j} + 2\mathbf{k}$, $\mathbf{c} = 4\mathbf{i} + 3\mathbf{j}$.

(a) Find the area of the triangle ABC.

(b) Find the volume of the tetrahedron $OABC$.

(c) Obtain vector $\mathbf{p}$ and $\mathbf{q}$ so that the equation of the line L passing through A and B may be expressed in the form $\mathbf{r} \times \mathbf{p} = \mathbf{q}$.

(d) Find the shortest distance from the point C to the line L.

U.L. P3 (7) June 91

20. With respect to an origin O, the straight line l_1 and l_2 have equations

$l_1 : \mathbf{r} = p\,\mathbf{i} - 2\mathbf{j} + 2\mathbf{k} + \lambda\,(\mathbf{i} - \mathbf{k})$.

$l_2 : \mathbf{r} = 3\mathbf{i} - \mathbf{j} + \mu\,(2\mathbf{i} + \mathbf{j} - 3\mathbf{k})$,

where λ and μ are scalar parameters and p is a scalar constant. The lines intersect at the point A.

(a) Find the coordinates of A and show that $p = 2$.
The plane π passes through A and is perpendicular to l_2.

(b) Find a cartesian equation of π.

(c) Find the acute angle between the plane π and the line l_1, giving your answer in degree to 1 decimal place. (11 marks)

U.L. P1 (14) June 1991

21. Referred to a fixed origin O, the line l_1 and l_2 have equation

$\mathbf{r} = 3\mathbf{i} + 6\mathbf{j} + \mathbf{k} + s\,(2\mathbf{i} + 3\mathbf{j} - \mathbf{k})$,

$\mathbf{r} = 3\mathbf{i} - \mathbf{j} + 4\mathbf{k} + t\,(\mathbf{i} - 2\mathbf{j} + \mathbf{k})$

respectively, where s and t are scalar parameters.

(a) Show that l_1 and l_2 intersect and determine the position vector of their point of intersection.

(b) Show that the vector $(-\mathbf{i} + 3\mathbf{j} + 7\mathbf{k})$ is perpendicular to both l_1 and l_2.

(c) Find, in the form $\mathbf{r} \cdot \mathbf{n} = p$, an equation of the plane containing l_1 and l_2. (9 marks)

U.L. P1 (12) June 1990

22. The points A, B, C, D have position vectors

$\mathbf{a} = (2\mathbf{i} + \mathbf{j})$ m, $\mathbf{b} = (3\mathbf{i} - \mathbf{j} + \mathbf{k})$ m,

$\mathbf{c} = (-2\mathbf{j} - \mathbf{k})$ m, $\mathbf{d} = (2\mathbf{i} - \mathbf{j} + 3\mathbf{k})$ m

respectively.

(a) Find $\overrightarrow{AB} \times \overrightarrow{BC}$ and $\overrightarrow{BD} \times \overrightarrow{DC}$.

(b) Hence, or otherwise, find

(i) an equation of the plane ABC in the form $\mathbf{r} \cdot \mathbf{n} = p$,
(ii) the area of $\Delta\, ABC$,
(iii) the volume of the tetrahedron $ABCD$,
(iv) the length of the perpendicular from the point A onto the plane BCD.

U.L. P3 (6) Jan. 1990

23. Referred to a fixed origin O, the point A and B have position vectors a (5**i** − **j** − **k**) and a (**i** − 5**j** + 7**k**) respectively, where a is a positive constant.

(a) Find an equation of the line AB.

(b) Show that the point C with position vector a (4**i** − 2**j** + **k**) lies on AB.

(c) Show that OC is perpendicular to AB.

(d) Find the position vector of the point D, where $D \neq A$, on AB such that $|\overrightarrow{OD}| = |\overrightarrow{OA}|$. (8 marks)

U.L. P1 (9) Jan. 1990

24. The points A and B have position vectors $\mathbf{a} = 4\mathbf{i} + 5\mathbf{j} + 6\mathbf{k}$ and $\mathbf{b} = 4\mathbf{i} + 6\mathbf{j} + 2\mathbf{k}$ respectively relative to a fixed origin O. The line l_1 has vector equation $\mathbf{r} = \mathbf{i} + 5\mathbf{j} - 3\mathbf{k} + s(\mathbf{i} + \mathbf{j} - \mathbf{k})$ where s is a scalar parameter.

(a) (i) Write down a vector equation for the line l_2 which passes through the points A and B, giving the equation in term of a scalar parameter t. (2 marks)

(ii) Show that the line l_1 and l_2 intersect and state the position vector of the point of intersection. (3 marks)

(iii) Calculate the size of the acute angle between the lines l_1 and l_2. (4 marks)

(b) Given that P is a general point on the line l_1 with position vector **r**, find the vector $\mathbf{r} - \mathbf{a}$ and show that $AP^2 = 3\{(s + 2)^2 + 26\}$. (4 marks)

State the values of s for which AP^2 is a minimum and hence, or otherwise, obtain the position vector of the point on the line l_1 closest to A. (3 marks)

(Ans. (a) (i) $\mathbf{r} = 4\mathbf{i} + 5\mathbf{j} + 6\mathbf{k} + t(\mathbf{j} - 4\mathbf{k})$ (ii) $4\mathbf{i} + 8\mathbf{j} - 6\mathbf{k}$; (iii) 45.6°
(b) $s = -2$; $-\mathbf{i} + 3\mathbf{j} - \mathbf{k}$)

AEB P1 (12) June 1993

25. The lines l_1, l_2 have vector equations

$l_1 : \mathbf{r} = 2\mathbf{i} + 3\mathbf{j} + 5\mathbf{k} + \lambda (\mathbf{i} + \mathbf{j} + 2\mathbf{k})$

$l_2 : \mathbf{r} = 4\mathbf{j} + 6\mathbf{k} + \mu (-\mathbf{i} + 2\mathbf{j} + 3\mathbf{k})$.

(a) Show that l_1 and l_2 intersect and find the position vector of the point of intersection. (4 marks)

(b) Find the acute angle between l_1 and l_2, giving your answer correct to the nearest degree. (3 marks)

Ans. (a) $\mathbf{i} + 2\mathbf{j} + 3\mathbf{k}$; (b) 40°. **AEB P1 (5) Nov. 1992**

26. The points A, B, C have position vector $\mathbf{i} + 2\mathbf{j} - 3\mathbf{k}$, $\mathbf{i} + 5\mathbf{j}$ and $5\mathbf{i} + 6\mathbf{j} - \mathbf{k}$ respectively relative to an origin O.

(a) Show that AB is perpendicular to BC, and find the area of the triangle ABC. (4 marks)

(b) Find the vector product $\overrightarrow{AB} \times \overrightarrow{BC}$. Hence find an equation of the plane ABC in the form $\mathbf{r} \cdot \mathbf{n} = p$. (4 marks)

(c) The point D has position vector $4\mathbf{i} - \mathbf{j} + 3\mathbf{k}$. Find the distance of the point D from the plane ABC. Hence show that the volume of the tetrahedron $ABCD$ is equal to 21. (4 marks)

(d) Give, in cartesian form, the equation of the plane π which contains D, and which has the property that for each point E in π, the volume of the tetrahedron $ABCD$ is still 21. (3 marks)

(Ans. (a) 9; (b) $-6\mathbf{i} + 12\mathbf{j} - 12\mathbf{k}$); (c) 7, 21; (d) $x - 2y + 2z = 12$.)
AEB P2 (6) Nov. 1992

27. The line l_1 has vector equation $\mathbf{r} = (-7\mathbf{i} + 5\mathbf{j}) + \lambda (8\mathbf{i} - 3\mathbf{j} + \mathbf{k})$ and the plane π_1 has equation $\mathbf{r} \cdot (\mathbf{i} - 2\mathbf{j} - \mathbf{k}) = 9$.

(a) Calculate, to the nearest degree, the acute angle between the line l_1 and the plane π_1. (4 marks)

(b) Find the coordinates of the point of intersection of the line l_1 and the plane π_1. (3 marks)

(c) Evaluate the vector product $(8\mathbf{i} - 3\mathbf{j} + \mathbf{k}) \times (\mathbf{i} - 2\mathbf{j} - \mathbf{k})$ and hence, or otherwise, determine an equation of the plane π_2 which contains l_1 and which is perpendicular to π_1. (4 marks)

(d) Determine a vector equation of the line of intersection of the plane π_1 and π_2. (4 marks)

(Ans. (a) 38°; (b) (9, − 1, 2); (c) 5**i** + 9**j** − 13**k**, **r** . (5**i** + 9**j** − 13**k**) = 10
(d) **r** = 9**i** − **j** + 2**k** + λ (35**i** + 8**j** + 19**k**))

AEB P2 (7) June 1993

28. With respect to an origin O the points A, B and C have position vectors 3**i** − 2**j**, − 2**i** + 5**j** − 4**k** and − **i** + 4**k** respectively.

(a) Calculate the scalar product $\overrightarrow{AB} \cdot \overrightarrow{CB}$ and hence find the angle ABC to the nearest degree. (4 marks)

(b) Given that A, B and C are three vertices of a parallelogram $ABCD$, find the position vector of D and show that AC is perpendicular to BD. (3 marks)

(c) Calculate the area of the parallelogram $ABCD$. (3 marks)

(d) The point E lies on BC produced so that $\overrightarrow{CE} = 2\,\overrightarrow{BC}$. Show that the position vector of E is **i** − 10**j** + 20**k**. (2 marks)

(e) The line AE cuts CD at X. Find the position vector of X. (4 marks)

AEB P1 (11) Nov. 1993

29. The points A (2, 0, − 1) and B (4, 3, 1) have position vectors **a** and **b** with respect to a fixed origin O.

(a) Find **a** × **b**.

The plane Π_1 contains the points O, A and B.

(b) Verify that an equation of Π_1 is $x - 2y + 2z = 0$.

The plane Π_2 has equation **r** . **n** = d when **n** = 3**i** + **j** − **k** and d is constant. Given that B lies on Π_2,

(c) find the value of d.

The plane Π_1 and Π_2 intersect in the line L.

(d) Find an equation of L in the form **r** = **p** + t **q**, where t is a parameter.

(e) Find the position vector of the point X on L where OX is perpendicular to L. (17 marks)

U.L. P4 (10) Jan. 1993

8. VECTORS IN TWO AND THREE DIMENSIONS

INDEX